Better Embedded System Software

Better Embedded System Software

Philip Koopman

Carnegie Mellon University

Drumnadrochit Press

ISBN-13: 978-0-9844490-0-2
ISBN-10: 0-9844490-0-0
Drumnadrochit Education LLC

Printed on acid-free paper in the United States of America
2010 2011 2012 2013 2014 2015   9 8 7 6 5 4 3 2 1

To Sue

Topic Quick Reference

Contents

Preface

I wrote this book to help embedded software developers reduce risk and create better products. The topics and ideas are the distillation of more than a decade of experience performing 90+ design reviews on embedded system products across a range of industries. Every chapter in this book contains ideas and methods corresponding to the recommendations of design reviews on real embedded system products. Be sure to see the Topic Quick Reference page for a list of chapters.

If you find even one chapter useful, that should make owning this book worthwhile. But, we hope that you'll keep this book in your library and find many chapters that are useful in various future projects. To help you do this, the book is organized to let you dive into any chapter for a relatively self-contained chunk of good embedded software practice. Some chapters will be more helpful than others depending on your particular industry and project. Nobody can instantly start doing everything recommended by this book. But everyone can pick one or two ideas that will have quick payoff for making their products or development practices a little better.

This book can be used to supply readings for an advanced embedded systems course, although it is written as a professional book and not specifically as a textbook. We assume that the reader already knows the basics of embedded systems, and has some experience and maturity in design. Given that background, each chapter could be used as the basis for a lecture to guide students through the process of transforming from someone who merely writes code to someone who uses a methodical approach to designing embedded systems, with all their interlocking constraints and complex requirements.

If you're experienced at non-embedded software design, you'll probably find some of these chapters familiar material. But there is significant coverage of embedded-specific topics you'll find useful, especially in the sections on Implementation and Critical System Properties.

If you're relatively new to writing software, you should probably read an introductory embedded software book before diving into this one. We assume you've seen the basics to creating embedded systems, such as reading data from sensors, driving actuators, creating interrupt handlers, implementing control loops, and working with assembly language. There are many intro-level books on the market, and any of the highly rated ones are a good way to get started. This book is intended to help you take the next steps beyond those basics.

The material in this book is organized into several sections:

- **Software Development Process.** This discusses how formal the development process should be, with an emphasis on how much "paper" should be produced. Developers often try to avoid paperwork, but having some formality and some level of documentation can make a huge difference in your ability to succeed. We give you ways to create just enough paper to be useful, without going overboard.

- **Requirements and Architecture.** Every project has requirements and an architecture, whether they are written down or not. We discuss good ways to create and manage requirements, including both functional and non-functional requirements. We also discuss how to create a useful but simple architectural diagram, and how to achieve good modularity.

- **Design.** Software design is the part that goes between requirements+architecture and writing code. There are important benefits to getting things right at a higher level representation than source code. We discuss good techniques for representing designs (especially statecharts, which are under-used in the embedded systems industry), real time scheduling, and user interfaces.

- **Implementation.** While we all want to show our creativity, there are some common practices that can really make a difference in reducing risk and increasing our productivity. These include being extremely selective in the use of assembly language, using a consistent coding style, avoiding global variables, and using data concurrency techniques properly. We give you some economic ammunition to help fend off the nightmare of having to squeeze too much functionality into too small a processor.

- **Verification and Validation.** There is more to this topic than just testing! Your life can be made significantly easier by being clever about using compiler warnings, holding peer reviews, creating (and following) a test plan, tracking defects, and building in a way to keep run-time error logs.

- **Critical System Properties.** Embedded system failures can have dramatic consequences. We take you on a guided tour of techniques used to improve dependability, security, and safety. Additionally, we discuss how to get two of the most important aspects of critical systems right: watchdog timers and system resets.

For each chapter we provide a list of good starting points for further reading (if there are any we know of). They vary from academic papers to introductory tutorials in the trade press, but in each case they are the best places we know of to start. Beyond that, we recognize that the Web is where working developers get most of their information. But rather than list web sites that probably won't be there next year (or maybe even next week), we give search terms that tend to give hits on the most important topics covered by each chapter. Obviously we can't vouch for the accuracy of web sites you find this way! But we've tested each keyword phrase with several search engines and they tend to get you pointed in the right direction to understand more.

The introduction has more about the overall chapter organization. We hope you'll find the book easy to navigate, and the organization helpful in quickly finding information you can put to use right away in your current and future projects.

Acknowledgments

I want to thank the many embedded system designers who have been through the design reviews I've held. It's very difficult having someone from outside come in to tell you everything you did wrong, or even just ways to improve. I'm truly impressed by the many working engineers I've met who eagerly seek criticism and do their best at product development.

If embedded systems didn't work, people would notice in a hurry. But most ordinary people don't notice embedded computers at all. That is a testament to the amazing abilities of the engineers I've had the privilege to work with in industry. It's an imperfect world and nobody ever has time and resources to do everything they'd like during product design. Embedded system designers succeed under tougher constraints than in any other area of computing. I sincerely hope that the ideas in this book make it easier to keep succeeding, especially as products get more complex over time.

I'd also like to thank the students in my embedded systems courses. While this isn't really a text, much of the material in this book has been taught in lectures and course projects at the Electrical and Computer Engineering Department of Carnegie Mellon University. Working with students has been tremendously helpful in understanding how to explain many topics. Unfortunately, sometimes that understanding has come as a result of students suffering through my failed attempts at teaching a tricky concept. But in the end I hope that most students have gotten the skills they need to succeed from my classes. If you've taken a class from me, I'd love to hear how things have worked out for you, and what topics you'd suggest I add to my courses to make sure you're prepared for jobs in industry.

Several people have provided editing suggestions, comments, and source material. These include Rick Miu, Alex Dean, Marilyn Wolf, Justin Ray, Jen Black, Brian Finamore, Jessica Liao, and Roger Gatchell. I appreciate their comments.

I want to especially mention the support and encouragement given to me over the years by Bill Trosky, who is the founding Director of the Emerson Electric Software Center of Excellence. The opportunities he has provided to me were crucial to learning enough to create this book. He has done an amazing job at catalyzing software engineering process improvements across the various divisions of his diverse corporation.

Most importantly, I want to thank Sue Kennedy for her support, encouragement, and careful proofreading. Without her, I'd never have had the motivation and energy to write this book. Finally, I'd like to thank our children Ben, David, Hannah, and Sean for enriching my life.

Everyone can improve, and I'm no exception. If you see something in this book that you disagree with or, worse, an outright mistake, please let me know via an e-mail to:

BetterSoftware@Koopman.us

I'll post errata and other support material on a web page at:

http://www.ece.cmu.edu/~koopman/books.html

Philip Koopman
Pittsburgh, PA, April 2010

Chapter 1
Introduction

- This chapter discusses how to use this book, as well as some things to keep in mind when using it.
- The book is organized to be easy to skim, with self-contained chapters.
- Pick the one chapter that seems most compelling, and try out those ideas first.
- Be sure to take a look at the Topic Quick Reference page for a brief list of chapters.

Contents:

1.1. Overview

Embedded systems are different than desktop computing systems in some fundamental and important ways. They must meet real time deadlines. They must also meet demanding cost targets which constrain the amount of computing hardware available. They usually control the release of energy into the environment in some manner, which means safety is often a relevant concern. And, by and large, people expect them to be free of software bugs.

Getting embedded systems right is a difficult proposition. There are just so many things you have to know about and do! This book is a source of ideas, techniques, and lessons learned to help you get things right. In particular, it concentrates on areas that commonly come up as issues in embedded software design reviews. We assume you already know your way around embedded systems. Our goal is to help you take the next steps in becoming even better.

Some things in this book you're probably already doing. Some probably don't apply to your current project. But, there are almost certainly some ideas in this book that apply to you and can be used to decrease your project's risk and increase its final quality.

1.2. Using this book

Probably you won't read this book from front to back. It is organized as a tool kit, with each chapter a relatively self-contained unit. Most readers will skim through chapter summaries and dive into those that seem most relevant to them. Take a look at the Topic Quick Reference before the detailed Table of Contents (and on the back cover) for a list of chapters.

1.3. Chapter organization

Chapters tend to follow the same flow, and are organized to be reasonably self-contained.

1.3.1. Chapter sections

Each chapter in this book is divided into the following sections, if applicable:

- **Summary:** Describes the main ideas in the chapter.
- **Overview:** Some background and general discussion.
- **Importance:** Why should you care?
- **Symptoms:** If any of these things apply to your project (or seem likely to apply), you can benefit from the ideas in this chapter.
- **Risks:** The types of problems you might encounter if you have the symptoms and don't do something to treat them.
- **Discussion:** A discussion of the topic, and techniques for improving your product or processes.

- **Summary Boxes:** Many of the main points (the take-aways) for each chapter are summarized in text boxes throughout. If you want to just skim the chapter, look for these boxes.

- **Pitfalls:** Common ways that developers get into trouble in this area. If you see your situation described in a pitfall, don't feel bad. We have plenty of scars from learning things the hard way too!

- **More Information:** Places to look for related information.

Every chapter follows a similar organization.

1.3.2. Getting more information

It's challenging to provide really good sources of additional information that are accessible to working developers. So, instead of creating a long list of papers and articles that your local library might or might not have, and books you might or might not be able to obtain, we decided to provide the following information as appropriate:

- **Keyword search terms.** This lets you access the most recent available information on the Web. Evaluating the quality of that information is up to you.

- **Recommended reading.** These are articles that augment or provide a different perspective on the topic of the chapter. They are largely web accessible. The emphasis is on articles rather than books.

- **Additional resources.** These are articles or books that are more academic in nature, or are likely to be harder to obtain. We only list ones that we find particularly useful or important.

- **References.** This isn't an academic tome, so we aren't going to provide references for every idea. But, in some cases it's important to identify where something came from or to let you look at the source yourself to evaluate whether the idea is likely to be relevant to your particular situation.

There is really no point in attempting to track down every single relevant article on every topic. Rather, we give some examples so you can get an idea what others have to say on each topic. In most cases you'll find more than enough additional current information with a Web search.

1.4. What do you do first?

Nobody can expect to pick up this book and start doing everything in it on their current project. That's just unrealistic, even if everything here would in fact be helpful. We recommend finding the one chapter that looks like it will help you the most right now, on your current project. Try out the ideas. Tailor them to your situation. See how they can help you improve your project, refine your development process, and maybe even let you go home a little early once in a while to enjoy your life outside the cube. (You do have one, don't you? A life, we mean, not a cube.)

Pick the one chapter that seems most compelling, and try out those ideas first.

If the chapter works out and you're happy, try out another chapter. And if it doesn't, well, this book didn't cost nearly as much as getting an outside expert to visit and give you similar ideas to try out. Put it on your bookshelf with the all other books and take a look through in a few months to see if something else looks promising.

1.5. It's printed in a book, so it must be true, right?

This book has facts, opinions, things in between, and most likely some "facts" (things which we think are true based on what we've seen, but which might really be wrong). The problem with embedded systems is that there isn't much rigorous research to help us sort out which are which. Therefore, this book is our best shot at giving good advice, but isn't perfect. For areas where we disagree with other experts, we try to give pointers to some opposing views.

Each chapter has our best shot at identifying areas that are common embedded system problems and possible solutions. You should use your own knowledge and experience in evaluating whether you think what we say makes sense in your particular situation.

1.6. For more information

The resources below provide general embedded software and embedded system information. In other chapters, this section suggests ways to find out more about the chapter topic.

1.6.1. General topic search keywords

These search terms tended to work well with search engines at the time the book was published. Of course not every search hit will be relevant, and we can't vouch for the accuracy of information you find on the web using these terms.
- Embedded software
- Embedded system design

1.6.2. Other resources

http://www.embedded.com
> This is probably the best one-stop shopping place for embedded system developers. If you don't subscribe to Embedded System Design Magazine, then get a subscription (it's free for qualified subscribers), or at least take a look at the

extensive on-line article archive at this web site. Many of the reading suggestions in this book are available for free at this web site.

Ebert, C. & Jones, C., "Embedded software: facts, figures, and future," *IEEE Computer*, April 2009, pp. 42-52.
Describes the characteristics of large embedded software projects, and provides summary quantitative data on software size trends and defect rates. A table of defect prevention and removal techniques indicates that the three most effective approaches are: static code analysis, design inspections, and code inspections.

SOFTWARE DEVELOPMENT PROCESS

Chapter 2
Written Development Plan

- A written development plan documents what tasks should be performed during development and what outputs should be produced.
- Include both paper outputs and actual software in the plan.
- Spell out how risks are going to be managed to reduce the chance of a catastrophic project failure.

Contents:

2.1. Overview

A written development plan is a document that describes all the steps your organization should be taking to develop software. This includes both actions that should be performed (e.g., perform acceptance testing) and documents that should be created (e.g., write a test plan).

2.1.1. Importance of a written development plan

Successful development processes can vary widely, with differing levels of formality and approaches. But all such processes can benefit from a written development plan in the following ways:

- Knowing what your process is supposed to be helps keep you on the desired path during the course of development.
- Having a defined path helps you push back at management when they pressure you to take shortcuts. You can correctly say that the shortcut deviates from the development plan. This tactic works better if management agreed to the development plan before the project started.
- Having a defined path can help you face reality when it's time to make hard decisions about killing (or changing) a project.
- Having a path that everyone on a team follows helps keep things consistent across a project or series of projects.

It's possible to have a written development plan that everyone ignores, but that is the subject of another chapter (see *Chapter 4: How Much Paper Is Too Much?*).

2.1.2. Possible symptoms

Some symptoms that indicate you need to spend more effort on creating or maintaining your development plan include:

✘ Different projects or different portions of the same project vary wildly in quality and style.

✘ Projects that are doomed to failure keep consuming resources well after they should have been killed.

✘ Essential portions of the development process, such as testing, are subject to drastic shortcuts or omitted entirely.

✘ Management estimates project completion time based on how long it will take to implement code, rather than on how long it takes to also accomplish all the other activities necessary for success.

2.1.3. Risks of an inadequate development plan

Having an inadequate development plan or one that isn't written down can expose you to the following risks:

➤ Quality of the software might be poor overall because necessary steps are skipped or skimped upon. For example, you might have poor testing because testing is fit into time available before ship date rather than being based upon defined completeness criteria.

➤ Various portions of a project might be over- or under-engineered because there is no consistent set of guidelines for the steps and thoroughness to use in development.

➤ Maintenance and upgrades might be difficult because important documents aren't generated during development, and therefore aren't available later when the information is needed.

➤ Resources might be wasted on projects that are doomed to failure. This can happen if important project management checkpoints (often called gates) are skipped or delayed.

2.2. Development plan overview

Good engineering is largely about using a methodical approach to design. If you just slap something together without any plan, that isn't good engineering. You need a process (a way to be methodical), and a development plan is the description of that process.

> You must have a written development plan if you want to claim you have a methodical way of developing software.

2.2.1. Benefits of a development plan

To be effective, the development plan has to actually be in writing. If it's not in writing, but rather is just a group consensus, it is too easy to let it erode over time, forget about it in the heat of the moment, or not realize that different team members have dramatically different ideas about what the process is.

Perhaps just as importantly, if the development plan isn't in writing then there is no document to refer to when management is pressuring you to take process shortcuts to meet a near-term goal. Never underestimate the importance of having a printed document to wave around in a meeting when it supports your position! (Although a really thick and heavy document might be more intimidating when you wave it around or toss it at someone, we nonetheless recommend keeping it to a minimum useful length - see *Chapter 3: How Much Paper Is Enough?*)

Such a document is especially useful if it is created at a calm time during which there is no schedule crisis, and management agrees that the process is the right thing to be doing (preferably indicating that by actually signing the document). A written development plan isn't an impervious shield to management shortsightedness or, for that matter, to developers who want to take shortcuts. But, pointing out that skipping something violates the plan should at least give managers pause for thought. There is something in this for managers as well. Having a written development plan makes it easier to make sure that all the tasks and work products that are supposed to get done actually do get done.

2.2.2. Creating a development plan

Creating a development plan for the first time will take some time and effort. One outcome might be that you find out different people have a different idea of what should be in the process. This is not a problem! Rather, it is an opportunity to start the social process of converging upon what a reasonable development process should be for your organization and projects you perform. A significant benefit of creating a development plan is getting people to talk about what the right process is. If this takes a while, that's OK. Achieving a common approach via social processes and cultural change takes time. But, it is time well invested.

The level of detail and rigor of your development plan will depend on your situation. And, the plan will evolve over time. A reasonable software development plan will want to address the following high level points:

- What are the steps we are going to follow to create our product?
- What *paper* (documents, electronic or otherwise) are we going to generate as we follow those steps?
- How are we going to manage risk as we follow those steps?
- How are we going to know we succeeded?

> A development plan should include:
> development steps,
> a list of what paper is created,
> a risk management approach, and
> a way to measure success.

Each step is an activity such as writing requirements or performing tests. Steps might be arranged in a variety of ways, and don't necessarily have to follow a fixed sequence. The paper created might be matched to steps (e.g., a requirements document for a requirement step) or might only loosely correspond to the individual steps (e.g., a requirements document that is the combined result of several different steps).

2.2.3. Risk management and success criteria

The last two elements of the plan, risk management and success criteria, might be a bit unexpected, but are crucial for any project's success. If you aren't doing something about risky aspects of your project, you are leaving its success to chance. And if you don't have a metric for success, it's hard to know if you've actually succeeded.

Typical risk management items at this level of detail can include having project checkpoints or gates at which stakeholders decide whether the project is on track or not. Ideally, there are several checkpoints distributed throughout the process rather than one big checkpoint at the end. For example, there might be checkpoints every so many weeks, at the end of each step in the design process, or as a major revision of each piece of paper is released. The more rigorous the engineering process, the more heavyweight these checkpoints become. In some organizations, a project is not allowed to continue with its tasks beyond a particular point unless it passes a corresponding checkpoint review.

It is important to note that different projects might have different development plans, even within the same group of developers. For example, the level of rigor in a process appropriate for a 100 line text file processing script is likely to be substantially different than the more rigorous process appropriate for a 1 million line real time control program upon which the entire marketing fate of the product line rests.

2.3. Starting point for a development plan

Here is a framework for a development plan.

> The development plan should address: development approach, requirements, architecture, testing, design, implementation, reviews, and maintenance.

2.3.1. Process steps and paper generated

The below process steps can overlap and be performed in various orders. The order in which they are performed and the way in which they are coordinated is often referred to as the software *process model*. The waterfall, spiral, and V process models are commonly used in embedded systems (see the section: For More Information at the end of this chapter). In this list, primary bullets are process steps, and the secondary bullets are corresponding paper that can be produced as an output of that process step:

- Determine process model to be followed
  - Output: Software development plan tailored for this project
  - Output: Schedule and staffing plan
- Collect and set marketing requirements
  - Output: Customer requirements document
  - Output: User guide
  - Output: Marketing materials
- Create engineering requirements and system architecture
  - Output: Engineering requirements

- ○ Output: Architecture diagrams
- Create tests (performed in parallel with design)
  - ○ Output: Test plan
- Create software design
  - ○ Output: Design documents (e.g., flowcharts and statecharts)
- Create software implementation
  - ○ Output: Implementation (commented source code)
- Test and review software
  - ○ Output: Test reports
  - ○ Output: Peer review reports
- Maintenance
  - ○ Output: Bug reports and upgrade requests

See *Chapter 3. How Much Paper Is Enough?* for further discussion of the above outputs.

2.3.2. Risk management

This risk management plan outline is based on having several activities occurring in parallel across all the process steps outlined above.

2.3.2.1. Peer reviews

Every paper output of a process step should be subject to peer review and modification as necessary. Briefly, peer reviews involve other developers conducting a methodical review of written documents and code. (See *Chapter 22: Peer Reviews* for more detail.)

2.3.2.2. Gate reviews

At certain predefined points, management should conduct checkpoint "gate" reviews to assess the progress of the project. Common predefined points are after marketing requirements have been generated (this is typically a business-oriented review rather than a purely technical review), after the engineering requirements have been generated, and after testing has been completed. Holding gate reviews after other phases, and in particular the architecture and design phases, can be helpful as well.

The result of a gate review should be a management choice of one of these outcomes:

- The project should continue, usually with minor action items that must be completed before the next gate review.
- The project team should perform more work and attempt the same gate review again.
- The project should be killed.

Gate Reviews should be held after every major project phase.

There is clearly more to risk management than this. However, if the above reviews take place, it is likely that things will start heading in the right direction. Skipping reviews often means that bad news isn't found out until after it is too late to really fix the problems.

2.3.3. Success criteria

If there is no objective measure of success, how do you know you're ready to ship the product? The development plan should specify a concrete set of success criteria so that there is little question as to whether developers have done what they need to do.

While the ultimate success of a product usually can't be known until it is deployed, narrower success criteria for the development phase might include items such as:

- All acceptance tests have passed with no major issues outstanding.
- All gate reviews have been successfully completed and action items have been closed.
- All code and development documents have been peer reviewed.

The specifics of the criteria can vary. What does matter is that you actually have the criteria defined in a way that is compatible with your project and business environment.

2.4. Pitfalls

The obvious pitfall in writing a development plan is going overboard. Not every team should have a super-heavyweight process. And, even teams that might benefit from one eventually are unlikely to do well by attempting to jump from chaos to ultimate methodical rigor in a single leap. Thus, the process should be just thorough enough to get the job done. Or, if you aren't sure how thorough that is, try making the process a little more thorough on the next project than on the previous one and see if the increase in paper was worthwhile.

2.5. For more information

2.5.1. General topic search keywords

- Software project plan
- Software risk management
- Software development process

2.5.2. Recommended reading

2.5.2.1. General project management

Briggs, S., "Manage your embedded project," *Embedded Systems Programming*, pp. 26-46, April 2000.
This is an overview of project management, including risk management, costing, and other factors.

2.5.2.2. Software development plans

Hawley, G., "Ensure quality with a good development plan," *Embedded Systems Programming*, pp. 28-44 October 1998.
This article gives a somewhat more extensive list of things to include in a development plan.

2.5.2.3. Software development models

Any reasonable book on software engineering will explain the various software development models. Below are some starting points:

Boehm, B. W., "A spiral model of software development and enhancement," *Computer*, v. 21 n. 5, pp. 61-72, May 1988.
This is the original paper describing the spiral development approach, which emphasizes reducing risks over time rather than a linear progression of development steps. It also has a good description of the waterfall model.

INCOSE, *Guide to the Systems Engineering Body of Knowledge - G2SEBoK*.
http://g2sebok.incose.org/
This web site contains an extensive overview of system engineering and related concepts that is worth a look. Section 2.2.3 has a summary of the Vee model (more often called the V model) of development.

Beck, K., "Embracing change with extreme programming," *Computer*, v. 32, n. 10, pp. 70-77, October 1999.
Extreme programming is promoted as a way to be more flexible and responsive to change. Its suitability for embedded system can hinge upon whether it produces the right amount of paper for your situation.

2.5.2.4. Software risk management

Schmidt, R.; Lytinen, K.; Keil, M.; Cule, P., "Identifying software project risks: an international Delphi study," *Journal of Management Information Systems*, v. 17, n. 4., pp. 5-36 Spring 2001.
Table 3 has a list of common risk factors in software development projects, many of which are non-technical.

Chapter 3
How Much Paper Is Enough?

- A good software development process produces more than just source code.
- You should produce at least one document as a result of every distinct development process step or activity.
- A starting list of useful paper to create includes: customer requirements, engineering requirements, architecture, design, implementation, test plan, bug list, user guide, marketing materials, schedule, staffing plan, and a software development plan.

Contents:

Every development process step should produce a document. You should specify how thorough the paper trail should be in the software development plan. If code isn't important enough to document, then you should throw it away.

This section suggests documents to create for each phase of project development.

3.1. Overview

Many programmers would rather be writing code than doing anything else. Writing code is fun! Tasks other than creating executable code aren't nearly as much fun. Left to our own devices, we'd all rather do fun stuff. For most of us, the fun stuff doesn't include writing documentation.

Beyond the fun aspect, there is often pressure from management or customers to get something working quickly. Documentation isn't executable code, and doesn't produce obvious functionality. So, superficially at least, it can just seem like a waste of time. Moreover, documentation isn't visible at most customer demos, and customers tend to be less impressed by piles of paper than by a seemingly working piece of software. (And, when you were in school your programming assignments were probably graded based far more on "does the code seem to work?" rather than on "did you do all the documentation?")

Some development methods make a virtue of minimizing the amount of paper generated. And, this is not necessarily a bad thing - unless you are creating too little paper instead of just enough paper.

3.1.1. Importance of creating enough paper

The purpose of generating paper is to capture information so that someone else can understand a project. Sometimes well documented source code is good enough. But most often for embedded systems it isn't. Generating paper costs time and effort. The question is whether that extra cost for more paper is worth it overall. The answer depends on the situation, but having zero paper is never the right answer.

There's really no point in going on any more about this … we all know the allure of skipping documentation and getting right to the fun stuff. The problem is that in the end, skipping the paperwork results in higher total costs, longer time to create production-ready software, and more headaches downstream. More paper is not automatically better, but if you are seeing the types of problems listed below, then you don't have enough paper.

3.1.2. Possible symptoms

If any of the below are happening, you might not be generating enough paper.

✘ A developer leaves or retires, and you have no choice but to hire that developer back as a consultant to avoid project failure.

✘ You need to update some old software, and find you don't have enough information to understand what is there (in extreme cases, this is true even though you are the person who developed it).

✖ Someone has been assigned to document or perhaps even reverse engineer some existing code to understand what it does after it has been written and deployed.

✖ You have had a truly significant project failure or bug because of mis-communication that wouldn't have happened if that point had been written down.

✖ You are working with a partner (outsourcing or otherwise) and are spending a lot of time on phone calls to resolve misunderstandings.

✖ Someone is seriously, unpleasantly surprised during the development process (for example, a customer finds that features that were expected are missing or work the wrong way).

✖ Poorly documented, supposedly throwaway code seems to take on a life of its own, and doesn't get thrown away. It's still hanging around 10 or 20 years later.

✖ There is no paper except the source code listing for the implementation.

3.1.3. Risks of insufficient amounts of paper

Failing to generate enough paper is likely to increase the following risks:

➤ Risk of losing expertise due to developer turnover. This can make it difficult or impossible to make use of existing code.

➤ Risk that developers will introduce bugs when making changes because the assumptions and limitations of code aren't known.

➤ Risk of bugs because pieces of software don't work well together.

➤ Risk of the wrong software being written, or the wrong tests being performed, because people have different ideas about what the software is supposed to do.

It is difficult to find the time and energy to create more paper. This is especially true if you haven't experienced a disaster sufficient to motivate generating that paper. But even an incremental approach of adding just a little more paper (whichever missing item you think is most useful) is a step in the right direction, and will likely reduce some of the above risks.

3.2. Good ideas for creating paper

If a substantial piece of software has no documentation or comments at all, then that is almost certainly a high-risk situation. The following rule might seem extreme, but in practice this is what happens in the long run in many cases.

> Any project that isn't appropriately documented should be abandoned when the original developer switches to working on a new project.

Or, more pointedly:

> **If code isn't important enough to document,**
> **then throw it away right now.**

The rationale for this is that if you start working on something new, you'll forget the nuances of the previous project. If you leave the company, nobody else will know them either (unless they are written down). Who wants a project built on code that nobody understands? Well, yes, that happens all the time, but developers stuck dealing with undocumented code aren't particularly happy about the situation. And once in a while it turns out OK. But most of the time huge amounts of pain are involved, and often undocumented code has to be thrown away in the end. We're simply suggesting you fast-forward the process to reduce pain and suffering along the way.

While these rules might seem extreme (and perhaps they are), consider the alternatives. If nothing is written down, someone (perhaps even the same developer) will have to re-learn what is going on, and is likely to have incorrect or incomplete knowledge. That leads to mistakes. Moreover, re-learning code takes a lot of time and energy. Learning a piece of undocumented code and creating decent documentation for it can easily cost more than just starting to recode everything from scratch. Partly this is because understanding undocumented code is difficult. But this can also be because undocumented code often has really messy structure – so creating a clean description of it is a lot of work, or might even be impossible.

The alternative to re-learning code is worse: not knowing what code built into a product does, nor how it will react to changes. So we will argue the position that you simply should not go down that path. This gives two alternative strategies:

1. Skip documentation, and have the resolve to really throw the code away in the short term. This might be OK for special-purpose tools or small programs intended to try out specific hardware features. But few of us have the willpower, time, and political clout to follow through and actually throw the code away. So, in most cases, this option is more wishful thinking than reality.

2. Create adequate documentation if, in practice, the code is going to live on after it is developed. In most cases this includes supposedly disposable prototypes, because there is irresistible pressure to "just clean it up" into a product.

Therefore, the question for embedded software is not really "*should* I document." Rather, the right questions to be asking are "*what* should I document?" and "*how much* should I document?" The answers depend on the situation, but the following are some general guidelines.

3.2.1. What paper should I create?

Ideally, every development phase generates some paper (not necessarily a huge amount of paper, but at least some paper). The exact phases depend on the development process model you use, but might include just enough to answer the following questions:

- **Customer requirements.** What does the customer expect?

- **Engineering requirements.** What is the software we are building supposed to do (for example, what functions does it perform to meet customer expectations)?

- **Architecture.** What components or objects are in the software, and what are their relationships?

- **Design.** What does each component do?

- **Implementation.** How does the code work? (This is often in the form of code comments.)

- **Test plan.** How are we going to find out whether the system really works?

- **Test results.** How do we know that the system really does work?

- **Bug list.** What's wrong with the software, and has it been fixed yet?

- **User guide.** What does the user need to know to use and maintain the product?

- **Marketing materials.** What paper do you need to help sell your product?

- **Schedule and staffing plan.** When are things supposed to be done, and who is supposed to be doing them?

- **A software development plan.** What development process are you going to follow? How much and what kind of paper must be generated?

Every development process step should produce a document.

There are many types of paper that can be created, but the above are the basics. If you don't have at least one document, drawing, e-mail folder, or the equivalent for each of the above, then it is likely you aren't generating enough paper, and it is only a matter of time before you're bitten by it.

3.2.2. How much paper should I create?

Some people will say that close teamwork can be a successful substitute for creating paper. This can be true – but only to a point. Let's say you are using a small team that works so closely together you are just as effective as a single developer who can hold everything in her head during development. (If you use a cross-checking style of development, such as pair programming, you might be able to get away with less paperwork during the actual implementation phase. But, scalability to large, long-lived projects is still a significant issue.)

The biggest problem comes when the code lives on after the team disbands and development is finished. For applications that only live for a few weeks or months, this might be OK, since knowledge doesn't evaporate from developers' heads instantaneously. But, over a period of weeks, months, or years, developers will forget details, get new jobs, retire, win the lottery, get hit by a beer truck, or otherwise not be able to provide all the details that weren't written down. Some software only lasts a few weeks or months. But many embedded systems must live for years or decades, and it is over that timescale that a lack of paper truly exacts its toll.

It is difficult to give a precise formula for how much paper should be generated. But, having the development team formulate a plan for how much paper to create can at least make the decision an informed one:

> **The items and thoroughness of paper (documentation)
> must be specified – on paper.**

That's right, there has to be at least a little bit of paper to specify how much paper to generate. This is an essential part of the software development plan. Minimally, all that is needed is a simple list of documents and what should be in each one. In fact, it could just be a copy of the bullets listing different documents suggested in this chapter with the addition of a target for thoroughness (e.g., "all customer requirements shall be itemized" and "every component shall have a design").

With the understanding that situations are different, here are some suggestions for how to decide how much paper is enough:

- How much paper would you want if you had to pick up the project after the original developer left for greener pastures? Assume that you have a customer screaming at you at least once per hour to fix a bug that has shut down his entire business. Further assume that you are due to take your family on a vacation you've promised them for a year or so … with a nonrefundable flight tomorrow morning.

- Start with the lists in the next section and tailor them to your situation by adding or deleting elements. All documents you produce must have all (or almost all) the elements on these modified lists.

- Optionally, you can set an upper bound on document length to reduce the problems caused by too much paper.

You can decide to skip some of the documents we recommend. But, realize you do so at the cost of increasing risk. The tradeoff is up to you.

3.3. A starting point for what paper to create

This section has a minimal list of recommended documents that should be part of an embedded software development process. You can certainly add more. But, rather than going crazy with creating huge piles of paper, we suggest you start out just by trying the bare minimum, and then adding elements as you see they bring value to your situation.

Each section below gives a purpose and a list of items that should be in the document, along with a suggested criterion to determine how thorough the document should be. Note that this section generally corresponds to the items in *Chapter 2: Written Development Plan*, but is intended to be a different way of presenting the same general ideas.

3.3.1. Customer requirements

Answers the question: What does the customer expect?

- Numbered list of functions or services the customer expects.
- Constraints on the system (e.g., cost).
- Success criteria (how will the customer judge you a success?).

All items the customer expects should be documented in enough detail that the customer can sign off on them as complete, and the design team is unlikely to miss anything important by using this as their list of features and constraints.

3.3.2. Engineering requirements

Answers the question: What is the software we are building supposed to do (for example, what functions does it perform to meet customer expectations)?

- Numbered list of functions that should be performed by the software at a more detailed level than customer expectations.
- Performance criteria (speed, size, reliability, cost, safety, security).

This list should be thorough enough that designers can use it as the only list of requirements for the product. If the final software does everything listed in this document, and nothing more, then it is by definition complete.

3.3.3. Architecture

Answers the question: What components or objects are in the software, and what are their relationships?

- List of objects, functions, or other software elements with their interface information.
- If there is a network, a message dictionary of all message formats and meanings.

All components, objects, and other high level entities in the system should be listed.

3.3.4. Design

Answers the question: What does each component do?

- Flowcharts, statecharts, pseudocode, or other depictions of software behavior at a more abstract level than code.

Every architectural item should have a corresponding design. Every implementation module should also have a corresponding design.

3.3.5. Implementation

Answers the question: How does the code really work?

- The code itself.
- Code comments, preferably according to a brief style sheet that standardizes how and when to comment.

Every code module should follow a defined style sheet.

3.3.6. Test plan

Answers the question: How do we know that the system really works?

- List of tests to be performed, often in spreadsheet form.
- List of test results (passed, failed, not yet run).
- Records of peer review results.

Every requirement should be tested. In many cases this means there are actually two test plans: an engineering test plan (which tests each and every engineering requirement), and an acceptance test plan (which tests each and every customer requirement). Testing can be more thorough than this, but an acceptance test plan is the minimum requirement.

Additionally, every written document should be subject to peer review. We've bundled peer reviews with the test plan because they are both trying to find problems with the software and its supporting documents. Peer Reviews could instead be a separate topic in your document plan.

3.3.7. Bug list

Answers the questions: What's wrong with the software? And have the bugs been fixed yet?

- List of bugs and other issues discovered after some defined point in the development process.
- Status and priority of each bug (e.g., high/medium/low priority and fixed/open/deferred).

Every important bug should be in the bug list. There is leeway in deciding when to start tracking bugs (for example, perhaps only bugs that appear in acceptance tests are tracked). This can alternatively be called an issue list and include things beyond bugs.

3.3.8. User Guide

Answers the question: How does someone use and maintain the system?

- Instructions on how to use each feature and general instructions.
- List of required maintenance procedures with instructions.
- Troubleshooting and problem resolution guide.

Every feature and maintenance procedure should be documented. Common problems and reasonably foreseeable user mistakes should be addressed. Many times software developers provide inputs to this guide and a professional writer then produces a finished User Guide document.

3.3.9. Marketing materials

Answers the question: Why will a customer want to buy this product?

- List of features and advantages over previous models and the competition.
- Requirements to use the product (compatibility requirements, training requirements, environmental assumptions).
- Technical specifications (*e.g.*, speed, power, response time, standards met).

While it is common for marketing professionals to fully develop these materials, they need input from the development team. The input to marketing writers should contain a compete list of features, usage constraints, and limitations.

3.3.10. Schedule and staffing plan

Answers the question: When are things supposed to be done, and who is supposed to be doing them?

- Staff assignments and percentage of effort assigned.
- Schedule and milestones (both planned and actual performance).

All significant tasks used to estimate the schedule should be included. It should be possible to define an unambiguous owner for each piece of paper in the project, including both documentation and code.

3.3.11. A software development plan

Answers the question: What development process are you going to follow?

- General approach to software (steps in development process)
- Names of documents that must be produced with an outline for the sections of each document.
- On a per-document basis, minimum requirements for an acceptable document so that an impartial reviewer could reasonably decide if a particular document is acceptable.

The approach should give a flow of steps in the software creation process along with which pieces of paper are generated where. The list in this chapter is a reasonable starting point for the document names and acceptance criteria.

You don't need to create a software development plan from scratch for every project. A common approach is to maintain a reference software development plan as a company or group document which describes how typical projects are run. Each individual project can then have a mini-development plan that just says how this project's process will differ from the reference plan, if it differs at all.

3.4. Pitfalls

The biggest pitfall is creating paper for paper's sake. If you aren't used to creating a lot of paper right now, diving headlong into a heavy, paper-intensive process just for the sake of generating more paper is a bad idea. Partly that is because people won't really buy into the idea of generating paper until they see that it really makes things better instead of worse. And, partly this is because you'll generate the wrong paper if you don't experiment with what paper is useful and what isn't for your particular situation.

Another pitfall is failing to carry through on modifying paper (*all* the paper) to reflect changes made to the project over time. Some pieces of paper are only useful for a short while to help developers think through things (for example, sketches on a white board). It's fine to throw transient paper away when it is no longer useful. The important thing is to make sure you actually throw it away when it falls out of date.

Both of these pitfalls are addressed in *Chapter 4: How Much Paper Is Too Much?*

3.5. For more information

There are shelves full of books written about how to generate paper in support of software development. And there are many, many more types of paper that can be generated than what we've described.

3.5.1. General topic search keywords
• Software documentation
• Software lifecycle

3.5.2. Suggested reading

Douglass, "Designing Real-Time Systems with UML - I," *Embedded Systems Programming*, March 1998. (Parts II and III appear in the April 1998 and May 1998 issues).
This three-part series illustrates the use of the Unified Modeling Language (UML), which is a set of standardized diagrams that can be used to document the architecture and design of a project.

Ambler, S., "Agile documentation strategies," Dr. Dobbs Journal on-line, February 5, 2007.

http://www.embedded.com/columns/technicalinsights/197003518?_request id=441800
This is an essay that describes an agile methods approach to determining how much documentation is enough. Folks in this camp advocate a lot less documentation than we think is necessary, but that is because their main target audience develops shorter-lived software than is found in many embedded systems.

3.5.3. Examples of documentation standards

These references give examples of different approaches to documentation. Many of these are much heavier weight than is appropriate for a typical embedded system. But, they do serve as lists to help pick and choose which documentation ideas are right for a particular project. If you do end up creating very complex or safety critical systems, some of these references reflect what actually has to be done on such projects.

MIL-STD-2167A Defense Systems Software Development, 1988.
This is the grand-daddy of many heavyweight software processes, and is useful for historical perspective. Many people still use the terminology in this standard, and its successor MIL-STD-498.

NASA Software Documentation Standard, NASA-STD-2100-91, July 29, 1991.
This is a heavyweight software process developed by NASA.

Ganssle, *A Firmware Development Standard*, Version 1.2, January 2004.
This is a reasonable starting place for a coding style sheet.

There are also IEEE standards describing approaches for many of the suggested types of documents:

IEEE Std. 829-1998. *IEEE Standard for Software Test Documentation.*

IEEE Std. 830-1998. *IEEE Recommended Practice for Software Requirements Specification.*

IEEE Std. 1016-1998. *IEEE Recommended Practice for Software Design Descriptions.*

IEEE Std. 1044-1993. *IEEE Standard Classification for Software Anomalies.*

IEEE Std. 1059-1993. *IEEE Guide for Software Verification and Validation Plans.*

IEEE Std. 1063-2001. *IEEE Standard for Software User Documentation.*

IEEE Std. 1074-2006. *IEEE Standard for Developing a Software Project Life Cycle Process.*

IEEE Std. 1223-1998. *IEEE Guide for Developing System Requirements Specifications.*

IEEE Std. 1471-2000. *IEEE Recommended Practice for Architectural Description of Software-Intensive Systems.*

3.5.4. Additional reading

Lethbridge, T.C.; Singer, J.; Forward, A.; "How software engineers use documentation: the state of the practice," *IEEE Software*, v. 20 no. 6, pp. 35-39, November-December 2003.

Discusses results of a study of documentation use in industry (mostly non-embedded industry). In practice, documentation seems valuable, but isn't always kept up to date.

Chapter 4
How Much Paper Is Too Much?

- Some paper to support your design is good, but too much paper can be wasteful.
- Paper is useful if someone's life is made more difficult in its absence, or if someone thinks it is useful enough to keep it up to date.
- Try to find ways to make basic documents useful and worth keeping up to date.

Contents:

Every piece of paper should be forced to earn its keep as a useful document. The notion of paper as "documentation" that is written after the work has been done is fundamentally flawed. If paper seems useless, ask how it can be made useful before deciding to abandon it. Throw out any paper that isn't kept updated.

Avoid the pitfall of declaring paper to be useless simply as an excuse to avoid having to create it.

4.1. Overview

Generating no paper, where paper includes electronic documentation, is a bad idea. But, more paper just for the sake of having paper isn't necessarily better. It's worth taking a critical look at how much paper is the right amount for your situation.

4.1.1. Importance of keeping useful paper

The problem with avoiding useless paper is knowing which paper is, in fact, really useless. It is all too easy say "this paper is useless" for reasons other than an objective assessment of the situation. For example, the person assigned to create the paper might prefer to spend the time writing code (or just going home on time).

Having truly useful paper can make a big difference in avoiding problems and creating a more effective development process. But, creating paper costs money and time. In general, you should make sure that any paper you generate provides value. If the paper isn't useful, then you need to either (a) find a way to make the paper useful, or (b) get rid of the paper. In many cases the right choice is making the paper useful, but sometimes getting rid of the paper is the best strategy. The trick is being able to tell which situation is which.

4.1.2. Possible symptoms

If you see the below symptoms, you are generating paper that is useless outright, or are failing to benefit from the effort of creating the paper.

✖ Documents are created near the end of the project, as "documentation" instead of being used to support the design process itself. (In our view, this is useless paper because you aren't benefitting in the development process from having created it. Whether the customer demands such useless paper as part of a software deliverable for reasons beyond what you care about is another matter.)

✖ A document in the design package isn't traced to other documents. For example, there is no effort to compare the states in a statechart to the elements of an implementation's case statement to be sure states were not omitted or added by accident.

✖ Documents aren't updated on a regular basis. For example, when a major code rewrite is performed, requirements aren't updated to reflect the new code functionality.

4.1.3. Risks of creating useless paper

There are two main risks in creating useless paper:

➤ Resources are wasted creating paper that nobody cares about.

➤ Paper that isn't kept up to date (because it is useless) will mislead someone later because it has outdated or incorrect information.

4.2. How to avoid useless paper

Creating paper takes time and effort, just like everything else. Given deadlines and resource limits, paper that isn't perceived as being useful is likely to be poorly written and not kept up to date. That, in turn, pretty much ensures it never will be of any use.

> **Every piece of paper should be forced to earn its keep as a useful document.**

Some projects generate truly useless paper. That's a pure waste of time, and should be avoided. But, it is more typically the case that projects generate paper that could be of use, if only a little more effort were put in, or it were created early in the project rather than at the end, or if it were a little different. In those cases, it is well worth making the extra effort or change to convert something that is wasteful into something that is useful.

Chapter 3. How Much Paper Is Enough?, gives a list of documents which are useful in pretty much every embedded project. Beyond that, it is likely that other paper can be made useful enough to be worth having.

4.2.1. Make paper useful

We propose the following rules for useful paper. Your own list might vary, so consider this a starting point. To be useful, a piece of paper must have the following properties:

- **Have a reasonably well defined structure and scope.** Paper should serve a well defined purpose and be formatted according to a relatively standard template within the project or organization. For example, a requirements document should have a defined purpose, scope, and style. Paper that is unstructured and unorganized is much less likely to be useful.

- **Have a named custodian.** Paper that doesn't have an owner won't be kept up to date as things change, and will quickly become useless.

- **Be reviewed.** Peer reviews are the best way to ensure high quality, useful paper. If it isn't worth reviewing, then it isn't important enough to be kept.

- **Have a defined consumer.** Paper is only useful if someone reads it. Who will read a particular piece of paper? If the answer is "nobody" or "we don't know," then it is difficult to say it is important enough to keep.

- **Be used as part of the development process.** Paper that is produced after the fact isn't useful, at least to the development team. In fact, it is often a warning sign if developers habitually refer to paper as "documentation" rather than design documents. The idea of first writing the code and then back-filling the design documentation is popular in software classes, but is fundamentally wrong. The whole point of creating paper is to help the design process as it unfolds. While it is true that after-the-fact documentation might help maintainers, such an approach misses out on the benefits to developers of creating documents as part of a methodical design process.

> **The notion of paper as documentation that is written after the work has been done is fundamentally flawed.**

- **Be traced to other documents.** Most paper fits into the grand scheme of the design process in that it consumes information from one document and produces information that feeds another document. For example, when looked at from a development process point of view, a design consumes requirements and produces the input to implementation. Documents should be traced to other documents to show where in the big picture they fit, and to make sure that the items consumed and produced match corresponding items in other documents. This traceability could be done as part of reviews, or could be documented in the paper itself.

- **Be short.** Like code, paper requires effort to create, effort to make useful, and effort to maintain. Short, concise documents are more useful and efficient than long, poorly organized ones.

> **If paper seems useless, ask how it can be made useful before deciding to abandon it.**

If you have paper that meets few or none of the above criteria, ask yourself how they could be changed to be more useful. You have already invested effort in creating the paper - why not invest just a little more to make it useful?

It is always possible to create paper that technically meets all these criteria and is still useless for practical purposes. But, in general, if you can meet these criteria and are trying to do the right thing, you'll be fine.

4.2.2. Keep paper up to date

Outdated paper can be worse than useless. It can mislead people by giving incorrect information. We recommend that any paper which falls out of date be immediately updated or discarded. A promise to update it later at some undetermined date means it should be thrown out, because later never comes.

> **Throw out any paper that isn't kept updated.**

There is an implication to this rule. The decision to create a piece of paper commits developers to expending effort (and thus development cost). That paper has to be not only created, but maintained for the life of the product. We still think that paper can be extremely valuable. But, this high cost means you should create just enough paper – not go crazy creating paper that isn't worth maintaining.

Some paper is archival in nature, rather than a living thing that changes as the project evolves. For example, reports of design reviews might be stored as a basis of statistical data for software process monitoring. Or test results might be stored as part of a record to demonstrate that a particular release of a product was sufficiently tested. In these cases, the maintenance of the document doesn't necessarily mean it is changed when the design changes. Maintenance is still required, however, to make sure the information remains accessible as operating systems, report generators, and viewing programs undergo version changes.

4.2.3. Eliminate paper that can't be made useful

There are many instances in which paper should be created on a temporary basis and then abandoned. Informal to-do lists, e-mail discussions to clarify thoughts that lead to a change of formal paper, and so on are all useful. But, they should just be considered an informal adjunct to the developers' memories, and not formal paper that is part of the design process. They don't have to be maintained so long as they are temporary in nature – the formal project documents can't rely upon them to provide details or explanations

4.3. Pitfalls

The most prevalent pitfalls to creating just enough paper are arguments that are used as false justification for doing away with paper entirely. A classic is:

> "There is no point wasting time on documentation, because it won't be kept up to date. Only things in the source code itself are kept up to date."

This may be true in a particular environment, but the problem is not that documents can't be kept up to date. When someone offers this explanation, what they really mean is simply:

> "Our development team doesn't maintain documentation."

The problem with this situation is that the design process is ignoring documents other than actual implementation. Therefore, developers don't find such documents useful, and don't maintain them. Using this as an excuse to avoid documentation isn't the best way to proceed. Rather, developers should consider how adding one or two simple documents might make the development process more efficient. If those documents seem useful (and simple, and short), then developers might be motivated to maintain them. Over time, additional documents might prove their worth and be maintained – or not. Giving an incremental approach to adding basic items of paper to the development process is worth a try.

"We'll create the documentation at the end of the project."

There are two problems with this approach. First, the end never comes, or there is some new crisis that causes the documentation of the old project to be skipped in favor of the new project. The documentation is seldom created.

Second, the point of design documents is to help with the design process itself, not just serve as a pile of paper talking about what happened as a history lesson. The most extreme example of this we've seen is the notion of an automatic flowchart generator. Feed your source code into a program, and out comes a very nicely drawn flowchart … that is never actually read by a person. Why bother? That flowchart certainly didn't help in creating the code! The flowchart won't help with later maintenance either. The true value in a flowchart is conveying the important parts of what is happening, especially while you're trying to grapple with the design. Drawing pretty boxes around lines of code you could read for yourself isn't particularly useful.

4.4. For more information

The ideas in this chapter are somewhat different than the usual approach to lightweight software development, which avoids paper whenever possible on general principles. We aren't arguing that paper should be omitted. Rather, we're arguing that it should be kept simple, and useful.

4.4.1. General topic search keywords

• Software documentation

4.4.2. Recommended reading

Parnas, D. L.; Clements, P., "A rational design process: how and why to fake it," *IEEE Transactions on Software Engineering*, v. SE-12, n. 2, pp. 251-257 February 1986.
This paper describes why a perfect software process can't exist, and approaches that can be used to create a good process that is nonetheless better than ad hoc approaches. Page 252 has a nice list of reasons why documents are useful. It also describes how to create useful documents, especially for requirements.

Knuth, D., "Literate programming," *The Computer Journal*, v. 27 n. 2, pp. 97-111, 1984.
This paper started a style of programming that includes comprehensive descriptions of a program intermingled with the code itself - far beyond mere "commenting." It is an alternate approach to what is described in this chapter.

REQUIREMENTS & ARCHITECTURE

Chapter 5
Written Requirements

- A requirements document describes everything your embedded software has to do (and not do), as well as any constraints it must meet.
- Good requirements must be consistent, precise, measurable, and traceable through the development process.
- Ideally, if your system does everything in your requirements (and nothing else), that means your system is perfect. If that's not the case, you should improve your requirements.

Contents:

5.1. Overview

Every system has requirements, whether they happen to be written down or not. Those requirements include behaviors the system is supposed to have and some behaviors that the system is supposed to avoid (for example, system crashes and unsafe operations). The requirements also include system properties such as performance and dependability, and constraints such as cost and size.

5.1.1. Importance of written requirements

Writing requirements down is an essential part of a good development process. Without written requirements, it is all too easy to omit important features, have confusion about what the system is supposed to do, or even create a system that does the wrong thing.

Skipping the written requirements phase simply defers the capture of requirements to potentially less efficient forms – such as implicitly embedding the requirements in the code itself. This deferral can dramatically increase the cost of finding and correcting requirements problems, both because problems may be discovered later in the development process, and because requirements problems may become entangled with other issues such as implementation decisions.

We're not saying that on the first day of the project you'll write flawless requirements and proceed from there. But we are saying you should take your best shot at a reasonable set of written requirements as soon as possible, and that you should explicitly write them down.

5.1.2. Possible symptoms

The usual symptom of a requirements problem is simply that they aren't written down:

✖ There is no single written document which gives all the requirements for the system.

You have a problem if such a document, however simple or complex, doesn't exist. But, another symptom is often:

✖ A requirements document exists, but is too informal or too intertwined with design information to be really useful.

5.1.3. Risks of inadequate requirements

If you have inadequate written requirements, you are at increased risk for:

➤ Misunderstandings about what the system is supposed to do, leading to rework or project failure.

➤ Discovery of requirement issues late in the design cycle, when they are expensive to fix (especially problems that a peer review of written requirements could have caught at the outset).

➤ Gaps in verification and validation because all requirements are not addressed. (For example, not testing a critical function because the test team didn't know it was supposed to be in the system.)

5.2. What to put in written requirements

The point of requirements is to provide a list of everything that should be in the product. This includes mechanical, electrical, software, human interface, power, safety, and other considerations - truly everything. That doesn't necessarily mean it has to be a 1000 page document for a simple product. But a single paragraph or a few illustrative scenarios just doesn't provide enough detail to cover everything that is needed.

5.2.1. The big picture on requirements

The main reasons you should have written, complete requirements are:

- They help you make sure you haven't forgotten anything.
- They help you understand the big picture up front, before you've wasted time building a system that can't handle everything that is required of it.
- They provide a way to keep the rest of the design process anchored. For example, a thorough test plan will make sure that it exercises everything in the requirements document.
- They provide a way to communicate with stakeholders by saying, in effect, "when we're done, the system will do what this document says."

Thus, you want your requirements to be thorough. The point is, everything has to be in there somehow, or you can't be sure the missing parts will get done.

> Requirements include:
> everything the product must do,
> everything the product must NOT do, and
> every constraint the product must meet.

Longer documents are more expensive to create and maintain than short documents. The right size for requirements depends on the context and is always a tradeoff. It's important that nothing significant be left out, but:

> Shorter is better.

Requirements need not be a piece of fine literature with fancy prose. Bullet points are fine. Phrases instead of sentences work, so long as the meaning is clear. Short but readable should be the goal.

Nobody is omniscient, and it is impractical to expect requirements to be perfectly correct, especially at the start of the project. Nonetheless, writing them down to the extent possible up front eliminates many needless problems. And, that written document serves as a vehicle for collecting additional requirements as they are discovered (or changed) during the course of development.

If the system is so novel or vaguely defined at the start that you can't write requirements, it's fine to spend some time prototyping. Prototyping on a resource-rich platform such as a desktop computer can make it easier to develop algorithms, get customer feedback on potential alternative approaches, and understand what the requirements should be. But don't mistake that prototype code for an initial product! When you are done prototyping:

(1) Throw the prototype away.

(2) Write some requirements based on what you learned.

(3) Start developing product-quality software.

5.2.2. Types of requirements

There are three types of requirements:

- **Functional requirements.** These are functions, behaviors, or features that must be provided by the system. Typically, functional requirements are implemented by hardware, software, or other system mechanisms.

  Example: "When the button is pressed, the door shall open."

- **Non-functional requirements.** These are also called quality attributes, or sometimes extra-functional requirements. These are properties the system must display that aren't overt functions or features, but rather are attributes of the system as a whole. Some examples are performance, security, safety, and usability.

  Example: "Response time to a button press shall be less than 200 msec."

- **Constraints.** These are limitations on how the system can be built. Typical constraints include mandated adherence to a particular set of international standards, use of a particular type of technology, limitations on production cost, a requirement to use a specific model of CPU, and adherence to a particular set of design rules.

  Example: "System shall conform to the requirements of IEC 61508 for SIL 2 software." (This means the system is slightly safety critical, and will conform to a standard that mandates certain techniques to ensure the software will be as safe as necessary for use.)

> **Every system has functional requirements,**
> **non-functional requirements, and constraints.**

Every system has all three types of requirements. Many requirements documents focus on functional requirements. But, including non-functional requirements and constraints is important to avoid a design that functions properly but fails to meet the other types of requirements. (See *Chapter 8. Non-Functional Requirements.*)

The essential part of a requirement is that it tells you *what* needs to be done, but not *how*. If it specifies *how* then it is really part of a design and might overly constrain engineering approaches. (In some cases, the *how* is mandated by law or by a specific customer request, in which case specifying *how* is appropriate. But those cases are only a small fraction of all requirements for a project.)

> *Bad Example:* "When the timer expires, the software shall increment 16-bit integer variable RollOverCount."
> (Does it really need to be 16 bits? What if 32-bit variables are easier to manipulate – are we prevented from doing that? Can we call the variable something else if there is a naming conflict? If we are testing the system, how do we know what the variable was incremented properly so we can ensure the requirement was met?)

> *Good Example:* "The system shall keep a count of how many timer expirations have occurred, with the ability to tally at least 15,000 expirations."

Beyond that, a well written requirement must be verifiable. It is important to be able to tell if a requirement has been met. If you can't tell that a requirement has been met, then there is not much point in making it a requirement! Verification might take place through testing, inspection, or design reviews. (People often say a requirement must be testable. Verifiable is a more general term for this same idea.)

> *Bad Example:* "The system shall be fast." (How fast is fast? Does everything have to be fast, or just some aspects of the system? How do we know it is fast enough? Is it OK if it is fast on average but slow sometimes?)

> *Good Example:* "The system shall have a worst-case response time of less than 500 msec."

5.3. Good requirement practices

Beyond the basics, there are many good requirement practices. Some widely used good ideas are listed below, and doubtless there are other good practices that you will discover or adopt for your projects. In general, requirements should conform to all the below practices, but sometimes there are good reasons not to do that. In each case, we give examples of requirements that are in general good and bad to illustrate the point.

5.3.1. Measurement

Any requirement that can be measured should be stated in a way that makes it easy to determine, via measurement, whether the requirement has been met. In many cases, this means the requirement must have a number.

Bad Example: "The system shall be fast."
(Again, how fast is fast?)

Good Example: "The system shall have a worst-case response time of less than 500 msec."

> **Requirements must be easily verified and, if practical do to so, directly measurable.**

5.3.2. Tolerance

Numeric values should have a tolerance associated with them if they are single values rather than ranges. This avoids accidentally over-engineering systems or complicating things to exactly meet a value that was really meant to be an approximate target.

Bad Example: "When the system is activated, the output signal shall be set high for 500 msec and then set low." (What if the available counter/timer can only provide 499 or 501 msec, but not exactly 500 msec – is that good enough?)

Good Example: "The system shall assert an output voltage for 500 +/- 5 msec."

Good Example: "The system shall have a worst-case response time of less than 500 msec." (No tolerance is required because the acceptable values form a range rather than an exact target value.)

5.3.3. Consistency

While it might seem boring and unimaginative, using extremely consistent terminology and precise verbs makes requirements much easier to interpret. For example, if two words are used for an idea, should the reader assume that two different things are meant because there are two different words, or not?

Bad Example: "When the button is pressed once, the output signal shall turn on. When the switch is pressed twice, the output signal shall turn off."
(Are the *button* and *switch* the same thing? Or different things? If they are the same, why are they called two different things? If something is a button, then it should be called button everywhere in the requirements document. Also, in this requirement, it is unclear whether *twice* means a second time, twice without any other intervening button presses regardless of time, or twice in quick succession.)

Good Example: "When the button is pressed once, the output signal shall turn on. When the button is pressed a second time, the output signal shall turn off."

Requirements should also be consistent in that they should avoid conflict with each other. Determining whether this can happen takes some thought, and often is more than a simple matter of phrasing.

5.3.4. Use of shall and should

Requirements need consistent terminology to indicate whether something is mandatory or desirable. *Shall* is used to denote a mandatory behavior. *Should* is used to denote a desirable behavior that should typically take place, but might not happen all the time or might be optional in uncommon cases. Most sentences in a requirements document need to use the word **shall** to be unambiguous, however boring that might be.

> **Every requirement should contain one of the words: *shall* or *should*.**

Bad Example: "When button is pressed, the user wants the light to turn on." (This tells us what the user is thinking, but that doesn't really tell us what the system is supposed to do. While it is somewhat obvious that the software should turn on the light, is this always what shall happen? What if there is some other situation that might force the light off? Will the user infer something from the light going on that is or isn't appropriate?)

Good Example: "When the button is pressed, the light shall turn on" (This is unambiguous – it has to happen.)

Good Example: "When the button is pressed, the light should turn on unless an error condition exists."
(*Should* means that the light turning on is normal operation. But there might be cases of unusual situations or very difficult to deal with operating conditions where it just isn't going to happen, and that's OK.)

5.3.5. Trackability

Every requirement should have a number or alphanumeric identifier so that it can be tracked and referred to easily in other parts of the design. For example, a test plan might list which requirements are verified by that particular test.

Good Example: "R17. When the button is pressed, the light shall turn on." (This is Requirement #17.)

In general, a requirement has two types of text: an actual requirement, and a rationale that amplifies the meaning of that requirement. Each actual requirement should have a unique identifier and should start its own paragraph or other item in the requirements document. Combining multiple requirements into a single item should be avoided, because this hinders traceability.

> **Every requirement should be uniquely numbered.**

There are many other characteristics of good requirements, most of which are common sense. For example, requirements should be feasible (this makes a requirement such as "the software shall be perfect" problematic). But the above list is a good starting point, and the rest can come after these basic good practices are in place.

5.3.6. Readability

The biggest practical problem with thorough requirements is that few people really want to read them. And yet those same people who won't read the requirements are sure to complain when the system doesn't do what they expected (because the requirements weren't what they imagined them to be).

The first line of defense against people not reading requirements is to create and maintain a *set* of requirements documents, with each document intended for a different audience. For example, it is common to have different documents for marketing requirements and engineering requirements. They have different audiences and different emphasis. Usually the marketing requirements document is much shorter. Yet, if you can trace all the requirements back and forth between those two documents, they are simply different but consistent descriptions of the same product. If someone takes the time to read and approve of the marketing requirements, then there should be no huge surprises even if they don't read the engineering requirements.

If people don't want to read any requirement document, you can try to convince them of the need to do so. For example, ask if they actually look at their credit card statements or checking account statements from the bank to see if everything looks right. Or if they would order a new car without checking to make sure the engine, transmission, sound system, trim options, and color were what they wanted. But, unfortunately, some people are happy to skip the fine print on the assumption that somehow things will work out just fine. For example, almost nobody reads the fine print on the huge pile of documents involved in buying a house. So, while attempting to convince people to read requirements is worth a try, don't expect that reason will actually work on everyone.

Another approach to get more people to spend time understanding the requirements is to make the document skimable. For example, for each chunk of related requirements include a plain English summary of what those requirements are trying to accomplish as a high level comment. This requires more work to create and maintain the requirements, but might be worth it if it gets more stakeholders to become involved in understanding and improving the requirements.

Finally, some projects give up on requirements and just create executable prototypes to show to stakeholders and ask "is this what you want?" There is certainly some validity to this approach, but it isn't well suited to many aspects of embedded system design. For example, people can tell if they like a user interface. But consider what will happen when they watch a data logger with no display being demonstrated. Can they tell that it is sampling every 250 msec in degrees Fahrenheit instead of every 25 msec in degrees Centigrade? They might care a lot, but only a requirements document is going to give them that type of information. Sometimes written requirements are the only practical way to define how a product works.

In the end, it is impossible to force everyone who needs to read the requirements to actually do so. But you can make it clear that if they don't understand the requirements, they don't have the moral high ground when they later complain things don't work as they expected. And you can try to find ways to make it easier for them to read the requirements if they decide to give it a try.

5.4. Pitfalls

(See also the pitfalls section of *Chapter 8. Non-Functional Requirements.*)

A common pitfall in requirements documents is gold plating. This refers to the tendency of engineers to include product features that don't really need to be there. Those extra features may be fun to put in, and might sound sexy, but every requirement adds cost to the development process. Only requirements that need to be implemented in the final system should be included in the requirements document.

5.5. For more information

5.5.1. General topic search keywords

- Software requirements
- Requirements specification

5.5.2. Recommended reading

The topic of requirements is well covered in articles and books. The hard part is finding something both practical and digestible on the topic.

Wiegers, K., *Software Requirements* 2nd Edition, Microsoft Press, 2003.
A comprehensive, well-written book on the topic by an author who has worked with embedded system developers.

Brombach, R., *Customer requirements and requirements analysis example*, SAE 2001-01-0018, Society of Automotive Engineers, 2001.
An example of requirements for an automotive lighting system, with commentary.

Gause, D. C.; Weinberg, G. M., *Exploring Requirements: Quality Before Design*, Dorset House, 1999.
A discussion of how to get requirements right.

5.5.3. Suggested standards

IEEE Std. 830-1998. *IEEE Recommended Practice for Software Requirements Specification.*

IEEE Std. 1223-1998. *IEEE Guide for Developing System Requirements Specifications.*

Chapter 6
Measurable Requirements

- If a requirement isn't measurable, you can't know if it has been satisfied.
- If something isn't directly measurable, you may need to identify an indirect measurement.
- Approaches to improve measurability include: identifying proxy measurements, having the test team identify a practical measure that is close enough to be useful, incorporating field data feedback into an iterated development process, measuring the design methodology instead of the actual product, and using formal methods to prove properties about the design.
- A benefit of emphasizing measurability is identifying impossible-to-meet requirements.

Contents:

Don't require perfect software. Include an objective pass/fail criterion with each requirement.

If you can't define a real measurement, create a proxy measurement that is likely to result in the property you desire. Get testers involved with making requirements measurable up front in the development process. Collect field data on requirements that are difficult to measure. Supplement your measurements with methodology requirements.

6.1. Overview

If you can't tell whether a requirement has been met, then why bother to include it in the requirements document? We're not trying to say you should skip the requirements phase of a project. Rather, we think that you should find ways to demonstrate that every requirement for your system has been met. Making requirements measurable is the first step in doing that.

6.1.1. Importance of having measurable requirements

It is relatively easy to write a requirement that sounds great, is obviously desirable, is easy to understand, and is impossible to measure or otherwise validate. Consider, for example, the requirement of "the software shall never crash." How long to you have to run the software to see if it crashes (or not) to meet this requirement? Answer: to be sure it is never, you need to test the program for longer than forever. And even if you didn't see a crash while testing, that doesn't prove the system couldn't crash in some circumstance you didn't happen to encounter. Clearly measuring *never* is impracticable, so you need a different requirement to attain measurability.

Some requirements are attributes that can be measured, but for which the requirement doesn't state a goal. For example, a requirement that "system response shall be fast" begs the question of how fast is *fast*.

Some requirements are things that can't be measured by testing, but rather are properties of the system as a whole that are difficult to understand until after the product has been shipped. For example, determining how reliable software will be is difficult before the system is shipped. These non-functional properties are the topic of a separate chapter (*Chapter 8. Non-Functional Requirements*), but the same issues of measurement apply.

If you care about meeting the requirements for your system (and, just as importantly, care about knowing that you have actually met them), then you need to make every requirement measurable somehow.

6.1.2. Possible symptoms

There are three types of symptoms that indicate you may have requirement measurability problems:

- ✘ Requirements specify absolute perfection, and in particular can only be achieved with defect-free software. Beware of words such as *never* or *always*.

- ✘ Requirements use descriptive adjectives or adverbs rather than numerical targets. Troublesome words include: fast, slow, big, small, friendly, inexpensive, and flexible. Imprecise terms such as these make it impossible to be sure you have met the actual requirement intended.

- ✘ Requirements specify targets for quantities or properties that can't realistically be measured. If, when reading a requirement, it isn't obvious how to measure success, then there is a problem.

6.1.3. Risks of unmeasurable requirements

➤ System fails to meet customer expectations because of imprecise communication of expectations. For example, the customer's idea of *fast* might be much faster than the developers' notion of *fast*.

➤ System development costs more than expected because of unrealistically stringent requirements. For example, the customer's idea of *fast* might be much more relaxed than the developers' notion of *fast*, leading to unnecessary effort making the system faster than necessary.

➤ The system fails in the field because desired properties weren't measured, but were assumed to be met.

➤ Product literature fails to disclose reasonable limitations, resulting in company liability. For example, a system that isn't designed to be highly reliable might need a "not for life-critical use" warning in its product manual.

6.2. Successful quantification of requirements

It is all too easy to write a requirement that sounds desirable, but can't be verified. Consider, for example, the ever-popular requirement to be *user friendly*. How friendly is that exactly? And how do you plan to measure it? Yes, extensive human subject studies can help quantify *user friendly*, but that is seldom what embedded designers have in mind. More often they mean something like "user friendly as perceived by design engineers," without the necessary perspective on how different from the general population most design engineers really are.

A good requirement needs to be quantifiable. For example, saying software needs to be fast or easy to use really doesn't help anybody understand what is meant. (How fast is *fast*? How easy is *easy*?) Thus, each requirement must be quantified so that it can be judged as a pass/fail criterion for success, or as a measurable number.

The problem with quantification is that you need to create a measure that actually matters without making measurement impractical. For example, it is very tempting to have a requirement of "this software shall never crash." But, that's simply unrealistic! *Never* is a really, really, really long time (and then some). So, be sure to create quantification approaches that either reflect your real requirements, or at least seem to be a reasonable proxy for the requirement you want to accomplish.

6.2.1. Avoid a requirement for perfection

We'd all like our systems to be perfect, but that is just unrealistic. Unless you are developing a safety critical system according to the highest level of safety integrity, you just have to assume that perfection isn't realistic. Thus, your requirements should avoid both a requirement of perfection and an assumption of perfection.

Here are some typical requirements that assume perfection:

Bad Example: "The software shall never crash."

Incomplete Example: "Mean time between hardware failures shall be at least 5000 hours." (But there is no mention of software failures! Entire system failure rate is what matters.)

Bad Example: "The system shall be safe." (What does *safe* mean? Nothing is perfectly and completely safe.)

Bad Example: "The system shall be secure." (Nobody knows how to make something perfectly resistant to attack. Moreover, new attacks emerge over time.)

Bad Example: "The system shall be easy to use." (Not only is this imprecise, but it fails to specify user demographics. Did you really mean to include everyone, such as people who can't see or can't hear? Perhaps, but in many cases that isn't the target user population.)

Don't require perfect software.

Avoiding a need for perfection can get tricky. It is overly cumbersome to include exceptions and error response situations in every requirement. For example, it would make the requirements too clumsy if you said something like "When the button is pressed the light shall illuminate, except when the button has failed, or the light has failed, or the software has crashed, or …" This can be solved by having a separate fault response portion of the requirements.

Ultimately, the difficult part of avoiding perfection is coming to terms with the limits of technology. You're not likely to create a system that never crashes, so when you write a requirement you need to put a number on crash frequency. That's often an uncomfortable thing to do. Customers don't want to hear that they are getting software that will crash once in a while, but that's reality. All we can say is that you should just bite the bullet and write requirements that actually address the issues.

Good Example: "Mean time between software crashes shall exceed 1000 operating hours. At least 90% of software crashes shall be followed by an automatic reboot to resume normal operation within one minute."

Good Example: "Mean time between failures from all sources shall be 4000 hours."

Good Example: "Mean time between hazardous system outputs shall be 100,000 hours."
(This one is difficult to measure because the number is quite large, but it is at least a well defined requirement.)

Good Example: "The system shall require password authentication according to company security standard XYZ."
(This defers the issue of security to an external document, but that's OK,
because it gives a way of knowing if the requirement has been met - either
you follow the standard or you don't.)

POSSIBLY Good Example: "The system shall be easy to use for the targeted
customer base."
(This doesn't provide a direct measurement, but we discuss that topic later
in the section on making things measurable.)

There are some legal implications of admitting in a requirements document
that imperfection is a fact of life. In some industries it is undesirable to write anything down suggesting less than perfect safety, for example. Unfortunately, requirements documents could appear in a courtroom during a lawsuit. In those
cases you need to follow the practices of your industry or company (which, often
times, means not putting such things in writing). If in doubt and you are new to
the industry, ask your colleagues about how such things are handled. It's important to follow typical practices for your situation.

6.2.2. Being precise

Some requirements sound great, but simply aren't precise enough to be useful.
Systems that are fast, inexpensive, and easy to use are always nice to have - but
quantifying these notions can be difficult.

Include an objective pass/fail criterion with each requirement.

The best way to solve the problem with imprecise requirements is to make
them more precise. For example, if response time matters, give the response
time in the requirements. That way, developers know what their goal is, and can
tell early in the development cycle whether they are likely to reach it.

Good Example: "Response time shall average 100 msec, and should not exceed 200 msec."

Sometimes requirements are relative to other products (whether your own
products, or competitor products). For example, a requirement might be:

Bad Example: "Response time shall be at least as fast as for the previous
product version."

That type of requirement is OK as far is it goes in terms of being unambiguous. But, it begs the question of "how fast is fast?" It is all too common to see
such a requirement and then find out that nobody really knows exactly how the
previous product version performs. It is better to give the target in the requirements document if possible, or at least attach an annex of relevant measurements so the developers can look up what the target is, such as:

Good Example: "Response time shall be at least as fast as for the previous product version (see Appendix A)."

(This assumes that Appendix A gives the relevant response time in a description of the previous product.)

You could leave it to the test team to figure out what the requirement is, for example by doing side-by-side comparisons between old and new systems to compare response times. In practice this is often what happens. But, consider, this approach doesn't provide any way for developers to know if they are going to meet the requirement until after development is completed and the testers find a problem (or don't).

6.3. Measuring the unmeasurable

There is no doubt that some things are difficult to measure. And that means it is difficult to write an easily measurable requirement for them. There are several possible approaches to dealing with difficult to measure quantities.

6.3.1. Don't ignore unmeasurable topics when writing requirements

Simply ignoring measurability of difficult topics is the default, and worst, option. For example, if you can't measure software reliability, then just omit that topic from the requirements. We strongly advise against this approach, as you might imagine. This approach just sweeps the problem under the rug. Don't do this.

6.3.2. Create a proxy measurement

It might be that you can't measure the property you want directly, but you can create a different measurement that is good enough for your purposes.

For example, let's say you want software that crashes less often than once per week. You might have a requirement that the software is able to run for two weeks during system acceptance tests without crashing. This won't guarantee that it will always run for at least one week without crashing, but you can be pretty sure that mean time between crashes in likely operational scenarios will be a lot longer than 5 minutes! In other words, you might be willing to believe that two weeks without a crash during acceptance test is a good enough proxy measurement for testing whether the system is unlikely to crash after one week of real use.

The idea of a proxy measurement is to figure out something that is measurable, and is likely to be correlated to the property you are interested in. It should also be unlikely to encourage developers to compromise the system overall just to meet that goal. Very often the proxy measurement is quite arbitrary compared to real system operating conditions, but sometimes that is the best that can be done.

> **If you can't define a real measurement, create a proxy measurement that is likely to result in the property you desire.**

For example, there is a requirement that it take no more than 90 seconds to evacuate all passengers from a jumbo jet airliner. An actual test involving a plane full of volunteers is performed, and they are timed to see if all of them get off within 90 seconds. If the test passes (and other tests pass as well), the FAA certifies the aircraft for regular use. But in real life, there is no guarantee that you'll have 90 seconds after a crash to evacuate. 90 seconds is a completely arbitrary (although not unreasonable) measurement. Nonetheless, that test gives some reasonable measure of how easy or hard it is to evacuate an aircraft. It is deemed good enough to be a useful proxy measurement for the real requirement that most or all passengers be able to evacuate after a survivable crash landing or other emergency.

Creating a proxy measurement is fraught with risk. It is easy to create a measurement that doesn't actually correlate with what you care about, or even one that makes things worse instead of better. Management texts and even a few comic strips are replete with stories of management metrics that lead to organizational dysfunction (for example, paying developers for each bug they find and fix, when they are in a position to insert bugs themselves). But, a well thought out proxy measurement is often the best that can be done.

6.3.3. Get testers involved up front

Another way to handle an imprecise requirement is to let testers resolve any ambiguity as they perform testing. For example, when presented with a requirement to be *fast*, the test group will have to resolve the question of how fast is *fast* before they can declare a speed test to have passed or failed. We don't recommend this approach as-is, because all it does is delay the clarification of the requirement until after the development work is done. Better to understand the requirement before all that effort is expended.

If design engineers get stuck on defining measurements, it can be useful to ask testers to help with defining measures up front, while requirements are being written. Testers might be able to suggest a proxy measurement that isn't too difficult for them to perform and that is a good enough measurement for requirements purposes. Having testers help define measures is an excellent reason to have testers involved in creating requirements.

> **Get testers involved with making requirements measurable up front in the development process.**

6.3.4. Create an engineering feedback system

Beyond creating proxy measurements, a good way to know if a difficult-to-measure requirement has been met is to gather data after the system has been deployed to see how things turn out. For example, if you have a mean time between software crash goal of 100,000 hours, then you aren't going to rack up enough testing time to know if you will meet that goal. (You might, however, be able to tell if you don't meet that goal. Multiple crashes during a few hundred hours of testing make it pretty unlikely the fielded system will run for 100,000 hours without a crash.)

Even as you do your best during development, you can take things a step further by collecting data on deployed systems and feed that data back to the development team. The data can be fed back as part of normal operations, can be collected during system maintenance, or can be collected from units returned as defective. If the data indicates you aren't meeting your requirement, then you might be able to find and fix the problem, or at least know you need to do better with your development efforts (and proxy measurements for that requirement) next time.

> Collect field data on requirements that are difficult to measure.

6.3.5. Rely upon process

In some cases there is no way to actually know if you are going to meet a particular requirement target during development, or even during initial system deployment. There are two general ways developers can deal with this: relying upon the quality of your development process, and formal methods.

Process-based approaches attempt to use a high quality software design process to reduce the chance defects will appear in a system. This is especially common for highly critical systems, which might have failure goals of only one catastrophic failure per billion (1,000,000,000) operating hours. The belief is that following a rigorous design methodology will improve quality.

There is certainly some validity to the claim that better software development methodology (*i.e.*, better software process) tends to increases software quality. Thus, if you create a particular requirement and follow a good process, you are more likely to meet that requirement than you are by following an ad hoc process. But, good process isn't a complete substitute for being able to actually measure the outcome.

There are fairly lightweight methodology approaches that can be included in any project plan. For example, if you are worried about software crashes, a compromise requirement might be: "All sources of software crashes discovered during system integration testing shall be tracked to root cause and eliminated." (The common alternative is to dismiss each such crash as a one-off problem that won't happen again, perhaps blamed on the hardware.) This is not a requirement on the system itself, but rather a requirement on the development methodology. It doesn't give you confidence you will reach any particular software reliability target. But, such a requirement will be effective at eliminating at least some sources of software crashes (specifically, it will eliminate sources of crashes that you discover during testing).

> **Supplement your measurements with methodology requirements, especially for difficult-to-measure aspects of your system.**

6.3.6. Formal methods

Formal methods are mathematical techniques for proving properties are true of a system. A common formal method is model checking, which involves creating an abstraction (a model) of your system, and using sophisticated programs to analyze that model for particular properties you care about. For example, you might try to prove that a particular system never asserts both a *stop* and a *go* signal to a motor at the same time.

These methods can be quite powerful, but developing systems this way requires special skills, and these methods have trouble scaling up to large, complex software systems. More importantly, they require assumptions and simplifications to create the model. Once you have proven the model perfect, there is still the issue that the actual implementation (the source code) might have bugs. Nonetheless, formal methods are important, and are commonly employed by methodologies for creating high criticality systems.

6.4. Pitfalls

In other chapters we're encouraging you to put a lot of things into your requirements beyond just a list of functions. But, the fact is that all these aspects of a system will have to be verified one way or another, and some things are difficult to measure. It is better to deal with measurement issues up front when creating requirements, rather than waiting for problems to emerge late in system development.

6.5. For more information

6.5.1. General topic search keywords

- System requirements validation
- Requirements engineering
- Model checking
- Requirements measurable

6.5.2. Recommended reading

Bahill, A. T.; Henerson, S. J., "Requirements development, verification and validation exhibited in famous failures," *Systems Engineering*, v. 8 n. 1 pp. 1-14, 2005.

This paper examines a number of famous system failures and suggests how those failures relate to requirements problems. It emphasizes the differences between verification vs. validation of both the requirements and the finished system.

Chapter 7
Tracing Requirements To Test

- If there is no test that covers a particular requirement, then you aren't actually testing whether that requirement has been met.
- Tracing requirements to tests means checking that each requirement is covered by a test *and* that each test corresponds to one or more requirements.
- It's useful to create a spreadsheet that documents traceability, and look for uncovered requirements and orphan tests.

Contents:

Every requirement should have one or more corresponding system acceptance tests. Every acceptance test should have one or more corresponding requirements. Do some exploratory testing and ask if those results indicate there is a gap in your requirements or test plan.

7.1. Overview

There are two high level reasons to have written requirements. The first, mentioned elsewhere, is making sure you know what you want to build. The second, of more interest in this chapter, is that written requirements provide a checklist to make sure that the thing you built does everything it is supposed to. In other words, you'd like to know: "does my system actually meet its requirements?"

7.1.1. Importance of tracing requirements

An example of traceability is: for every requirement, check to see which acceptance tests exercise that requirement. If there is a requirement that isn't exercised by at least one test, then you have a gap in your test plan that needs to be filled. If you don't test a requirement, then you have no idea whether it is being met.

There are some instances in which tests are impractical. In those cases some alternate method must be used to check that the requirement has been satisfied (See *Chapter 6. Measurable Requirements*). But for most systems, tests are used to check most, if not all, requirements.

It is also possible to trace individual tests back to requirements. This would check that every test corresponds to at least one requirement. If a test exists that doesn't have a requirement, something is missing in the requirements.

7.1.2. Possible symptoms

You have a problem with traceability between requirements and tests if both of the following are true:

✘ There is no spreadsheet showing the correspondence between requirements and tests to establish coverage.

  AND

✘ The test plan does not note which system requirements are covered by each test.

In some cases a test plan might simply be a procedure saying "go through the requirements and check to see that each one of them is covered." While quite informal, such an approach is a way to achieve traceability.

7.1.3. Risks of inadequate traceability

The main risks of not doing traceability between requirements and tests depend upon which direction has a traceability problem:

➤ Requirements with no corresponding tests. Requirements might not be met in a product, even though it passes all tests.

➤ Tests with no corresponding requirements. Tests might establish arbitrary requirements that have bypassed the normal reviews and approvals of the requirement process. For example, if the testing group creates a stress test with an arbitrary pass criterion but no requirement for system robustness in the specification, how does anyone know whether that outcome is the right amount of robustness?

7.2. Traceability

The concept of traceability is that there are many pieces of a design at different levels of abstraction, and they should all have well defined relationships. In particular, every element of each document with a design package should map onto other elements in other documents of the design package.

For example, a requirement such as:

"When the button is pressed, the light shall turn on"

might trace to architectural elements:

• The system has a button.

• The system has a light.

and might also trace to a system test:

• Test: Press the button. The test passes if the light turns on.

Traceability can happen at lower levels of detail as well. The requirement to turn a light on might trace to:

• An I/O routine to read the button.

• An I/O routine to turn the light on.

• A state machine that looks for a button press, and transitions to state "Light ON" when the button is pressed.

There are two types of *traceability*: forward traceability and backward traceability. In forward traceability, something in the design package causes another thing to be created. Example: a requirement to turn a light on traces forward into a test to see if the light actually turns on. Perfect forward traceability means everything in a high-level or early part of the design process traces to one or more things in later phases.

Backward traceability means that everything created was created for a reason, and traces backward to some reason for existence. For example, a test to see if a light turns on should trace backward to some requirement for that light turning on. Perfect backward traceability means nothing is there without a reason.

7.2.1. Requirement to test traceability

A well designed system has both forward and backward traceability throughout the entire design package. But the following is the most important thing to get right:

> **Every requirement should have one or more corresponding system acceptance tests.**

	Requirements								
Tests	**R1**	**R2**	**R3**	**R4**	**R5**	**R6**	**R7**	**R8**	**R9**
T1	X				X				
T2		X	X						
T3									
T4			X						
T5				X	X				
T6					X		X	X	
T7								X	
T8									X

Figure 7.1. Example requirements to test traceability matrix.

By system acceptance test, we mean a test that determines whether the system as a whole works properly. This means that you should have 100% forward traceability from requirements to test if that is practical. It's important to be a little flexible about the word *test* in this rule. Some properties have to be verified by design review or other methods that aren't tests in the strictest sense of the word (we could more correctly say they are system acceptance criteria).

There is a complementary rule that helps ensure both the right tests are being performed and that your requirements are complete:

> **Every test should have one or more corresponding requirements.**

If you have a test that isn't provoked by a requirement, then why are you doing it? Either this is a situation in which something is missing from the requirements, or you are wasting time doing unnecessary tests.

It might be that some tests are just a good idea to cover problems that might have, for example, troubled previous projects. That's a fine reason to test, and can be very simply covered in the requirements by referring to a set of standard acceptance tests for this type of product. (This infers that a list of standard tests is kept in a standard procedure somewhere, so they aren't skipped by accident or forgotten over time. This is also a good idea.)

In addition to adding traceability information into a test plan, it can also be useful to use a matrix approach to visualize the traceability of a system. One way to do this is have requirements as columns and tests as rows. Figure 7.1 shows an example.

In this traceability matrix, an "X" indicates that the requirement in that column is covered by the test in that row. For example, in Fig. 7.1 requirement R5 is covered at least in part by each of tests T1, T5, and T6. Similarly, test T6 covers, at least in part, requirements R5, R7, and R8.

Checking for full traceability can be done by inspecting the traceability matrix for empty columns or rows. In Fig. 7.1, requirement R6 is never tested (its column has no "X" marks). Additionally, test T3 does not correspond to any requirement (its row has no "X" marks). Both R6 and T3 have traceability problems that should be addressed.

Creating a traceability matrix doesn't take much time if someone has already done the analysis of which test traces to which requirement. But the effort spent in creating such a matrix can yield significant benefit if it leads to a discovery of traceability problems.

> **Every project should have a traceability matrix between tests and requirements.**

7.2.2. Exploratory testing and traceability

Not every test plan is perfect, and not every set of requirements is perfect. There is plenty of room in testing to look for the unexpected.

Exploratory testing is an approach in which a knowledgeable tester sees what problems can be found without necessarily adhering strictly to a list of predefined tests nor to the written requirements. In other words, the tester goes exploring. This type of testing can be very valuable, and should be performed on any product as part of an overall testing strategy.

Exploratory testing by its nature doesn't always trace to requirements. This means it should be *in addition to* tests that trace to requirements to make sure that all requirements are checked by other, non-exploratory testing.

When exploratory testing finds a problem, this should be taken as an opportunity to examine the quality of both the requirements and the non-exploratory test plan. In particular, for each issue found by exploratory testing, ask yourself:

- Does this problem reveal an important gap in the requirements?
- Does this problem reveal an important gap in the test plan?

> **Do some exploratory testing.**
> **When that finds problems, ask yourself if you have revealed an important gap in the requirements or test plan.**

In some cases exploratory testing might simply find different ways to test general areas already covered in the test plan (for example, ways to test a requirement in different operating situations than those specified in the test plan). But in other cases a good exploratory tester can find gaps in requirements and combinations of system conditions that can and should be the subject of more formal design attention and corresponding updates to both requirements and the test plan.

7.2.3. Other uses of traceability

A traceability matrix can have the added advantage of making it easy to see the implications of a change in the system. It reveals, for example, what tests might need to be changed if a requirement is modified.

Traceability can be used for other purposes, such as tracing requirements to design. Anyone considering increasing the formality of their design process should definitely consider traceability at every step in the design. But, the most critical application of traceability is between requirements and tests.

7.3. Pitfalls

It is impossible in practice to achieve complete or perfect testing. Just because you have tests that cover all the requirements doesn't mean you have covered all possible combinations of situations over all possible operating conditions. In other words, don't mistake full traceability for perfect testing. On the other hand, if you don't have full traceability, you can be pretty sure your test plan is falling short of where it ought to be. Relying solely upon open ended exploratory testing is likely to miss things, and should only be done in conjunction with testing that traces to requirements.

Traceability is a safety net to ensure you don't make any really gross mistakes, such as completely forgetting to test a requirement. It is no substitute for careful consideration of a test plan, nor for expert testers who have a good idea of both your system and the types of things that are important to find.

7.4. For more information

7.4.1. General topic search keywords
- Requirements traceability
- Traceability matrix

7.4.2. Recommended reading

Jarke, M., "Requirements tracing," *Communications of the ACM*, v. 51, n. 12, pp. 32-36 December 1998.
   This gives a broad view of traceability well beyond requirements to test traceability.

In addition, most texts on software engineering address requirements traceability approaches.

Chapter 8
Non-Functional Requirements

- Non-functional requirements are attributes that can't be implemented directly in software or hardware.

- Typical non-functional requirements include: performance, resource usage, dependability, fault handling, security, intellectual property protection, safety, usability, conformance to standards, and certifications.

- System requirements must address non-functional aspects for the project to succeed.

Contents:

Every technical aspect of the system that is required for success, functional or non-functional, should be included in the requirements. This section lists many of the relevant non-functional considerations.

8.1. Overview

Requirements often concentrate on the functionality required of the system. But, to be complete, they need to encompass all aspects of the system that developers must get right for the product to be a success. These attributes are often called non-functional requirements. They are also called quality attributes or extra-functional properties.

Non-functional requirements are, for our purposes, requirements that aren't really overt behaviors, and therefore can't be implemented directly in software or hardware. Most often, they are emergent properties or they are constraints. Emergent properties are things that are true of the system as a whole, but not easily attributable to any one system piece. For example, system processing speed is generally a property of the system as a whole. You must know how much time every portion of the software in the system takes to execute if you want to know how much the total CPU load will be for running all the software concurrently; there isn't a single subroutine that somehow makes the system go faster to meet its deadlines.

A second type of non-functional requirement is a constraint, which is a rule that must be followed when creating the system. The term *rule* can be used very loosely, but denotes something the developers have to do regardless of whether it helps or hurts the overall system. Example rules include "must run on Linux" or "must conform to UL safety standards." Constraints aren't necessarily good or bad – they are simply a fact of life that must be taken into account. In most cases there is no single place in the code you can look to see if the constraint is completely satisfied.

8.1.1. Importance of meeting non-functional requirements

If your system doesn't implement its non-functional requirements correctly, then it's just as faulty as if it omits significant functions.

As an example, software that crashes once per minute is pretty likely to be faulty. A crash only once per week might or might not be considered a success, depending on the application environment. But either way, software isn't supposed to have a specific module that is in charge of causing crashes. Rather, whether the software crashes or not has to do with the interaction of modules throughout the system. Nonetheless, lack of frequent crashes is an important success criterion for software. If the level of desired software stability isn't mentioned in the requirements, then how can you be sure you will get software that is stable enough for your purposes?

Requirements documents should address all the aspects of a system that are necessary for product success. Simply listing all the functions the system performs is important, but not enough to create a complete set of requirements. The non-functional requirements have to be included as well.

8.1.2. Possible symptoms

Many symptoms of incomplete requirements are difficult to see until the product nears shipment, because early in a project developers tend to focus on implementing functionality rather than on non-functional issues. Some of the symptoms to look for are:

✘ The requirements document doesn't have sections for all of the following topics: performance, resource usage, dependability, fault handling, security, intellectual property protection, safety, usability, conformance to standards, and certifications. (Possibly other topics are also important to your domain.)

✘ The test plan includes non-functional tests that don't correspond to requirements (for example, a software stability or stress test with no requirement for the software to be stable).

8.1.3. Risks of inadequate non-functional requirements

➤ The system is over-designed or under-designed in an important non-functional aspect. This can happen if the development team doesn't know how much (or how little) to emphasize non-functional aspects of the system.

➤ Non-functional requirements aren't met, or are met only via difficult and expensive last-minute efforts. Tradeoffs of non-functional aspects omitted by the requirements often must be made after the system design is largely completed, rather than as part of the design process, because there is no up-front discussion of these requirements.

8.2. Common non-functional requirements

The best way to avoid the risk of having problems with non-functional requirements is to explicitly include those requirements as items in the system requirements document. Leaving them out doesn't make them go away as requirements – it just delays the day of reckoning for determining how (or if) the system meets them.

Overall, the best way to look at this topic is to ask yourself two questions:

• If the system only does what is in the requirements, and nothing else, is it going to be successful?

• If the system has undesirable behavior not prohibited by the requirements (such as crashing frequently), is it going to be successful?

While good developers will often get unspecified things right, it is risky to simply assume that everything will turn out OK even though the requirements don't mention crucial aspects of the system.

> Every technical aspect of the system that is required for success,
> functional or non-functional,
> should be included in the requirements.

Each subsection below discusses a general type of non-functional requirement that is relevant to embedded systems.

8.2.1. Performance

Embedded systems interact with people or external physical systems, and both of these have real time performance issues. In general, timing requirements must be given for user interactions, control loops, data I/O servicing, and other real time events. An especially helpful type of requirement in this area is one that can be used to create deadlines for real time scheduling of various tasks (for example: "system shall respond to button press within 300 msec").

All processing deadlines should be included in requirements.

Not all performance values are purely a function of CPU speed. Other important performance metrics include the below, which should be addressed by requirements if relevant:

- Reboot speed (if fast turn-on time is required)

  Example requirement: "The system shall be ready for use within 3 seconds of a system reset."

- Energy consumption and battery life, assuming some operational profile.

  Example requirement: "The system shall operate for at least two years on a new set of AA Alkaline batteries."

- Thermal heat dissipation.

  Example requirement: "No fan will be required in the system for always-on operation within specified operating conditions."

  Example requirement: "The external case temperature shall not exceed 110 degrees F." (This minimizes risk of scalding when in contact with exposed human skin, but might be considered painfully hot to the touch.)

Energy related issues are to a large degree performance issues. Certainly hardware power saving techniques such as reducing operating voltage are important. But, once those techniques have been applied, further power management approaches depend upon having software that minimizes computational load or periodically puts the system to sleep to save power.

Energy consumption and thermal limits   **should be included in requirements.**

8.2.2. Resource usage

It's important to have slack resources in embedded systems for a variety of reasons. There is always the possibility that new requirements will emerge near the end of the development cycle or need to be addressed via mid-life product up-grades, and room must be left to accommodate them. Moreover, software development becomes very expensive as resources come close to being full (see *Chapter 18. The Cost of Nearly Full Resources*).

Rather than leaving slack capacity to chance, requirements should establish a target amount of spare capacity as a goal, so that the system hardware and software approaches can be sized appropriately at the outset.

> **Requirements should specify maximum resource usage for each important system resource.**

Areas in which resource usage matters can be many, but here are some common ones:

- **CPU capacity.** How full should the CPU be in terms of percent CPU usage?

- **Memory capacity.** How full can memory be?

- **I/O channels.** How many spare digital I/O pins and spare A/D converter channels should be available?

- **Network bandwidth.** How much spare bandwidth should be available?

- **Physical size.** How much spare area inside an enclosure should there be, or how many empty expansion slots should be provided?

- **Power supply.** How many spare milliamps of power capacity should the power supply have?

Requirements for resource usage are typically expressed in terms of the percent of resources that are used or unused. For example, a memory usage requirement might be:

> *Example:* "Each type of memory shall be less than 75% full when the system is initially deployed (applies individually to each type of memory: RAM, flash memory, and EEPROM)."

8.2.3. Dependability

All systems have some probability of failure in use. It is common to set a target for hardware failure rates. Typically this is given as a Mean Time Between Failures (*MTBF*), which can often be thousands of hours of system use between expected failures. Performing dependability calculations can be a bit of work (see *Chapter 26. Dependability*). But, doing so for electronics and mechanical systems has a fairly well established procedure.

On the other hand, software dependability is a much more slippery topic. Nonetheless, ignoring the topic of dependability invites having a system that is undependable. Developers need a dependability target to strive for, and testers need a dependability target to measure against.

There are different aspects to dependability, only some of which are relevant to any particular project. The relevant aspects listed below should appear in your requirements. Each aspect has an example requirement, but it is important to realize these are just examples, and real requirements can be dramatically different.

- **Reliability.** This is the time the system stays operational between failures.

  Example requirement: "The system shall have less than a 10% chance of crashing within the first two weeks after it is rebooted."

- **Availability.** This is the fraction of "up-time" compared to total time, expressed as a percentage.

  Example requirement: "The system shall have at least 99.999% up time" (This is 315 seconds of downtime per year.)

- **Maintainability.** This is the degree to which fixing problems disrupts system operation, and the speed with which problems can be corrected.

  Example requirement: "Applying system patches shall require less than one minute of downtime per month."

  Example requirement: "A typical service call shall be completed within 30 minutes of arrival of service personnel."

  Example requirement: "The system shall be patchable via the Internet under user control."

  (This example is in some ways a functional requirement, but might be overlooked because it supports a non-functional need to deploy patches.)

Requirements should specify a reliability or availability target.

Creating extremely dependable systems such as aircraft, which fail catastrophically perhaps only once per billion operating hours, requires specialized skills. But, for everyday systems, dependability can be assessed as part of the ordinary system test plan. For example, running several systems for a few weeks in a test environment to see how often they crash can go a long way toward understanding if dependability goals have been met.

Safety and security are often considered a part of dependability, but we cover them in more detail as separate items below.

8.2.4. Fault handling

No matter how dependable you think a system is, ultimately there will be system faults and failures. Handling and recording faults in an appropriate way is essential to creating a robust system. There are three different aspects of fault handling that appear as system requirements.

- **Fault detection.** Faults aren't always detected. For example, a corrupted piece of data might cause incorrect system operation but might not be detectable by the software. Requirements can improve fault detection by mandating the use of error detection codes and run-time fault checks.

  Example requirement: "All non-volatile data shall be protected by error detection codes capable of detecting all errors involving three or fewer corrupt bits within a single data block."

- **Fault recovery.** It is often undesirable for a system to crash and stay crashed after a fault occurs. Recovery is very often done using a watchdog timer, but other approaches are possible.

  Example requirement: "Any detected fault shall cause a system reset."

  Example requirement: "The failure of any task to complete within its deadline shall cause system reset."

- **Fault logging.** It can be extremely useful to keep a log of faults so that service personnel can determine what has been going wrong with a system that fails in the field. Fault logs are also useful when testing newly designed systems.

  Example requirement: "A history of the most recent 16 faults encountered shall be kept in non-volatile memory."

> Requirements should address
> fault detection, recovery, and logging.

It is impossible to detect, recover from, and log all possible faults. Rather, system designers decide what type of faults they care about and then decide how they handle them. For example, a system might be designed to detect and recover from data corruption faults, power supply brownouts, timing faults (system hangs) and failed sensor modules. But it might not be designed to automatically detect and recover from software design errors, completely burned out memory chips, and other things.

8.2.5. Security and intellectual property protection

Cyber-security isn't just for banks and desktop computers any more. Many embedded systems have security requirements to prevent unauthorized use, discourage unauthorized modification by system owners, deter reverse engineering by competitors, ensure the privacy of users, and so on. It's important that these aspects of system operation be addressed by the requirements.

Typical embedded system requirements need to address the following security issues to the degree that they are relevant to the system:

- **Authentication.** How are users (and other embedded systems on a network) authenticated so that the system knows they are authorized to actually use the system?

  Example requirement: "System access shall be password protected, with passwords having a minimum of 6 total alphanumeric characters, at least one alphabetic character, and at least 1 numeric character."

- **Privileges.** This is a specific topic within the general umbrella of authentication. Are there multiple types of users that should have different levels of access to the system? If so, which users can perform what operations?

  Example requirement: "System shall support four user classes: Administrator, Power User, User, and Factory Technician."
  (This requirement implies that various other requirements will be annotated with which classes of users have access to that functionality.)

- **Secrecy.** Are there any secrets that must be kept by the system? Secrets might include trade secrets in the code itself, or information supplied by the user.

  Example requirement: "System shall encrypt all user-supplied data with AES using a 256-bit key."

- **Integrity and tamper evidence.** In some systems, especially safety critical systems, it is important to ensure that the system hasn't been tampered with, or at least be able to tell if tampering has taken place. A system with compromised integrity can't be trusted to be safe.

  Example requirement: "The system shall check code integrity with a secure hash function at startup and shall halt if code has been altered." (In some systems a cyclic redundancy code (CRC) is a good enough hash function, although CRCs are not cryptographically secure.)

  Example requirement: "Only patches cryptographically signed by the manufacturer shall be accepted for installation in the equipment."

Chapter 27. Security discusses aspects of security at length. It is common to need a security plan to specifically address security issues and ensure that security is adequate.

> Requirements should address security, including at least
> authentication, secrecy, and integrity.

8.2.6. Safety and critical functions

A surprising number of embedded systems have some degree of safety criticality. Often they aren't highly critical, but they can have safety issues nonetheless. As with security and dependability, creating a top-notch safety critical system requires some very specialized skills. However, with everyday embedded systems there are some fairly simple requirements that can go a long way toward avoiding problems in this area.

The word *safety* sometimes carries too much legal baggage with it (the word *unsafe* fairly screams "lawsuit!" in the United States, regardless of the context). So for our purposes we'll just call this area critical system properties, which includes not only safety, but other functions that must work correctly to avoid unacceptable problems.

Requirements should list critical properties (things that need extra attention to make sure they are right), specify recovery actions if critical properties are violated due to failure, and give some sense as to how important these properties are so developers know how much additional system cost is worth incurring to ensure they are done properly.

- **List of critical properties.** Requirements should either annotate requirements that are critical or have a separate list of them. For example, a * by a property might mean it is critical. A critical property might be something such as:

  Example requirement: "*Critical*: Temperature shall never exceed 200 degrees F.
  Rationale: this will help avoid system pressurization caused by steam formation."

- **Critical recovery actions.** System faults can cause critical properties to be violated no matter how much attention has been paid to getting them right in the design. Specifying recovery actions or mitigation techniques can help make it clear how the system is supposed to behave (and ensure that code to actually perform that recovery is included in the system).

  Example requirement: "*Critical*: When temperature exceeds 200 degrees F, system shall de-energize all heating elements."
  (Note that in most critical systems, there would also be a hardware safety mechanism in case the system overheats due to a software defect.)

- **Critical property assurance.** Some systems are more critical than others. Critical properties should be assessed as to how severe a failure might be, either in terms of probability or according to an established standardized approach.

  Example requirement: "*Critical*: An over-temperature condition shall occur no more often than once per 100,000 operating hours."

  Example requirement: "*Critical*: Temperature control shall be treated as a SIL 3 function in accordance with IEC 61508."

See *Chapter 28. Safety* for an explanation of the Safety Integrity Level (SIL) approach to creating critical systems.

> Requirements should list:
> critical properties,
> critical recovery actions, and
> critical assurance levels.

8.2.7. Usability

Designing good human-computer interfaces is an entire discipline, with methodologies and design practices that many embedded system designers have not yet encountered (see *Chapter 15. User Interface Design*). While it is not the role of a requirements document to spell out how human interfaces should be designed, it is important for requirements to provide the raw material needed to do a good job at human interfaces. There are two major elements to this: defining interface standards and defining the user population.

- **Interface standards.** There should be a standard or guideline for the user interface so that, for example, screens in a graphical user interface have a consistent look and feel. That standard isn't necessarily part of the requirements itself, but should be referred to.

  Example requirement: "The Company X user interface guidelines shall be followed to provide consistent look and feel."

- **User population.** Every product has an intended user population. That population should be identified so that designers can make appropriate tradeoffs in functionality vs. complexity and testers can make sure that the entire user population can properly use the product. The requirements might simply list the characteristics of users, or might have itemized requirements such as:

  Example requirement: "The product shall support internationalization for at least four languages including: English, German, Chinese, and one language to be provided via a later system upgrade."

- **Operating conditions.** Beyond the limits and diversity of the user population, there are operating conditions that must be taken into account, such as whether displays are visible in bright sunlight, and how well the system can be used with gloved hands.

  Example requirement: "The display shall be visible in direct sunlight by users wearing vertically polarized sunglasses."

> Requirements should address interface standards and
> specific needs of target user populations.

8.2.8. Conformance to standards and certification requirements

There is a wide variety of standards, regulations, and certification requirements that might apply to a system. All of the relevant ones should be referenced in the requirements so that they can be addressed during system design. Many standards are industry-specific, so a comprehensive list is impossible. But, some general types of standards include:

- Safety standards to ensure safe operation: Underwriter Laboratories (UL) standards, IEC 61508, medical device safety, aviation safety, and so on.
- Communication standards to ensure compatibility with other communication equipment.
- Domain-specific conformance requirements (building codes, automotive regulations, medical equipment labeling requirements).
- Quality and manufacturing standards.
- Certification requirements, such as electromagnetic emission certification (FCC certification in the US) for hardware, and any required software or system-level certifications.

> **Requirements should list all applicable standards.**

8.3. Pitfalls

We're encouraging you to put a lot of things into your requirements beyond just a list of functions! But, the fact is that all these aspects of a system will have to be addressed one way or another. It is better to deal with the non-functional requirements up-front, so as to avoid a need to rework things after the design is mostly done.

8.4. For more information

8.4.1. General topic search keywords

- Non-functional requirements
- Quality attributes

Chapter 9
Requirement Churn

- Requirement changes should be monitored for signs of excessive change (churn).
- Churn can be avoided by filtering out non-critical changes or delaying them to later revisions, as well as by making it clear what additional cost each change will have on the overall project.
- Having a single person or group approve all changes can help moderate requirement churn.

Contents:

Requirement changes should become less frequent as development progresses.

All requirement changes should be approved by a Change Control Board. There should be a requirement freeze date well in advance of the product release date. Approval for requirement changes should be based, in part, on the cost and impact to schedule.

9.1. Overview

Requirement changes are part of life. It's difficult to get everything perfect in an up-front requirements process. Customer desires change. Developers come to realize that their initial requirements aren't feasible, or have ideas for cool new features. Business needs change based on competitive forces or a new business emphasis.

Requirement changes come in two flavors. Requirement creep (also known as feature creep) is the tendency for a project to accumulate additional requirements over time as new ideas are inserted into the product. Requirement modifications, on the other hand, occur when a requirement turns out to be wrong or inadequate and must be revised.

9.1.1. Importance of minimizing requirement churn

Requirement changes can cause huge disruption to project schedules, software quality, and team morale. In general, the later in the development cycle a requirement change is made, the more disruptive it will be. The biggest problems occur when the rate of requirement changes escalates from a normal level across some fuzzy threshold into being so high that it becomes requirement *churn*.

While just one more tiny requirement change might be needed to close the next sale, an accumulation of disruptive requirement changes can undermine software quality and shorten the effective market lifetime of a product. It is unrealistic for requirements to remain unchanged. But that doesn't mean we should be fatalistic about requirement changes and the impact of those changes on the project. Rather, we should be realistic and accept the fact that after some number of changes it will be time to scrap the project and start over with a next generation system. So spend your changes wisely.

9.1.2. Possible symptoms

Requirement churn may be a problem if:

✘ There is no single point of final approval for requirement changes (either a person or a group of people). This can make it easy for individual requirements to be changed without anybody realizing that too many changes have been made overall.

✘ Schedules are not re-evaluated and adjusted in response to significant requirement changes.

✘ There is no cut-off or freeze date for final requirement changes well in advance of a release date.

✘ A high fraction of requirements have changed since the project was started. How high is too high depends on the situation.

✘ Requirements documents are not up to date with the implementation. This is because changes are so frequent developers have given up on trying to keep requirements documents up to date.

9.1.3. Risks of frequent requirement changes

The main risk of requirement churn is that it is difficult to hit a moving target.

➤ Deadlines can be missed if requirement changes require significant rework.

➤ If changes don't go through a formal approval process, they may slip directly into code, causing a mismatch between the implementation and other design documents. This is especially common if changes are made directly to systems during testing or customer site installation, bypassing normal development procedures.

➤ The software becomes brittle because too many changes have been made during the development process, degrading the software structure to the point it is more bug-prone.

9.2. Tracking requirement churn

Requirement *churn* is an informal term for having a high rate of requirement changes. A related term is requirement *creep*, which is the gradual accumulation of additional requirements over time. While having some requirement changes is a normal fact of life, a high rate of change leads to problems, because it disrupts development efforts. There are three common ways to help manage the effects of requirement changes to prevent them from becoming a full-fledged requirement churn situation: tracking, controlling, and assessing.

9.2.1. Tracking the requirement change rate

The first part of doing something to manage requirement churn is knowing that you have a problem (or, if you already think you have a problem, communicating that problem in an effective way to people who can help you fix it). A good way to do this is to keep an up to date graph of requirement changes over time within each phase, iterated development cycle, or software release. Figure 9.1 has some hypothetical examples, where data is shown for the first 50 weeks of a project. Which project seems most likely to you to be heading to a requirement churn train wreck? (Why?)

We think that project 2 looks worse than project 1 because project 2 has a higher average rate of requirement churn. But, other factors must be understood before saying which project was lower risk. Project 2 might have much more detailed, fine-grain requirements, and the changes might be much less effort to make than Project 1. But, in the absence of any other information, a lower rate of churn is better.

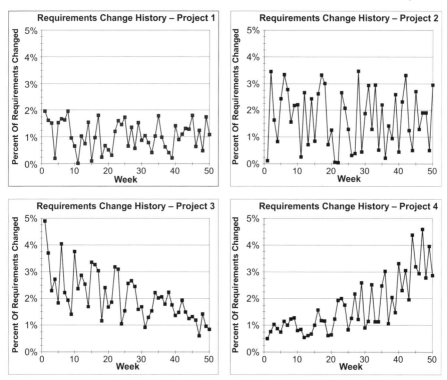

Figure 9.1. Requirement change rates for four hypothetical projects.

Project 3 has more total changes than Projects 1 and 2. But, it has a trend indicating more changes early in the project and fewer changes later in the project. That suggests a good requirements management process is in place, and that the developers have been successful at finding requirement changes early in the development process (or, at least, in deferring requirement changes to later revisions as the first revision release date draws near). Even though this project has more total changes than Project 2, the total cost and impact on schedule is likely to be less, because requirement changes early in the project are far less disruptive than requirement changes later in the project. We'd all be happiest if our requirement change graph sloped down as Project 3 does.

Project 4 looks like an impending train wreck. The total number of requirement changes is about the same as Project 2, and is in fact lower than Project 3. But, here is a project where requirement changes aren't being discovered until late in the development cycle, where they are very disruptive and difficult to fix. This graph predicts an unhappy outcome to the project development effort.

You should graph your requirement change rate periodically (perhaps weekly, but it depends on how short or long a project you have). There are two important things to look for in the graph:

- **The fraction of requirements changed per unit time.** If you're changing a high fraction of your requirements in a relatively short amount of time, you're in trouble. The raw change rate doesn't take into account the possible disruption that only a single really big change can make. But a high rate of churn indicates a lot is happening, and you need to be more aggressive in managing requirement churn.

- **The trend.** Requirement changes should become less frequent with time, not more frequent. If requirements start changing frequently late in the project, it often means the initial requirements weren't thought out very well or that customers didn't really think hard enough about they want until near the delivery date. (Or both!)

> Requirement changes should become less frequent as development progresses.

Merely tracking the change rate does not in itself solve a requirement churn problem. But, historical data might be useful in persuading someone that a problem really exists. The difficulty with requirement churn is not that any one, single requirement change will cause project failure. It is that an accumulation of many small changes can, in aggregate, cause project failure via requirement churn. Keeping track of historical churn and showing someone a chart of requirement change rates can be a good tool in a situation where someone says "What's the big deal? It's only a tiny requirement change." The insightful response is not "this one isolated change will kill us" but rather "this trend will kill us!"

9.3. Controlling requirement churn

Once you have the ability to identify that too-frequent changes are a problem, there has to be some way to control those changes. While being responsive to customers is important, being over-responsive to the point that it causes project failure is in nobody's best interest.

9.3.1. The Change Control Board

The usual method of controlling requirement changes is with a Change Control Board (CCB). This board is a group (or perhaps only a single person) which takes ownership of the project requirements after they have been reviewed and approved by all stakeholders, but before significant development effort has started. From that point on, a change to the requirements requires the CCB's approval.

Approval can be as simple as an e-mail from a single-person CCB saying "approved," to a weekly meeting of many people who discuss each proposed change at length. The level of formality involved in making a change should be appropriate to the circumstance. But, having no CCB and no single owner of requirements is just asking for requirement churn, because there is no single person with a big picture view of what is happening. It helps if the CCB has representation from both stakeholders who benefit from changes (for example, marketing), and stakeholders who have to bear the costs of approved changes (for example, engineering).

> _All_ requirement changes should be approved by a single person or group.

It might sound like having a CCB is painful, because a hoop must be jumped through to make a requirement change. But that is, in fact, part of the point. Making changes a little bit difficult helps filter out changes that are unimportant or not really thought through.

9.3.2. Requirement freezes

Beyond having a CCB, it's important to have a cutoff date for requirement changes for a particular release or version. The amount of lead time varies according to the situation, but it is completely reasonable to say something like: "Any change requested within two months of the scheduled ship date will be deferred until the next release." Some reasons that a requirement freeze date like this is required include:

- Eliminating last-minute requirement changes that can lead to bugs from hasty development and overloaded developers.
- Leaving sufficient time for testing. It is difficult or impossible to test last-minute changes adequately.
- Encouraging people to plan ahead, rather than not really thinking things through until the last minute.

> Requirements should be frozen at a defined date significantly prior to the release date.

There may be times when a change is so important that it must go in despite being past the freeze date. Those changes should be exceedingly rare, and should involve fixes of problems that are likely to be catastrophic for systems in the field.

9.3.3. Assessing the cost of changes

Some managers (and customers) think that software is more or less free. (Hint: developer time isn't free, so neither is software.) They also think a change should just be "a few lines of code" and not any big deal. If developers go along with that misperception, or foster it themselves, then they are inviting requirement churn.

The fact is that software is expensive to develop, and software changes are even more expensive (cost per line of code modified) than development (cost per line of code written). Developers should never accept changes without insisting on an appropriate change to the development schedule, budget, and other necessary plans. One way of ensuring this is to require the CCB to evaluate not just the technical and marketing merits of a proposed change, but also cost and impact on schedule when making a decision as to whether a change should be accepted, rejected, or deferred to a later software release.

Determining the cost of a change might not be simple. But, at a minimum, the approach used to create an initial project schedule should be revisited periodically in light of change requests. It may be that some changes are so small that there is no discernable schedule impact, especially early in the project for requirements that haven't really been addressed in the design to date. But, as the project progresses, every requirement change will have a ripple effect throughout the project. Sources of cost and schedule disruption include:

- Addition or deletion of architectural elements
- Changes to design
- Changes to implementation
- Changes to test plan or regression test suite
- Need to re-test portions of the system
- Changes to user documentation
- Changes to real time task schedule

> **Approval for requirement changes should be based, in part, on the cost and impact to schedule.**

Because change is inevitable, it is wise to build in a little schedule slack for changes. Even if such slack is present, the true cost of a change isn't free – it eats up some of that built-in-slack, which will eventually run out if too many changes are made.

9.4. Pitfalls

It is important to be flexible. It is also important to not get steam-rolled by your stakeholders. Successful change management plans create a tiered approach to changes, where changes that are big or made late in the development cycle are more difficult to get approved and result in proportionally larger deadline extensions than changes requested early. At some point, you will find that deadline extensions are so long and costs are so high that it is better to skip a proposed change – it's simply not worth the cost. Identifying such a situation is the main point of doing change management!

It is important not to make the change management process so difficult to use that developers skip it and just make changes directly to the implementation without reflecting those changes in the requirements. It should be difficult for people to make changes on a whim. But the change process shouldn't be so onerous that it kills worthwhile change ideas.

Sometimes requirement churn occurs because you simply don't understand the problem well enough to create a reasonable set of requirements. In this situation what is really happening is that you are doing research (working to understand the problem) rather than development (working to create a solution). If you see very high requirement churn be sure to ask yourself whether the source of the churn is that you don't actually understand the problem. You could still be in a research phase even though the schedule says it's almost time to ship the finished product. If this is the case, traditional project management approaches aren't really going to help much. That's because project development approaches assume you understand the problem you are trying to solve at the outset, or at least that with every development iteration you are converging on a final solution.

9.5. For more information

9.5.1. General topic search keywords
- Requirement churn
- Software change
- Requirement creep
- Change control

9.5.2. Recommended reading

Jones, C., "Strategies for managing requirements creep," *IEEE Computer*, v. 29, n. 6, June 1996, pp. 92-94.
    Requirement creep and some ways to reduce or manage it.

Chapter 10
Software Architecture

- A software architecture is a set of components, their behaviors, and their interconnections within a system.

- Every system should have, as a minimum, a boxes and arrows diagram that describes the overall software structure.

- Creating an architecture diagram helps you think about how to make the architecture cleaner, and therefore make the system less problem-prone.

Contents:

10.1. Overview

The *architecture* of a system is the highest level of design, providing a master plan for the overall organization and operation of every aspect of the system. If your system doesn't have a documented software architecture, then there is no master plan except what is inside the developers' heads.

A drawing of an architecture is some figure that has boxes and arrows representing components and interconnections. Many different architectural drawings are possible, and it is common for multiple such drawings to be useful in describing different aspects of a single system. Having at least one useful architectural drawing is much more important than which particular style of drawing you use.

10.1.1. Importance of a well defined software architecture

Systems often have problems because they were designed without a master plan. Consider living in a house where each room was added on as an afterthought, compared to a house designed according to a master plan. It's possible to live in both – but the well planned house will be much more livable, and likely suffer from fewer problems. Software is no different.

Many embedded systems are created without benefit of a documented architecture. So, what's the big deal? At an intuitive level, all systems have an architecture whether it is documented or not (this is because all systems have both components and connections between those components, whether a picture of them has been drawn or not). But, many systems do not have a *good* architecture. A system with a bad architecture – one that is a hodgepodge of items with no coherent master plan – tends to be difficult to understand, difficult to design/debug/maintain, and difficult to get right.

Some developers are born architects, and will create beautiful systems simply by keeping everything in their head. But, born architects are few and far between. For the rest of us, documenting an architecture forces thinking things through, and provides a way to recognize messy architectural approaches.

> A messy architecture picture means
> you have a messy architecture.

10.1.2. Possible symptoms

If your project has any of the following symptoms, you should invest more effort in defining and documenting your software architecture:

✘ There is no one-page picture of the software architecture for your system. Backup pictures to show details are OK, but there should be a high level depiction that fits on one piece of paper. Flowcharts don't count – those are design diagrams, and not architecture diagrams.

✖ No single person can give a top-level view of how the software is organized. For example, nobody can draw how the software is organized overall if given a whiteboard, a marker, and 15 minutes to draw the picture.

✖ Modifying or adding to the software is error-prone because the feel of the software varies wildly across the code base. If drawn, the architectural diagram for this type of system tends to look very messy.

10.1.3. Risks of an inadequately defined software architecture

The problems you might encounter due to an undefined or inadequate architecture include:

➤ Difficulties and high expense in modifying or improving the system due to inconsistent architectural approaches.

➤ A high defect rate.

➤ A high fault reinjection rate (new bugs caused as a side effect of fixing some other bug) due to poor system organization.

➤ Difficulty in understanding the big picture system organization, making the learning curve for new personnel difficult.

➤ Early code wearout, in which software becomes so brittle and disorganized due to changes that throwing it away is more cost effective than continued maintenance.

➤ Failure of a project to be completed at all, if the complexity of the project isn't properly managed using a good architectural approach.

10.2. Representing software architecture

A software *architecture* is a combination of:

• **Components** of a system. A component could be an object, a separately compiled module, a library, a subroutine, or some other natural chunk of software.

• **Behaviors** and other properties of the components. This might include methods for objects.

• **Connections** between components. This might include data flows, subroutine call dependencies, or data sharing dependencies.

An architecture is best represented as a boxes and arrows diagram.

Every system should have an architectural diagram which:
(1) has boxes and arrows with well-defined meanings
(2) fits on a single letter-size sheet of paper (no tiny fonts!)
(3) is homogeneous, clean, and relevant.

In many cases, several distinct architectural drawings are useful and desirable, but each such picture must conform to the criteria described in the rule above.

10.2.1. Common architectural representations

The business of creating architectures is sufficiently squishy that it is difficult to say which approaches are better than others, especially for specialized embedded systems. However, there are certainly some standard approaches that can be used, and there is no point in inventing your own architectural notation without good reason. Here are some typical architectural representations.

- **Call Graph.** Shows subroutine call dependencies.

  ○ Boxes = subroutines or objects, with functions they provide

  ○ Arrows = subroutine or method calls

  ○ Strengths: Shows flow of control; especially helpful for debugging and understanding how changes in common routines affect other modules.

- **Class Diagram.** Shows class hierarchy and inheritance.

  ○ Boxes = object classes with methods

  ○ Arrows = inheritance

  ○ Strengths: Shows relationship of classes to each other.

- **Data Flow Diagram.** Shows how data is communicated among modules.

  ○ Boxes = computation or data transformation

  ○ Arrows = streams of data

  ○ Strengths: Especially useful for DSP algorithms; concentrates on transformations of data flowing through a system.

- **Hardware Allocation Diagram.** Shows how software is mapped to hardware.

  ○ Boxes = CPUs, with annotation showing which software modules are resident on that CPU

  ○ Arrows = communication network links and types of messages that flow across those links

  ○ Strengths: Helps show how software is allocated across a distributed system (for example, which software modules execute on a server, and which modules execute on a client).

- **Control Hierarchy Diagram.** Shows structure of control loops.

  ○ Boxes = controllers (or control loop software), with control laws

  ○ Arrows = set-points, inputs, and outputs

  ○ Strengths: Shows how different hierarchical control loops interact with each other, emphasizing the control aspects of the system.

It is important to have a well defined notion of what it means to be a *box* or *arrow*. What boxes and arrows represent varies depending on the type of architectural diagram being drawn. But, the representation approach should be consistent within any single diagram.

There are additionally some architectural elements that are very useful to have even though they are not strictly in terms of boxes-and-arrows diagrams. They include:

- **Message dictionary.** For any distributed embedded system, it is essential to have a list of messages used by the system, including message types, payload definitions, frequency of transmission, and so on.

- **Real time schedule.** Most embedded systems have real time deadlines, and thus require real time scheduling. At a minimum, the schedule information should have a list of all tasks with their maximum run time, how often they need to run, and deadlines.

- **Memory map.** A memory map is a picture of how memory is allocated for system use, including things such as program memory, global variable memory, stack memory, heap memory, and memory-mapped I/O.

10.2.2. Multiple architectural diagrams

Once an architectural diagram is created, it will become apparent that it has limitations in that it only captures a particular way of looking at things. For example, a class diagram focuses on issues related to object hierarchies, but doesn't deal with data flow or timing at all. All systems can benefit from having multiple architectural diagrams. But, it is not always the case that more is better. The only reason to create an additional architectural diagram is if it helps developers and reviewers in understanding essential aspects of the organization of the system.

> **Embedded systems should have multiple architecture diagrams, each with a different perspective.**

There are two good reasons for a proliferation of architecture diagrams: representing multiple views, and decomposition.

- **Multiple views.** It is entirely appropriate to have multiple architectural diagrams that represent multiple views of the same system. For example, a control diagram might show control loop organization while a class diagram shows the various object classes used in creating the system. Both views of the system are likely to be useful, and the diagrams can be completely different (so long as they are non-conflicting) while still representing the exact same system.

- **Decomposition.** It is vitally important to have architectural diagrams that are simple enough to be understood. The whole point of architecture is to help people understand the system organization. If the architectural diagram is so full of fine print and complex interconnections that it is difficult to understand, then it has failed at its purpose of communicating high-level organizational concepts. It is, however, quite reasonable to have a hierarchy of architectural diagrams to help understand the different layers of a complex system. This is commonly done in hardware design, where a single high-level schematic might show a system in terms of a collection of circuit boards or hardware blocks, and each block at the top level in turn has its own schematic revealing more detail.

In the software realm, the entire system might have an architecture diagram showing a number of quite complex subsystems as boxes. Each subsystem box might then have its own set of architectural diagrams. At some point it isn't useful to create more layers of decomposition. But, so long as architectural diagrams provide value to designers, they are worth creating.

10.3. What makes an architecture good?

Creating architectures is more art than science. Nonetheless, there are some general rules that help in understanding what makes a good architecture. Violating these properties makes it likely the architecture is bad. (You can follow these rules and still have a bad architecture if you try hard enough – but the rules help in getting things right.)

- **Conciseness.** A good architecture can be summed up on a single sheet of paper. If it doesn't fit on a single sheet of paper, then you need to think harder about a higher level representation that does fit on one page. It's OK to have detail pages behind that top level sheet that, for example, describe what is inside a particular high level box. But, getting things boiled down to a single-page diagram makes a huge difference in attaining a consistent, useful architecture. It's cheating if the paper is bigger than letter size, or if the fonts are too small to read.

- **Homogeneity.** A good architecture has an underlying principle that provides homogeneity across the components, behaviors, and connections. For example, homogeneity might mean that each and every box represents a subroutine, and each and every arrow represents a call dependency (this particular set of meanings makes the architectural diagram a call graph). There are other possible ways to assign meaning to boxes and arrows. The point of homogeneity is that there are only one (or possibly a few) types of boxes, and only one (or possibly a few) types of arrows. If every box and every arrow means something different, then the architecture is non-homogenous, which isn't good.

- **Cleanliness.** A good architecture is clean in that it is as uncomplicated and easy to understand as possible. The real point of an architecture is helping designers keep things organized. If the architectural drawing is a mess, it is likely that the designer's understanding of that architecture is also a mess. Despite the limitations of 2-dimensional drawings on paper, it is worth considerable effort to find a way to depict an architecture in a clean way on a piece of paper (or, to change the architecture so that its drawing is less messy).

• **Relevance.** A good architectural representation is relevant to issues that matter to designers. Drawing a homogeneous, clean picture of aspects of a system that just don't matter is a waste of effort. In any system there are some things that matter a lot, and some things that aren't too important. One or more high-level architectural drawings should be created that focus on the things that matter.

> Good architectures are concise, homogeneous, clean, and relevant.

Ultimately, the goodness of an architecture and the documented representation of that architecture is in the eye of the beholder. But, any architectural representation has to provide a useful answer to the following question: "What is the high level view of this system?"

10.3.1. Architectural patterns

An architectural pattern shows a particular architectural arrangement in the form of boxes and arrows that have particular meanings. For example, a fault tolerance pattern might include three CPUs and a voting circuit to choose a majority vote of the CPUs' outputs. Many catalogs of architectural and design patterns have been published. These patterns can be very useful in giving architectural ideas. But, randomly choosing a set of patterns is unlikely to result in a good architecture. Look at architectural patterns as a useful set of ideas for architectural building blocks.

10.4. Pitfalls

Having a less-than-perfect architecture diagram is better than having no architecture diagram. Nonetheless, it is important for an architectural diagram to have real meaning, rather than being a meaningless collection of boxes and arrows.

A common problem when creating architectural diagrams is creating boxes or arrows with fuzzy meanings. For example, if there are two boxes that do similar things, then an arrow might be used to connect them. But, what does this arrow mean? Perhaps it means "is similar to" – but it is unclear how that helps in creating the system. Perhaps it should instead mean "is a sub-class of" or have some other well defined meaning.

When reviewing an architectural diagram, pick a few arrows at random and ask "what does this arrow mean" to see how well defined and homogeneous the architecture diagram really is. Do the same with boxes, asking both "what function does this box perform" and "are any two randomly selected boxes the same type of component?" When you're starting out, label every arrow with its meaning in the diagram (e.g., "is a subclass of," "calls," or "is composed of") and see how consistent you are.

We'd love it if we could show some example architectures and say "just make diagrams like this and everything will be fine." But, unfortunately, creating architectures is pretty squishy stuff. To become good you'll need to do a lot of reading (start with the references discussed below), get some mentorship from an experienced architect, and practice a lot. There aren't any shortcuts that we know of.

10.5. For more information

10.5.1. General topic search keywords
- Software architecture
- Design pattern
- System architecting

(System architecting is a related concept, and deals with how you create an architecture – software or otherwise)

10.5.2. Recommended reading

Garlan, D. & M. Shaw, *An Introduction to Software Architecture*, Carnegie Mellon University Technical Report, CMU-CS-94-166, January 1994.
The starting point for much current work in software architecture, although many of the ideas existed before this work. There is a book published in 1996 by the same authors that builds on these ideas.

Rechtin, E., *Systems Architecting*, First edition, Prentice Hall, 1990.
This is the best book on creating system architectures. The second edition, published in 2000, has more material, but in our opinion the first edition keeps things simpler and easier to understand.

Rechtin, E., "The art of systems architecting," *IEEE Spectrum*, Oct. 1992, pp. 66-69.
This is a brief overview of the material in the Systems Architecting book by Rechtin.

Chapter 11
Modularity

- Breaking software up into modules helps manage complexity.

- Good modules are moderately short, are used to contain a related set of operations (high cohesion), have few detailed dependencies upon other modules (low coupling), hide implementation details from other modules, aren't too complex, and permit flexible composition in creating a complete system.

- The most common modularity problem in embedded systems is having modules that are too long to readily understand.

- While judging the effectiveness of modularity is as much art as science, there are rules of thumb that are helpful.

Contents:

11.1. Overview

It's a good idea for software to be written in a number of reasonably small chunks of code (*modules*) that work together, rather than as a few really big pieces of code. While the general idea of modularity is taught in introductory programming courses, there is considerable art in creating good modules. Making code chunks small is just the beginning.

11.1.1. Importance of modular systems

In general, modular programs tend to have fewer defects, because there is less risk of unexpected interactions among spread out fragments of code. Modular programs also tend to be easier to understand, debug, and maintain. But, these benefits only appear if the modules have been created with careful attention to how they interact with each other, and how they can be combined to create the system as a whole.

11.1.2. Possible symptoms

While modularity and complexity can be somewhat squishy terms, code that is highly modular is composed of many small, non-complex pieces. Software written in big pieces can't be considered modular. Thus, typical symptoms of poor modularity are:

✘ Source code for a single procedure, method, or other unit of code is more than one to four printed pages in length, depending on the application and language. Interrupt service routines should, as a rule, be shorter – half a printed page at most.

✘ Many unrelated operations or ideas are combined into a single code module.

✘ A large number of unrelated parameters is passed from one module to another.

✘ Global variables are used to pass information among different modules.

11.1.3. Risks of non-modular systems

➤ Increased number of bugs due to higher than necessary complexity.

➤ Increased number of bugs due to interactions among modules that should have been made more independent from each other.

➤ Difficulty in understanding code.

11.2. Evaluating modularity

The main idea behind *modularity* is that a program should be created as a set of building blocks that are composed to form a solution. There are many strategies for determining what a building block should be. Building blocks might be commonly used functions (subroutine libraries), different phases of computations (based on boxes in a flowchart), different system states (based on boxes in a statechart), objects with corresponding access methods, control loops, items within the system that are likely to change, or even just which programmer has been assigned to implement a particular portion of a system.

From this list, it should be clear that the approach to modularity that is best depends on the situation, and that merely breaking a program into arbitrary small chunks doesn't necessarily help if the chunks aren't the right chunks. At a high level, the question of how to break a system into modules is a matter of architecture. The modules should correspond to the software architecture (see *Chapter 10. Software Architecture*). At a finer granularity, modules should support making the design clearer. We'll discuss a few strategies for that but, more importantly, we'll also explain some of the criteria that are used to evaluate how good a program is with respect to modularity. Unfortunately, there is no real way to know if you have the best possible approach to modularity compared to just a reasonable approach. But being perfect isn't the point. Rather, the important thing is to avoid really bad approaches.

Programs are considered to have good modularity when they exhibit as many of these desirable properties as possible: medium-small size, high cohesion, low coupling, good information hiding, good composability, and moderate complexity. Let's look at each in turn.

11.2.1. Small size

Smaller is better, up to a point. In most programming languages, building an entire program out of one-line long subroutines would be a bad idea, because the size of each programming chunk would be too small to contain a collection of related operations within a single module. (There are languages in which this is not true, such as APL and Forth, but that is due to relatively dense notation that permits many distinct operations in a single line of code, and an ability to pass parameters between functions without explicitly giving parameter lists.)

For embedded systems written in C or C++, there should be a reasonable distribution of module sizes. Some small helper functions or methods might only be a couple lines long. Many procedures will be a half-page to a page in length. A few of the most complex modules should fit on two pages. Any module that takes more than two printed pages (call it 120 lines of code including comments) is probably longer than it should be and should be redesigned into smaller chunks.

Length is an issue in part because it is much easier to see what is going on if you can look at everything in a module at one time, rather than having to flip through pages of printout (or screens full of information) to see various parts that interact. Secondarily, long modules tend to have high complexity (discussed later). If a procedure is long, it usually has several components which could benefit from being moved into separate modules based on an evaluation of the rest of the criteria in the following sections.

> Most modules should be a page or two in length.
> ISRs should be at most half a page long.

Interrupt service routines are a special case. Interrupts are inherently complex because they invite concurrency and real time scheduling problems. Therefore, they should be as short and simple as possible. A good rule is no ISR should be more than half a page long (or, perhaps, one full page if the ISR is written in assembly language).

11.2.2. High cohesion

Cohesion is a measure of the degree to which operations are related within a module. When a module has high *cohesion*, it means all the operations fit naturally together, work on related data, and perform related actions. In other words, a module with high cohesion does a good job of binning together a set of operations that are highly related to each other in many respects.

In contrast, a module with low cohesion has a variety of functions that are unrelated in one or more respects, or are related in superficial ways. As an example, a module that initializes all the data structures in a program has relatively low cohesion, because all the initialization operations are designed to take place at the same time, but otherwise have little to do with each other. A better approach would be to create separate initialization routines for each type of data structure, grouped with each structure's access methods.

If initialization functions are separate from data structure access methods, putting those functions on the same physical source code listing page as the data declaration is better than having them in an entirely different program file. It is better, from a cohesion point of view, to avoid a separate explicit initialization phase by having data objects initialize themselves upon first use, such as is done with object oriented program constructors.

> Modules should have high cohesion.

Actually measuring cohesion can be tricky, because there are different ways in which sets of operations within a module can be related. Thus, in practice this is a subjective criterion. Nonetheless, high cohesion is something that experienced developers can recognize when they are doing a peer review, and is desirable.

11.2.3. Low coupling

Two modules are said to have high *coupling* when they are highly dependent on each other due to some type of sharing. The sharing might be that they share data, share hardware resources, control each other's execution, or each need detailed knowledge of how the other module works to do their job properly.

High coupling is bad. This is because the point of modularity is to encapsulate a set of related details within a single module, freeing other modules from worrying about those details.

As an everyday example, consider the difference between an automatic and manual transmission in an automobile. A manual transmission has high coupling between the driver and the vehicle (if you want to consider these things two modules) because the clutch pedal is part of the interface, and must be operated in a precise manner for every gear shift. The automatic transmission has lower coupling, because it doesn't require the clutch pedal, and requires the driver to have much less knowledge about how gear shifting is done. This analogy also points out that coupling is often a tradeoff. Some drivers prefer a manual transmission because it provides more control over a vehicle's performance. High coupling might bring the opportunity for better optimization in the form of ability to control details, but at the cost of increased complexity and development difficulty.

As with cohesion, coupling can be difficult to measure. Signs of high coupling include very large parameter lists, use of global variables, and ripple effects in which a change in one module forces changes elsewhere.

Modules should have low coupling.

Low coupling among modules is best. If you feel you really need high coupling to optimize the system, it is possible you are right in the narrowest sense. But, very often the real problem is that you should re-think how different modules are split to find a better strategy for determining which modules do what. Or just buy a faster CPU (see *Chapter 18. The Cost of Nearly Full Resources*).

11.2.4. Information hiding

One reason to use modules is to hide information from other portions of the software that don't need to have access to that information. The point of *information hiding* (also called *encapsulation*) is to ensure that other portions of the code don't make assumptions about details of a particular implementation that could cause problems downstream. Information hiding can be thought of as a specific technique which promotes low module coupling.

**Modules should hide their implementation details
from other modules.**

For example, consider a device driver module for a serial port. Part of the reason for using a device driver is to hide the details of interfacing to the serial port from the rest of the program. Information such as the exact port address, control register layout, bit rate, parity, and so on should be hidden from the rest of the application. The device driver needs to know these things, but letting other parts of the program know this information can make it more difficult to make changes if the serial port operating details change or the code is ported to a new processor.

Another common use of information hiding is making variables visible only within a module so that there is no possibility of other modules changing those variables in unanticipated ways. An example of this is using locally scoped variables rather than global variables (see *Chapter 19. Global Variables Are Evil*).

11.2.5. Composability

A set of modules is composable if those modules can be used within a system in many different combinations, and if they perform distinct operations with minimal overlap. For example, if your program needs to perform 17 different complex operations on a data structure, some analysis might reveal that all those complex operations are really just combinations of 3 primitive functions that are applied in different sequences. A set of modules that performs those 3 primitive functions would be more composable than a set of 17 modules in which each module performs exactly one of the complex combinations. With the 3 primitive functions, you can not only compose combinations to implement the 17 complex operations you need, but also create even more combinations if you find out you need them later.

> **Modules should have good composability.**

We are so used to seeing composable designs in well thought out systems that we don't necessarily notice that they are composable. For example, in a set of procedures to manipulate linked lists, we might have procedures to: insert an element, delete an element, traverse to next element, and go to the first element. If you have that basic set of functions, you can do pretty much anything you need to with a linked list.

But, consider, you might also want the following functions to be provided for a linked list: swap order of two elements, go to last element, insert at end of list, delete first element on list, sort the list, reverse order of the list, replace an element with a new one, and delete duplicate elements. It might be entirely appropriate to provide these functions, but the question is, how are they built? If they are expressed as combinations of the basic functions (insert, delete, traverse, go to first), then you only have to write, test, and optimize the four basic functions to avoid getting something wrong with the linked list mechanics in any other function. But, if you decide to optimize something like sorting for speed, that sort routine now becomes dependent on the implementation details of the linked list for proper operation. (For example, is the list singly linked or doubly linked? It matters if you are manipulating the links directly, but doesn't matter if you are just calling the four basic functions.)

It should be clear that composability is often at odds with optimized performance. That isn't always the case, but often it works out that way. You should avoid compromising composability for speed unless the speed gains are truly worth the increased complexity and development cost. Usually they aren't.

11.2.6. Low complexity

The simplest complexity metric is the sheer size of a module, on the principle that it's difficult to see at a glance what is going on with a big module. But, that is only one aspect of complexity, and we need to dig deeper into that topic to really deal with modularity.

Software complexity is a slippery subject. Superficially, software complexity can be expressed in terms of Lines Of Code (LOC). Very likely, something that is 100,000 LOC is significantly more complex overall than something that is 100 LOC. But that doesn't help us understand what complexity is really about. And, for two pieces of code that are closer together in size, it might be that the shorter code is more complex. For example, a 50 line interrupt service routine might be far more complex (and more full of bugs) than a 200 line case statement that implements a simple statechart.

Rather than delving too deeply into the cognitive psychology or theory of complexity, let's keep things practical. We care about complexity primarily because complex code is likely to be difficult to understand, and therefore likely to be buggy. (Or, in short: *complex code tends to be buggy code*.) How complex is too complex is a difficult question, but lower complexity is better down to the point where making code less complex starts to introduce high coupling or low cohesion.

> Modules should have the lowest complexity practical.
> (But, how you define complexity is up to you.)

There are a few measures of complexity listed below – none of them perfect. You'll need to decide which measures are most useful and appropriate for your situation.

11.2.6.1. LOC (lines of code)

LOC, sometimes called Source Lines Of Code (SLOC), is a count of the number of lines of source code excluding comments and blank lines. This metric is relatively easy to compute, but not every line of code is equivalent. So it isn't terribly useful if you are talking about small differences. But, despite its limitations, it is the most prevalent complexity measure in use because it is relatively easy to measure.

11.2.6.2. McCabe cyclomatic complexity

This is a measure of complexity based on the structure of the program. The complexity is determined by looking at a program control flow graph, and counting the number of edges, nodes, and connected components. The more connected the nodes in the graph, and the bigger the graph, the higher the cyclomatic complexity. Thus, control flow structures such as loops and conditional branches increase cyclomatic complexity. A simple way to look at this is: if you draw a flowchart or other control flow graph of the program, count up the number of closed loops you see and add one. That gives you the complexity metric.

The limit to this complexity metric is that it is based on control flow and not data flow. So, for example, using a double-indirect pointer instead of a direct variable reference doesn't increase complexity according to this metric; neither does using a conditional branch that checks 23 different conditions instead of only 1 condition. Nonetheless, many find this a useful metric.

11.2.6.3. Short term memory chunks

A common approach to thinking about complexity is to relate it to a human's short term memory capacity, which is considered to be 7 plus or minus 2 chunks or concepts (Miller, 1956). Some people can hold 5 things at a time in their short-term memory, and some can hold 9, with most people coming in between those numbers. Based on this, one can argue that any given module should have 9 or fewer things going on in it, to make it easier for a person to understand everything that is going on. This doesn't mean 9 lines of code, but rather 9 things that are related chunks of concept (for example, perhaps, 9 states in a statechart, or 9 boxes in a flowchart). With this metric, clearly there is not much gain in having modules simpler than 5 chunks in complexity, and any module more complex than 9 chunks is clearly too complex. Deciding what a chunk is, though, isn't a clear cut process.

It should be noted that some consider this application of Miller's work to be unfounded, since the studies didn't involve computer programming tasks. It is a matter of opinion how much weight this effect should be given when estimating complexity. But, we've found the idea to be useful, and it seems to work well in some situations.

11.2.6.4. Function points

This is a relatively complicated way of counting up different aspects of a piece of software and determining a complexity metric. It is based on both data and control flow, and is too complex to summarize here. It is likely more accurate than cyclomatic complexity, but it's a lot of work to use. You shouldn't use function points unless you're well down the path of collecting and using a variety of software metrics already. If you haven't already had experience with one of the other measures we discuss, you shouldn't start with this one.

11.2.6.5. Using complexity metrics

Once you have a complexity metric, even if it is just counting lines of code, how do you use it? In some cases, organizations set a target for the maximum complexity of any module. But, other organizations find this too rigid, and instead do something like require a special design review session for any code above a certain complexity. In general, the right question to be asking is: is there a good way to simplify complex modules without making other aspects of modularity too bad? At its simplest, complexity should be used in peer reviews along the lines of: "You have a 10 page interrupt service routine and we'd like to see it be less than 1 page in length. Are you sure there is no better way to do this?"

11.3. Improving modularity

Ultimately, excellent modularity stems from having a great architecture, and it's difficult to give a recipe for architecture that works in all cases (see *Chapter 10. Software Architecture*). However, there are some general design and implementation-level techniques that tend to help.

At the design level, use the right design representation for the task at hand. If you have something with behavior that changes depending on the state the system is in, use a statechart to design it (see *Chapter 13. Statecharts and Modes*). If you have a very long sequence of events represented by a flowchart, try to break that sequence into related chunks of behaviors that have good cohesion and low coupling. And so on.

At the implementation level there are some techniques that can help, including factoring and aggregation, which we discuss below. These techniques are really just a bottom-up way to improve the architecture. But, if you are starting with a detailed implementation, they can be useful.

> **Factoring and aggregation can help improve modularity.**

11.3.1. Factoring

Factoring involves taking a segment of code, identifying portions of that code that might make a nice subroutine, and putting them into a subroutine, forming a nice chunk or, ideally, a reusable functional component. In other words, if you think a module is too complex, look for pieces of it that can stand on their own and put them into a subroutine. Ideally, such a subroutine will have high cohesion (it will be a sensible chunk of code) and low coupling (it will only take a few parameters, and its implementation approach will be relatively independent of the calling module).

Consider the following simple code example:

```
Sum = 0;
for (I = 0; I < NumItemsX; I++)
{ Sum = Sum + X[i]; }
```

While the meaning of this code is fairly clear (it sums elements of the array X), it has a loop and takes a moment to understand. If this is part of a two-page program, it adds to the complexity of understanding the program as a whole. Every time you see it, you have to stop and say "what are these lines of code doing?" In a well commented program we might have a comment that says, "this loop sums elements in X[]". But, we can do better, and replace that code segment with:

```
Sum = SumArrayItems(X, NumItemsX);
```

where we have defined SumArrayItems to be a procedure that sums up all the elements of the array. Now, in part due to using a descriptive name, the code tells us what is happening more directly. Moreover, we have a reusable routine that can sum array items in other places as well. And, if we are using a complexity metric even as simple as cyclomatic complexity, we have reduced complexity by moving a loop from a long program into its own subroutine.

While factoring can be carried to extremes, it is often worth doing in moderation to make code easier to understand and test. Factoring should be used if you can identify a chunk of code that has a sensible, meaningful name, and that doesn't take so many parameters as to be unwieldy to call. If you are worried about performance, you can tell most compilers to inline the function to eliminate the call overhead.

11.3.2. Aggregation

While factoring is about splitting up pieces of code, aggregation is about associating pieces of data. One of the problems with passing around a lot of data (high data coupling) is that it can be difficult to keep track of what each piece of data is doing. Aggregating data can simplify what is happening. If you have a procedure call with more than 5 or so parameters, it is really difficult to figure out what is going on, and aggregation can help.

Here is an example of aggregation. Suppose you are keeping track of Cartesian X, Y coordinates in a graphics program. The simplistic, and very common, way to do this is have two variables, X and Y, to hold the coordinate values of one point. For example, plotting a line on a graphics display between point 1 and point 2 might be done via:

```
void DrawLine(X1, Y1, X2, Y2);
```

This involves four parameters. And, it has the disadvantage of requiring the programmer to keep track of which parameters are X values and which are Y values. Instead, you could create a data type for a point P that holds an X,Y pair. Then, you would have:

```
void DrawLine(P1, P2);
```

which cuts the number of parameters in half. Equally important, it makes it clear that the parameters are points, which is conceptually closer to what is actually happening.

The important thing with data aggregation is to make sure that the data being bound together has a fundamental cohesion. Putting unrelated data together just to reduce the number of parameters in a procedure call is counterproductive. But, if the data is naturally referenced as a set, aggregating data can simplify code and make it easier to understand.

11.4. Pitfalls

11.4.1. Using performance as an excuse for poor modularity

At one time it might have been true that subroutine calls took a lot of time to execute. But, this just isn't the case in most situations. For very small subroutines, compilers just place the actual instructions in-line with the calling procedure, completely eliminating the overhead. For larger subroutines, optimizing compilers are quite good at reducing the overhead to a bare minimum. Unless you have a poor compiler and a huge number of very small subroutines, performance isn't a reasonable justification for writing longer, flat routines instead of modular code. You should concentrate on writing code you can understand and get right. Let the compiler worry about performance.

11.4.2. Over-aggressive simplification

Overly aggressive simplification can also be a problem. If every procedure in a program is just one line of code, then trying to figure out how all the fragments fit together will be as much (or more) of a problem as figuring out what is happening in a 20-page long subroutine. (Some programming languages work really well with short fragments. But, writing good programs in such languages takes significant skill and is a different experience than writing good code for most other languages.)

11.5. For more information

11.5.1. General topic search keywords
- Modular code
- Software metric
- Software complexity

11.5.2. References

Miller, G., "The Magical Number Seven, Plus or Minus Two: Some Limits on Our Capacity for Processing Information", *Psychological Review*, vol. 63, pp. 81-97, 1956.
Discusses typical limits of short term memory and chunking.

Parnas, D. L., "On the criteria to be used in decomposing systems into modules," *Communications of the ACM*, vol. 15, no. 12, Dec, 1972, pp. 1053-1058.
The most famous paper promoting modularity.

DESIGN

Chapter 12
Software Design

- A software design is a high level representation that shows the structure of the code without giving line-by-line specifics.
- Common design representations are pseudocode, flowcharts, and statecharts.
- Creating a written design can help organize thoughts and help identify problems more efficiently than skipping design and going straight to writing code.
- Model-based design is a way to work entirely at the design level and have implementation created automatically with synthesis tools.

Contents:

12.1. Overview

When creating software, there can be enormous pressure to jump into writing code. And, for fairly simple programs, we can often get away with doing just that without causing huge problems. Then, if someone forces us to, we might draw a hasty flowchart or write some pseudocode to try to explain what we did. But, what worked in homework assignments while we were in school won't necessarily cut it in the Real World. When programs are more complex than the toy problems we worked on when learning programming, we need help in dealing with that complexity. A good source of help is figuring out what your program is supposed to do at a higher level of abstraction than the code itself. That's where design comes into play.

Design is a middle ground between architecture and implementation. Architecture deals with the organization and function of modules. Design deals with the internals of a single module, and how it is built in general. *Implementation* is the actual code.

As an example, an architecture might have a box that filters sensor data. The corresponding design might have a description of how the filtering is done, such as: there is a buffer that keeps the last few samples, and we average those samples to provide data upon request. The corresponding implementation deals with details that don't matter to the design, such as the name of the buffer, how the buffer keeps track of the newest sample position, how we can compute the average efficiently, how we avoid numeric overflow, and so on.

12.1.1. Importance of having a good design

You need a design so that developers can think about how create a program without getting bogged down in details. For example, if you need to create a filter for sensor data, the most important thing to decide is what the filtering technique will be, not the name of the variables used in loops to index into the sample buffer. Design helps us understand what is going on by abstracting away (hiding) the details that don't matter to the big picture. This, in turn, lets us see what is going on better, and makes it easier to find mistakes before we invest a lot of time creating code.

12.1.2. Possible symptoms

The first type of symptom is that the design isn't at the right level of abstraction:

✖ There is no design. No design exists – just the implementation (the source code). Comments in the implementation are helpful, and might be thought to be a design by the developers. But in our experience, comments don't really provide the benefit of a true design.

✖ The design is too detailed. For example, lines of executable code appear in the design. An overly detailed design is really a different expression of the implementation. Sometimes there are designs in the form of flowcharts that aren't really designs, but graphical versions of the implementation. For example, a flowchart in which each box has exactly one line of code written in it is really a pictorial form of the implementation. It isn't a design unless it is somehow at a higher level of abstraction than the implementation itself.

A second type of symptom is when designs are backfilled after implementation. Typical symptoms of this problem include:

✘ Design documents are generated automatically based on the implementation. For example, programs exist that will create flowcharts automatically from source code. An important point of doing design is to help the developer understand what is going on before the code is written. Documenting the design after the fact might be nice, but shouldn't be the primary purpose of having design documents.

✘ Design documents have creation dates near the end of the project. They should have creation and modification dates throughout the project.

12.1.3. Risks of not having a concrete design

Software can, occasionally, be created successfully by jumping right into writing code. But, doing so incurs a significant risk of increased cost and defect rates. The reason is that complexity is difficult to manage, and a system's implementation is more complex than its design. By skipping the design phase, developers lose an important opportunity to find problems and create cleaner solution approaches early in development rather than later. Typical risks are mostly in the form of lost opportunities:

➤ Mistakes in general approach are put into the implementation, delaying the time when they are found and increasing the cost to correct them.

➤ Messy implementations arise from not having a conceptually clean design approach.

➤ High defect rates result in increased development costs.

12.2. The role of design

A design is a simplified representation of the implementation that helps the developer understand how the implementation will be structured and how it will function, without getting bogged down in details.

12.2.1. The right level of design abstraction

The right level for a design can vary depending on the system. The best level of abstraction for a design is one that makes the problem simpler to understand. In general, it means the design should avoid details that aren't required to understand the general approach. For example, if a routine is supposed to add up all the numbers in a list, then a design will concentrate on notions such as "add to a running sum" and "select every element on the list." Details such as whether an

8-bit or 16-bit integer is used as a loop counter, and the order that the numbers are added in aren't important to seeing that the point is to add up all the numbers. Those details should (and must) be in the implementation, but ordinarily have no place in the design.

One way to think about the right level of abstraction is to ask: "Is this detail essential to understanding what has to happen?" A good heuristic to apply when creating a design is to ask: "Can I make this description simpler and still get the point across?"

The design shouldn't have anything to do with the programming language you are using. If it does, it smacks of implementation. Any time variable names or lines of code show up in a design representation, you should ask whether you've crossed the line into implementation. It is certainly true that this sort of shorthand can be useful in expressing a high-level idea. But it can also be the start of a path to creating an implementation instead of a design. The best way to get a good design is to avoid including executable code.

> Designs should not have any elements of implementation –
> no executable code allowed!

12.2.2. Going straight to implementation

If you skip design and go straight to implementation, there is still a design of sorts – but it exists only in the developer's head while the code is being written. The developer might (or might not) put some of that design information into the comments. The case of comments being used to document the design are discussed in the Pitfalls section of this chapter.

The problems with skipping design and not writing it down at all tend to be:

- If the design isn't written down, it has to be re-created in the head of anyone else reading the code, taking additional time and effort compared to looking at a written design.

- Not having a written design misses the chance to find problems in the act of writing down the design. Many times a design is fuzzy, and being forced to write it down makes it easier to see where the problems are compared to keeping it in your head.

12.3. Different design representations

There are many different, reasonable ways to represent a design. Each approach has its strengths and weaknesses. In embedded systems, different representations are best for different portions of the system. In each case it is possible to abuse the design representation by putting in so much detail that it turns into an implementation. But, with care, each of these representations can help give developers (and later maintainers) a high level understanding of what is supposed to be going on.

For each design representation, it is important to be able to see everything that is going on in a piece of code easily. That way, the whole picture of what is happening can be understood at once. We suggest that whatever design representation is being used be limited to a single sheet of paper per module (possibly with details or subroutines on additional sheets).

> **Each design diagram or other module of design should fit on a single sheet of paper.**

12.3.1. Pseudocode

Pseudocode is a segment of text that is some sort of hybrid between a programming language and a narrative description of what is going on. Often, pseudocode mixes elements of implementation and design. We prefer pseudocode that avoids as many implementation details as possible.

Bad Example:
```
while (Element.Next)
   CurrentPtr = Element.Next;
if (Current element < Next element)
   Swap order of elements
```

The problem with this example is that it has actual pieces of code in it, and refers to specific variables and fields within those variables. Surely following a linked list can be described without having to know the name of the field with the pointer to the next element.

Better Example:
```
while (Not at end of list)
   Follow link to next item on list
if (Current element < Next element)
   Swap order of elements
```

While the above is better than something with all the gory details, but it still lets a lot of implementation detail creep in. For example, is it essential that you know a linked list is being used to store data being sorted? While that matters to the implementation, at the level of design it is unnecessary detail. A better approach for this set of functionality would be to just describe what is going on at a uniformly implementation-neutral manner:

Good Example:
```
For all items in sequence except last item
   Compare current item to next sequential item
if (Current item < Next item)
   Swap order of items
```

Pseudocode has the advantage that it can be entered and edited easily using e-mail and word processing software, without need for graphical tools. Historically, that was important because computer systems had neither graphic displays nor graphics printers. These days that just isn't a primary factor. Pseudocode is still the best form for putting design information into comments, but we think that is not the best way to go for design.

> **Use pseudocode only as a last resort.**
> **Instead, use a graphical approach if one is suitable.**

The main disadvantage to pseudocode is that there is a lot of room for informality, ambiguity, and mixing of implementation and design. If more than a dozen or so lines of pseudocode are presented in one chunk, it gets difficult to understand what is going on.

12.3.2. Flowcharts

Flowcharts are good at emphasizing the flow of control of a program. Their strength is at representing ideas such as "first this happens; then that happens; then if such-and-such condition is true this other thing happens." In some types of embedded applications, they are just the right representation.

Flowcharts have boxes, ovals, and arrows to represent a sequence of steps in solving a problem, with diamonds used to represent conditional branch points. Flowcharts can also have symbols for loops, subroutine calls, and so on. The important part of flowcharts from a design point of view is not the shape of all the various boxes. The important part is that it must be a useful abstraction of the implementation.

The meaning of the flowchart is divided between the drawing structure and the text in each box. A good flowchart is similar to good pseudocode, except it uses the drawing to represent flow of control. The pitfalls are similar to those for pseudocode. Putting variable assignments and other executable code segments in a flowchart is mixing implementation into the design, which should be avoided.

A good flowchart has to be understandable at a glance. For that reason, a good flowchart should fit entirely on a single page. (Details might be represented as subroutines, with each subroutine fitting on its own page.) In general, the use of off-page connectors indicates a flowchart that is too complex to be really helpful in understanding a design.

> **Flowcharts are best at representing sequences of actions.**

Flowcharts are particularly bad at representing state-based and modal behaviors. It is true that switch statements can be represented in a flowchart. But, if the motivation of the switch statement is to define behavior in various states, then the drawing is showing implementation and not design. Statecharts should be used to represent state-based behavior designs.

12.3.3. Statecharts

Statecharts are diagrams that show the different states or modes of operation of a system. They are considerably different than flowcharts in that they aren't meant to emphasize paths through a set of sequential steps. Rather, they give a concise representation of everything a module can do, and show what conditions change its behavior. *Chapter 13. Statecharts and Modes* discusses statecharts in more detail. It is the rare embedded system that can't benefit from using statecharts as a design representation for at least some portion of the system.

> **Statecharts should be used to represent**
> **finite state machines and modal behaviors.**

Statecharts are not good at representing long strings of sequential functions – that is what flowcharts are good for.

12.3.4. Other design representations

There are many other design representations that can and should be used when appropriate in embedded systems. Most of the ones currently in favor are collected in the Unified Modeling Language (UML). These charts include the following:

- **Sequence diagrams:** show a sequence of messages illustrating a particular interaction among objects.

- **Activity diagrams:** a different approach to flowcharting that supports representing multiple parallel paths being active at the same time, rather than a single flow of control as in a flowchart.

- **Collaboration diagrams:** show a sequenced set of messages illustrating a specific example of object interaction.

- **Implementation diagrams:** show the run-time dependencies and packaging structure of the deployed system

There are other UML diagrams as well, but the above are the ones most relevant to expressing designs. There are many tutorials and books on UML, with some starting points included at the end of this chapter.

12.3.5. Code synthesis and model-based design

Increasingly, embedded software is being created via synthesized code and model-based design. The general idea is that a very precise high-level description of system behavior is entered into a graphical tool, and that tool automatically creates the implementation. We'll call this general type of tool model-based design even though that terminology is more precisely applied to controls-oriented software. The idea of model-based design has been around for a long time, and has always had its strengths and weaknesses.

Model-based design can be powerful and very beneficial when used to create understandable, accurate designs. By understandable, we mean that the designs must have the right level of abstraction and be relatively free of implementation details, as with any other design representation.

The key to understanding the role of any model-based design system is realizing that every tool has a notion of the type of software it is good at synthesizing. For example, software that is good at synthesizing control loops may be very good indeed at that. But it probably isn't very clever at creating code to implement a real time scheduler, or code to perform database accesses. Therefore, just as with any other design representation, the key to effective use of model-based design tools is using them for what they are good at, and using other techniques when they make sense.

| If you have a lot of raw code in your model, your model-based design tool is a poor match for what you are trying to build. |

The signs that your design isn't mapping well onto the model your tool wants you to use are similar to the signs of problems with any other design representation. Lines of code as chunks of a model mean that implementation is leaking into the design (and, likely, this means that the model is having trouble representing the higher level concept you are trying to design with). Similarly, useful conceptual chunks of the system should fit onto a single printed page so you can see how they work, with multiple pages being arranged in a hierarchy to form the entire system.

Model-based design is a potentially powerful approach to creating systems at a higher level of abstraction than writing detailed implementations. But it isn't magic. Even for those designs in which it is a good fit, you still need a clean architecture and all the other things that help make a project successful.

12.4. Pitfall – using comments as the design

It is common for embedded developers to claim that they do indeed have a design – in the form of code comments. It is worth taking a critical look at this claim to see where it might, and might not, be reasonable.

To be valid, using comments as a design would mean that the comments describe what the code is doing at some higher level of abstraction than the actual implementation. This is certainly possible, but it immediately eliminates line-by-line comments about code operation from consideration. Any comment that, for example, explains that a shift left 3 bits was used to multiply by 8 is an aid to understanding implementation, but is certainly not a design.

What if there are comments describing what a section of code is all about that might in fact be design information? The usual problems with this approach are:

- Comments are text only, and the most powerful design techniques tend to be graphical. Usually a design approach based on comments uses pseudocode, which is the squishiest form of design representation. Thus, style and level of abstraction tend to vary tremendously depending on who wrote the comments.

- The big picture is more difficult to see. If pseudocode is scattered throughout the source code, it is difficult to get the big picture of what is happening. (If pseudocode for a whole module is at the start of the module, this problem is mitigated.)

Comments aren't a design.

Much more commonly, comments aren't really a design at all. Rather, they are documentation of design information as it applies to a particular section of code. While this may seem like hair-splitting, the ramifications are important. Essentially all design information expressed as comments that we've seen have the following limitations:

- They are a summarization of code, not a predecessor to code. That means that the benefits of looking the entire system over at a high level before diving into implementation details have been lost.

- They are not at a uniform level of abstraction, and are often missing. Having a separate design document makes it much more obvious when huge chunks of the design are missing. Having to go through dozens of files of code to see which ones have design comments is much more difficult to check.

- They are often out of date. People maintaining code put top priority on maintaining the implementation. It is easy for comments to get out of date, especially if their design value isn't perceived as being important. If the culture is that separate design documents won't be maintained, it is difficult to argue that high level code comments will be maintained (sometimes they are, but more often they're not).

There are tools which go through code, extract information, and create designs (or at least design documentation) from that information. If the result is a good design, that might be OK as far as it goes and can provide useful information such as summaries of calling parameters. But very often this approach is used to back-fill a design after the code has been written (i.e., generate documentation). Such extraction processes usually yield text files, significantly limiting the expressiveness of the design information. This type of approach is often worthwhile, but should not be mistaken for creating a good high-level design.

The usual reason given for putting design information into comments is that only the code will be maintained, and other documents will get out of date. While this might indeed be true of a particular developer or organization, that doesn't mean designs are useless. It just means that developers who think this don't find that other documents provide enough value to be worth keeping up to date.

Is it possible to use comments as the design? From a strictly theoretical point of view, it is. But we've never seen it work out well in practice.

12.5. For more information

12.5.1. General topic search keywords
- UML
- Unified Modeling Language
- Software design

12.5.2. Recommended reading

Douglass, "Designing real-time systems with UML" *Embedded Systems Programming*. Part I: v. 11 n. 3, March 1998; Part II: v. 11 n. 4, April 1998; Part III: v. 11 n. 5, May 1998
A three-part tutorial explaining UML, with an emphasis on design.

Chapter 13
Statecharts and Modes

- Statecharts are a good way to represent modal or state-based behaviors, in which system responses vary depending on the current status of an internal finite state machine.

- A case statement implementation of a state machine can make it straightforward to design and implement even complex state-dependent behaviors.

Contents:

A statechart is a finite state machine diagram tailored for representing software. Statecharts should be used whenever the system exhibits state-based or modal behavior. Statecharts are best implemented using a case or switch statement, with one case per state.

13.1. Overview

Almost all embedded systems have some state-based or modal behavior. For example, it is common for systems to behave quite differently in normal operation, start-up mode, diagnostic mode, and standby mode. Beyond that, different buttons and LEDs might mean different things depending on what state the system is in. As an example, consider the buttons on a digital wristwatch, which do different things depending on which buttons have been pressed previously.

A good way to design state-based and modal system operations is to use a statechart. Statecharts are a specific type of finite state machine diagram suitable for use in designing software. We'll discuss them at length in this chapter.

13.1.1. Importance of using statecharts

It's important to match the design representation being used to the software behavior being designed. It is common to use flowcharts for everything. But, using flowcharts for something that has state-based behavior leads to an implementation that is messy, difficult to understand, and bug prone.

State-based behaviors are a lot cleaner when represented as statecharts and implemented with a case statement structure. Using a better suited design representation tends to result in code that is easier to understand and far less bug-prone than a flowchart-only design approach.

13.1.2. Possible symptoms

You should consider using statecharts as a design approach for at least some of your system if:

✘ There are no statecharts, finite state machine diagrams, or other design documents describing state-based behavior. It is the rare embedded system that can't benefit from statecharts in at least one place. If you aren't using any, something is wrong.

✘ The code has deeply nested conditional statements, often with many of the conditional statements having similar or identical conditional tests. Deeply nested if statements can indicate state-based behavior in embedded systems.

✘ The system has suffered from bugs due to differing portions of the software disagreeing about what state the system is in, or due to incorrect mode-dependent behavior.

13.1.3. Risks of not using statecharts

Using something other than a statechart to design state-based behaviors is likely to result in:

➤ Creation of overly complex conditional statements and that are difficult to understand and get right.

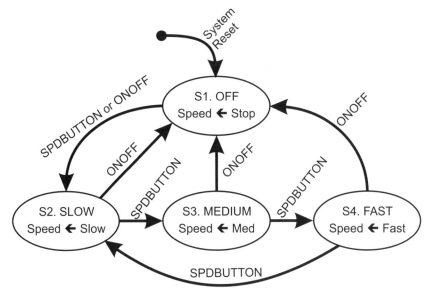

Figure 13.1. An example statechart.

➤ Incorrect state transition logic or per-state actions due to lack of clarity about state-dependent behaviors.

➤ In general, code with more complexity and more numerous bugs than could have been created using a better design approach.

13.2. Statecharts

Statecharts are diagrams that show the states and transitions of a finite state machine implemented in software.

13.2.1. Statechart construction

In its simplest form, a *statechart* consists of:

- **An initialization arc,** which indicates which state is entered when the system is reset. This arc has a small solid black dot at the tail of an arrow, with the head of the arrow indicating the reset state.

- **A set of states,** with each state represented by an oval. Each state has a name, and has actions associated with being in that state.

- **Arcs between states.** An arc is taken when its guard conditions (the conditions that permit the state change indicated by the arc) are true. Arcs may have actions associated with them that are performed as the arc is traversed, although we discourage that (discussed below).

The example shown in Figure 13.1 is a statechart depicting the operation of a three-speed fan with two buttons: an on/off button and a speed-select button.

The system is either in exactly one oval, or on an arc traversing between ovals at any given time.

There are four states represented by ovals: OFF, SLOW, MEDIUM, and FAST. Pressing the ONOFF button turns the system off if in SLOW, MEDIUM, or FAST speed, but causes the system to turn on at SLOW speed if the system was OFF. Pressing the SPDBUTTON causes the system to turn on at SLOW speed if it was OFF, and to cycle through the three available speeds if it is already ON. Note that the name and number of each state is solely for the benefit of the designer. The actual action being taken is solely a result of the Speed value assignment within each state and is unaffected by the state name.

In this example, the action the system takes when both ONOFF and SPDBUTTON are pressed at the same time is undefined. (The actual system will take some action by following the arc for either button, but the design doesn't limit what that action might be.) This example also assumes that the button is released before the next time a state transition is taken. In a real system, there would need to be additional states, button hardware, button device driver software, or some other mechanism to ensure that only one state transition is taken per button closure.

A statechart is completed when the following conditions have been met:

- All states of interest have been represented. This means it is impossible for the system to be in a state that isn't on the diagram.

- Every state has both a name (to benefit the designers) and defined effects (which tells implementers what to do when in that state).

- Every arc has a guard condition (to define when that arc is taken). The convention is that the system stays in the current state if no guard conditions are satisfied.

Statecharts can be much more complex, and there is a whole set of specialized notation that can be used for concurrency and creating hierarchies of states (see the reading section for this chapter). But, for many systems, the notation in Fig. 13.1 suffices.

As you can see, this notation is well suited to representing the behavior of systems which have state-based operation. In fact, it is so useful that it should always be used when a system has state-based behavior.

Statecharts should be used whenever the system exhibits state-based or modal behavior.

It may be possible to use flowcharts or some other techniques to attempt to describe state-based behavior, but they are simply the wrong tool for the job.

13.2.2. Statechart implementation

The best way to implement a statechart in code is with a case statement (known as a switch statement in C and C++). We'll use the terminology of switch statement because that is most familiar to embedded developers who use C and C++. But you can also think of it as a case statement from other languages.

> Use a switch or case statement to implement state charts –
> not nested if statements.

The general form of a statechart implementation involves several items:

- **A variable that remembers the current state.** The actual name could be anything, but let's refer to it as CurrState for this discussion. Each state in the system is assigned an integer value (or an enum value in C), and the value of that variable indicates which state the system is currently in. So for the example in Fig. 13.1, CurrState could have one of the following values: OFF, SLOW, MEDIUM, FAST. (In languages that require integers for case statement variables, we could just use the values 1, 2, 3 and 4 instead.) When the system starts, the variable needs to be initialized to the default state.

- **A case or switch statement** that executes code appropriate to the current state. It does this by performing the case or switch operation on the variable CurrState.

- **Code in each case to implement the action.** Once the switch statement is executed, only the code corresponding to the current state is run. In the example of Fig. 13.1, this code would set a value for the variable Speed, and perhaps send that value to an I/O port.

- **Code to check guard conditions and transition to different states.** Conditional branches are used to check for every guard condition relevant to transitions out of the current state. If any of the transitions are true, CurrState is changed to the value of the new state, and transition code is executed if applicable. If no guard is true, CurrState is left unchanged. If multiple guards are true, the statechart does not define the results.

The switch statement is executed periodically, with each state performing its actions. If a guard condition is true, the switch statement also changes CurrState to perform a transition to a new state. Traversing multiple arcs in the statechart requires multiple distinct executions of the case statement.

Below is a sketch of C-like code for an implementation of the statechart in Fig. 13.1. It is set to run in an infinite loop, but might instead be simply one task that is periodically performed out of many in a system.

```
enum CurrState
{OFF, SLOW, MEDIUM, FAST}; // define states

#define SpdOff   0    // define speed constant values
#define SpdSlow 10
#define SpdMed  15
#define SpdFast 25

CurrState = OFF;  // initialize state machine to OFF

while (1) // do forever
{
  switch (CurrState) {
  case OFF:      // State S1
    speed(SpdOff);            // Take action in state

    // Test arc guards and take transitions
    if (SpdButton() == TRUE || OnOffButton() == TRUE)
    {CurrState = SLOW;}
    break;   // go to end of switch statement

  case SLOW:      // State S2
    speed(SpdSlow);      // take action
    if (SpdButton() == TRUE)   {CurrState = MEDIUM;}
    if (OnOffButton() == TRUE) {CurrState = OFF;}
    break;

  case MEDIUM:    // State S3
    speed(SpdMed);      // take action
    if (SpdButton() == TRUE)   {CurrState = FAST;}
    if (OnOffButton() == TRUE) {CurrState = OFF;}
    break;

  case FAST:      // State S4
    speed(SpdFast);      // take action
    if (SpdButton() == TRUE)   {CurrState = SLOW;}
    if (OnOffButton() == TRUE) {CurrState = OFF;}
    break;

  default:        // Error — invalid state
    error("invalid state!"); // should never get here
  }
}
```

This code is simplistic and has some assumptions. In particular, we assume that **SpdButton** and **OnOffButton** are variables that reflect the current button value, and that they only return a value of true one time for each time they are pressed. This could be implemented in an object that keeps track of button status.

The virtue of this coding approach is that it is fairly straightforward to look at the code, look at the statechart, and determine whether the code matches the statechart.

13.3. Pitfalls

Statecharts are a formalism that, like all other formalisms, have strengths and weaknesses. They should be used for portions of a design where they are the best fit, which in general is state-intensive code. There are some common pitfalls in statechart use:

- **Forgetting the initialization state.** Forgetting to specify an initial state is easy to do, but can lead to the system being in an illegal or unexpected state at startup.

- **Multiple guard conditions true simultaneously.** Each state should have only one arc that can be taken at any given time. If two guard conditions are true, then which arc is taken will depend on the particulars of the way the code is written, which can be confusing or lead to incorrect behavior. You can fix this by making the guard conditions more specific.

While some might consider this a matter of taste, we prefer to avoid:

- **Actions on arcs.** It is possible to have actions associated with arcs in a statechart. This has the advantage of making sure that the action happens exactly one time, while the arc is being traversed. On a theoretical basis there's nothing wrong with this. But on a practical basis this approach creates opportunities for bugs:

  ○ Code executed as part of the arc shows up as code inside a guard condition if statement. Sometimes that type of code gets complex, which renders it more vulnerable to having bugs.

  ○ If the action on the arc fails, recovery can be messy. Do you leave the statechart in an in-between state for a retry operation on a subsequent execution? Or add a fault recovery state?.

We recommend putting actions only inside states and not on arcs, but realize that is a matter of preference.

13.4. For more information

13.4.1. General topic search keywords
- Switch statement
- Statechart

13.4.2. Recommended reading

Douglass, B. P., "UML Statecharts," *Embedded Systems Programming*, January 1999, pp. 22-42.

This introduction to UML statecharts introduces more advance concepts such as composite states.

Chapter 14
Real Time

- Meeting real time deadlines requires understanding the frequency, deadlines, and computation times of all various tasks within the system.
- Testing with no analysis is insufficient to ensure that real time deadlines will be met in the worst case, so it is important to use an approach with solid mathematical foundations.
- For simple systems, a purely static task scheduling approach can work, possibly with helper interrupts.
- For more complex systems, a rate monotonic scheduling system is often better.
- When possible, Earliest Deadline First (EDF) scheduling should be avoided, as should ad hoc approaches to task prioritization.

Contents:

uling uses the minimum of the task period and deadline for assigning task priorities.

Real time scheduling is a lot harder than it looks. If you aren't 100% sure you are getting it right, get some help. Don't try to bend the rules on your own.

14.1. Overview

Most embedded systems are also *real time* systems, because the usefulness of the computational results depends on when those results are produced. Timeliness is enforced via real time deadlines. Knowing that you are going to meet your deadlines is important, because late results can be just as bad as incorrect calculations. For all but the simplest systems, just performing computations as fast as you can may not be good enough. Although a system may compute much faster than required for typical cases, it might be possible for events to arrive in such a way as to cause a missed deadline, even if the system usually works just fine.

14.1.1. Importance of getting real time operation right

The point of real time analysis and scheduling is to make sure the system meets its deadlines. This can be ensured by first understanding the various tasks the system must perform, and then arranging for tasks to execute in an order that guarantees all deadlines are met. Real time issues are notoriously tricky to understand and get right. Therefore, it is a good idea to use one of several standard approaches that are known to work well.

The most common problem in real time operation arises from attempting to use testing to see if real time requirements are going to be met. Testing system operation can tell you if real time deadlines will *usually* be met, but not whether they will *always* be met, because creating the worst case situation for a test scenario is very difficult to do. Thus, the most important part of getting real time right is either designing the system so that testing the worst case is easy (via static scheduling), or designing the system so that worst case behavior can be understood mathematically without having to actually create and test that worst case situation (via rate monotonic scheduling).

14.1.2. Possible symptoms

You should take a closer look at real time scheduling for your project if:

✘ There is no written real time schedule.

✘ A hybrid or ad hoc scheduling technique is used instead of a single, consistent approach. (For example, a static schedule is used for most tasks, but some tasks are dynamically skipped during periods of heavy load.)

✘ Earliest deadline first scheduling or least laxity scheduling is used.

✘ Worst case execution time for various tasks isn't known and documented.

✘ A desktop operating system is being used without specific real time support.

14.1.3. Risks of inadequate real time design

If you are lacking a comprehensive approach to managing real time performance in your system, you might have the following problems:

➤ The system will miss deadlines in normal operation.

➤ The system will miss deadlines in particularly bad cases, but not typical cases, making it difficult to identify and debug real time problems.

➤ Significant effort will be spent on code optimization (or buying a faster CPU) that could have been avoided. Meeting real time deadlines is only partly about having fast code. Some slow code can be OK, so long as it doesn't get in the way of the parts of the system that need to be fast.

14.2. Real time analysis overview

Real time performance is seldom about being as fast as absolutely possible. Rather, it is about being just as fast as you need to be, and minimizing overall cost.

Real time isn't just going really fast.

To achieve real time operation, you need to follow several steps: understand the assumptions you need to make; understand your system; select a good real time scheduling approach; and perform analysis to assure you can meet your deadlines. We sketch an outline of approaches here that will work in simple embedded systems. There are many different special techniques that may be needed to adapt to specific situations – and plenty of specialized real time scheduling books available to provide the relevant theory. Consider this chapter a practical overview of the area.

14.2.1. Assumptions and terminology for analysis and scheduling

We're interested in determining whether or not a particular set of computations (which we will call *tasks*) can be performed while meeting a set of deadlines (mandatory completion times based on when a task becomes ready to run). The problem of figuring out how to execute all the tasks while ensuring their deadlines are met is called *real time scheduling*.

If you make no assumptions at all, it is impossible to ensure you meet real time deadlines under all circumstances. For example, if interrupts arrive faster than they can be processed, the CPU will be overloaded and deadlines will be missed. Nothing can prevent that, unless you make an assumption such that interrupts will arrive infrequently enough to leave time for everything else to execute.

So we have to make some assumptions. These assumptions are pretty optimistic, and aren't perfectly true in practice. But they are the best starting point:

14.2.1.1. All tasks T_i are perfectly periodic

We assume there are n tasks, each one named T_i with tasks being numbered $\{T_0, T_1, \ldots, T_{n-1}\}$. Each task can run only once within its period. We don't know exactly where within the period it will run, but it will need to run no faster than once per period.

In practice, we use the worst-case (fastest) inter-arrival time for tasks that aren't periodic. This may require enforcing a minimum delay before a task can be re-run. For example, an interrupt that tries to recur before its period has elapsed might need to be suppressed by hardware for a while.

If a task has varying period lengths, the fastest possible period is used for scheduling.

14.2.1.2. All tasks T_i are completely independent

This avoids issues of one task blocking another task. This assumption is often difficult to realize in practice, because any shared resource is a problem, including such diverse things as mutex-protected shared variables and multiplexed A/D converters. But, this assumption is required for simple scheduling approaches to work. If this assumption isn't true, tasks are said to have a non-zero blocking time, which complicates scheduling beyond what we will consider here.

14.2.1.3. Worst case execution time C_i for each task is known

We need to know how much CPU time each task will take to execute in isolation, and use the longest, worst-case execution time (WCET) in our calculations. This worst-case analysis includes taking the longest possible path through conditional branches in the code, the worst possible combination of cache memory misses, and so on. It does not include time spent waiting for other, completely independent, tasks to execute.

Actually determining the worst case can be a significant effort if the code is complex. Some processors come with tools to compute WCET, but more commonly developers must instrument real systems to determine execution time for a task. In the simplest case, a digital output pin can set at the start of a piece of code and reset at the end, and be monitored with an oscilloscope to determine timing. Many samples should be taken, and every effort should be made to ensure that the code is executing long computation paths rather than short paths during the measurement (for example, if there is a loop with a varying number of iterations, make sure you measure it for the longest possible number of iterations).

Determining WCET precisely can be difficult. It is a good idea to add a little margin to WCET values in case there is a tricky long path you missed.

14.2.1.4. The deadline D_i is greater than or equal to the period P_i

This means each task must complete execution before the next time that same task can start running. We don't force a task to complete, but rather create a schedule that ensures this will happen in a properly operating system.

If the deadline is shorter than the period, we assume a faster period to equal that deadline. For example, a task with a period of 100 msec and a deadline of 25 msec would be treated as if its period were 25 msec, even though it would run less frequently. This ensures that when it does need to run, it will complete by its required deadline.

14.2.1.5. There is zero overhead to switch between tasks

If switching between tasks is much faster than the shortest deadline, it can often be considered close enough to zero for practical purposes.

14.2.1.6. Meeting the assumptions

It's a good idea to leave a few percent unused CPU capacity to account for minor deviations from the assumptions. Chapter 18 (*The Cost of Nearly Full Resources*) argues that you should leave considerably more spare capacity to reduce development costs. But for the present discussion we assume that you want to load the CPU to the maximum capacity possible. (You can always assume a slower CPU than you actually have to create a real time schedule while leaving spare capacity.) Either way, it's still important to understand how much of the CPU you are using and how much is really unused.

> Basic real time scheduling requires assumptions:
> periodic, independent tasks;
> known worst case execution time;
> deadline equal to period; and
> zero-time task switching.

If you can, the best way to avoid problems is to modify your system to attempt to conform to the above assumptions, even if it means things aren't as highly optimized as you would like them to be. A working, but suboptimal system is better than an optimized system that doesn't actually work.

It is certainly possible to create a working real time system that doesn't meet all these assumptions. However, ensuring that such a system meets all its deadlines can become difficult, and requires significant specialized expertise. In other words, if any of the assumptions above don't apply to your system, you need to read a book dedicated to real time scheduling, and probably get some expert help as well.

14.2.2. Selecting an approach

Once you have modified your system to conform to the required assumptions, and gathered all the information for your system (in particular, P_i and C_i for each task T_i), you're ready to select a real time scheduling approach.

There are only three real time scheduling approaches that we recommend as being feasible for non-experts: purely static, static with small helper interrupts, and harmonic rate monotonic. Other scheduling approaches are possible, but without significant expertise it is difficult to get them right. If the approaches we recommend will do the job, you should use them to make your life easier, and reduce the risk of having real time performance problems.

We'll discuss each approach in turn below, including strengths and limitations. The most important point to remember is that for all three of these methods, we can show you how to guarantee you will meet your real time deadlines every time by building your system in a certain, structured way.

> Use a simple, defined real time scheduling approach.
> Don't invent your own!

14.3. Pure static scheduling (non-preemptive)

Pure static scheduling is a system in which all tasks run in a big loop. Each task runs all the way through one time, then the next task runs, and so on. When all tasks complete, they start over again with the first task. There are no interrupts, and no task preempts any other task. This is also known as a cyclic executive or a time triggered schedule.

Figure 14.1 shows the execution sequence in a typical statically scheduled system. Task 0 (T_0) executes to completion, followed by Task 1 (T_1), Task 2 (T_2), and so on through Task -1 (T_{N-1}). Then the system waits until its next scheduled execution start time, then goes back to the beginning and sequences through the tasks again. An example implementation is:

```
while (1) // loop forever
{ Task0();      // execute Task 0 to completion
  Task1();      // execute Task 1 to completion
  Task2();      // execute Task 2 to completion
```

MAIN LOOP

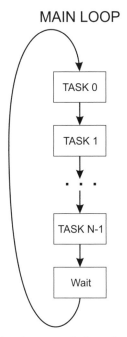

Figure 14.1. Task sequencing in pure static scheduling.

```
...
Task14();     // execute last task to completion
IdleUntil(100);   // wait for next 100 msec period
}
```

Often there is a wait function at the end of the main loop (e.g, after Task –1 in Fig. 14.1) so that the main loop runs at a fixed period rather than as fast as possible. For example, all tasks in the loop might take between 72 and 79 msec to execute depending on conditional branches taken, but a wait might be performed to start the loop once every 100 msec so that the overall system executes tasks at exactly 10 Hz.

For a system to have purely static scheduling, every task must be executed exactly once every time through the loop, whether tasks do useful work or not. This is crucial! If tasks are skipped depending on various factors, the loop timing will vary, and it will be difficult or impossible to understand execution time via testing.

> Pure static scheduling calls all tasks in order within
> a single main loop.

14.3.1. Pure static scheduling strengths

The main strength of this approach is its simplicity. There is no real time scheduling software to write, or operating system licenses to purchase. A single big loop that calls each task in turn suffices. Problems with shared variables and shared resources are minimized, because each task gets exclusive access while it is running. No interrupts or preemptions are possible.

Most importantly, this is the easiest system to test and validate, because it is so deterministic. This approach has been used with success for many years in safety critical systems for just this reason.

14.3.2. Pure static scheduling weaknesses

This is the least flexible scheduling approach. Everything has to run to completion before the next task can execute. There is no prioritization. All I/O has to be polled (interrupts aren't allowed!). If you can execute all tasks in the system faster than the fastest deadline, then none of these restrictions matter. But, as soon as you have deadlines shorter than the time required to execute all tasks in the main loop, this approach becomes difficult.

This approach is also potentially wasteful. Every task has to execute at the period of the fastest task in the system, whether it really needs to run or not.

Verifying this approach by testing is intuitively simple, but can be a bit difficult in practice. If every task takes the same time to execute every time it is run, then running the system for just a few iterations of the main loop will reveal whether or not it will ever miss a deadline. But, unfortunately, software varies in execution time for a variety of reasons. So, while testing is important, analysis based on determining worst case execution times for each task is also important in addition to testing. The important thing to look for is that every task can take its longest execution path and still have the main loop complete within its deadline.

14.3.3. Scheduling analysis

Ensuring a statically scheduled system will meet its deadlines is straightforward. So long as all assumptions are met, a statically scheduled system will meet its deadlines if the shortest deadline is less than the sum of the worst case, longest computation times for all tasks:

$$\sum_i C_i \leq \min(D_i) \tag{14.1}$$

If the system has a wait in it to force a constant period, the deadlines must be no shorter than the period at which the main loop executes, P_{main}:

$$\sum_i C_i \leq P_{main} \leq \min(D_i) \tag{14.2}$$

In other words, deadlines will be met if the main loop executes faster than the fastest deadline for any particular task. This is true because every task in the system is computed once per main loop. If any deadline is shorter than the time to execute the main loop, this approach won't work without embellishments (which are discussed in the next section).

> **Pure static scheduling meets its deadlines if the main loop executes at least as fast as the shortest deadline.**

14.3.4. Embellishments

A safe embellishment is running tasks that need to execute frequently more than once in the main loop. For example, run task T_0 once at the beginning of the main loop, and once again halfway through the execution of the main loop. This lets it have a deadline half as long as the main loop's execution time. This is easily implemented by having multiple calls to tasks coded right into the main loop. For math purposes this counts as multiple different tasks that just happen to call the same code, meaning if you run a task twice, you have to add its computation time twice to get a correct sum of total computation times, as you'd expect. Spacing apart the multiple task executions is essential. For example, calling Task 0 twice in a row in a 100 msec loop won't meet a 50 msec deadline.

Another reasonable embellishment is to run one background interrupt, such as a timer service routine. So long as that interrupt is short, runs strictly periodically, doesn't cause behavior changes in the main loop (for example, doesn't lock shared variables), and has a fixed execution time, this should be OK. The time spent running that interrupt can be subtracted from available CPU time when doing scheduling. But as soon as you get at all fancy with a background interrupt, you need to switch to the next scheduling technique, which includes interrupts.

14.3.5. Pure static scheduling pitfalls

It is *essential* that the order of the tasks and how often they are executed in the main loop remain fixed. As soon as any conditional execution logic is put in (for example, skip a task if it isn't really needed), you lose the benefit of the simplicity of this approach. A common pitfall is making a little change to task execution, along the lines of "this routine doesn't need to run very often, so if the system gets overloaded we'll just skip it for a while." While this might seem to make sense from a practical point of view, it invalidates the guarantee that your system will meet deadlines in every circumstance. If you find yourself in this position, what you need is a more flexible scheduling approach – not quick fixes such as conditional task execution.

> **Conditional task execution is strictly forbidden in static scheduling.**

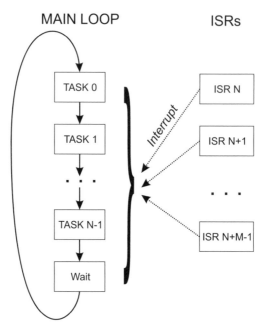

Figure 14.2. Task sequencing in pure static scheduling with helper interrupts.

Resist the temptation to put in a few special cases of conditional task execution. It is all too easy to create an unexpected timing problem this way. If you think you need to do this for some reason, then what you really need is a more capable scheduling approach.

14.4. Static scheduling with small helper interrupts

The next approach to real time scheduling is a variation of purely static scheduling in which interrupts are allowed. This approach is commonly used, but is trickier to analyze.

This system is constructed with a main loop, just as the pure static schedule system was. However, it also has helper Interrupt Service Routines (*ISRs*). We call them helper routines because there are very strict limits on what they can do. In general, they exist to do very quick I/O servicing or other functions that only take a few dozen instructions. Once you have a long, complex interrupt service routine, this approach runs into complications.

Figure 14.2 shows the arrangement of tasks in this type of systems. The N Tasks (numbered 0 through –1) form a main loop as before, with a wait at the end of the loop so that the loop runs once per desired period. There are also M ISRs which can interrupt execution of the main loop at any point. We've numbered the ISRs starting at N (meaning T_N, which is ISR #N, is the first ISR, and T_{N+-1} is the last ISR) to give unique numbers to each executing task, whether main task or ISR. This notation helps keep the math clean later on in the discussion.

The general operation of this system is that most of the computation takes place in the main loop, just as it did with static scheduling. However, ISRs can be used for the following purposes:

- Read input from an I/O device and put it into a data buffer for a main loop task
- Write output to an I/O device left in a data buffer by a main loop task
- Other similar short I/O operations
- Service counter/timers and make that information available to the main task
- Execute very small tasks to meet very fast deadlines, but only if the computation to meet the deadline is very quick. We'll discuss how quick that must be in the timing analysis discussion below.

Additionally, we assume the main loop in this system is triggered by a timer and runs at a fixed period (for example, a timer might trigger the main loop every 50 msec so that it runs exactly 20 times per second). This assumption is required to simplify the scheduling math, but is easily implemented by including a wait task that waits for the start of the next period to run the main task loop each time, as we saw with pure static scheduling.

> Helper ISRs can be used with a static schedule so long as they are short and don't cause data sharing problems.

14.4.1. Strengths

The obvious strength of this approach is you're allowed to use interrupts. This means that the main task doesn't have to do polled I/O; it can use interrupt-based I/O. Because the tightest deadlines in many embedded systems involve servicing I/O devices, this can significantly ease the time pressure on the main loop. The main loop doesn't have to worry about missing I/O events so long as data can be buffered and dealt with quickly by ISRs.

Other tight-deadline tasks can also be put into interrupts, so long as the very stringent timing limitations discussed below are met. The particular approach we use guarantees all interrupts will meet their deadlines regardless of the priority of any particular interrupt. This makes it a conservative approach, but keeps the scheduling math simpler than it would otherwise be. (And, really, it gets complex enough you wouldn't want it to be much worse!)

14.4.2. Weaknesses

As a practical matter, interrupts have to be kept to a few dozen instructions. Short interrupts are generally considered a good design practice, so that isn't really a huge additional limitation. However, the timing limitations on the interrupts are very important. Interrupts must be relatively short and infrequent for this approach to be useful in practice.

14.4.3. Scheduling analysis – the easy case

The big problem with determining if this approach will meet real time deadlines is making sure that ISRs don't steal too much CPU time away from the main loop. Even if ISRs are very short, they might run often enough that the main loop can't complete in time.

The easy case is meant to keep the math easy – not necessarily the system design itself. For the easy case, we assume that each ISR can run at most once per period. (How you ensure that is your problem! We just assume it is true for this analysis.) So, for example, if you have a system with a 50 msec main loop and four ISRs, each one of those four ISRs can run at most once every 50 msec. And, every task in the system, including ISRs, must have a deadline no shorter than 50 msec. As a practical matter, the easy analysis case is of limited use, because if ISRs have the same deadlines as main loop tasks, you might as well just execute them in the main loop as polled operations. But, understanding this case will help you understand the more difficult, but more useful, case presented next.

With the assumption that each ISR can run at most once per main loop period, from a timing point of view ISRs look just like any other task in the main loop. Each task and ISR can run once per main task period. The system will meet its deadlines so long as the main period is greater than the sum of the computation times, and the deadlines are no shorter than that main period. Mathematically, the deadlines must satisfy:

$$\sum_{i=0}^{i=N+M-1} C_i \leq P_{main} \leq \min_{i=0}^{i=N+M-1}(D_i) \tag{14.3}$$

which is the same as the deadline equation for pure static scheduling, but includes interrupts as well as main loop tasks. This means if all tasks in the system (both main loop and ISR) execute one time, the total execution time is less than or equal to the main loop period, and is also less than the shortest deadline of any task in the system.

14.4.4. Scheduling analysis – the difficult case

The difficult, but much more useful, case is when it is possible for an ISR to execute more than once per main loop period. This permits its deadline to be shorter than a main loop period (recall that we otherwise assume each deadline is longer than or equal to the task period).

Most systems have multiple ISRs, and use some sort of prioritization to determine which ISR executes next. If a high priority ISR executes more than once before a lower priority ISR can go, determining the worst case delay for that lower priority ISR gets complex. Worse, once a low priority ISR starts executing, it delays high priority ISRs until that low priority ISR completes execution. It is possible to analyze this situation mathematically, but it gets pretty messy and is easy to get wrong. So, instead, we're going to simply require that each ISR execute only once within the smallest ISR deadline. For example, if the shortest ISR deadline is 10 msec, there must be time for every single ISR to execute exactly one time within 10 msec (this is the worst case in which they all happen to trigger at once, not necessarily a typical case). This is conservative, but makes the math much simpler:

$$\sum_{i=N}^{i=N+M-1} C_i \leq \min_{i=N}^{i=N+M-1}(D_i) \tag{14.4}$$

This math looks suspiciously like the equation for the simple case above (but with sums starting at N instead of I), and that is no accident. Even though interrupts are prioritized, we're going to make sure they never run more than once during the smallest ISR deadline ($\min(D_i)$). Note that we still assume period is no less than deadline, even for ISRs. This guarantees that all ISRs will get a chance to run within a fixed amount of time, regardless of prioritization. Then we know we'll meet all deadlines no matter what happens, and the actual interrupt priorities won't get in the way of ensuring our schedule is correct. Put another way, we're finding a way to use periodic scheduling math on a prioritized system to make the analysis simple. So, we're able to schedule as if they were all executed in turn, even though they are prioritized.

This approach places a significant limitation on building your ISRs! You can't have a long-running ISR. The longest ISR execution time has to be much shorter than the shortest ISR deadline for this approach to guarantee schedulability. Furthermore, all the ISRs must be able to run consecutively within the time of the shortest deadline. From a practical point of view, these aren't significant limitations. You should be writing short ISRs anyway.

Once we know interrupts won't cause each other to miss deadlines, we have to determine their aggregate compute load. We have already constrained the timing of the main loop to run once every fixed number of milliseconds rather than running as fast as possible. (If you don't do this, the math is even messier than what we end up with below.) Thus, we have to make sure all deadlines for non-ISR tasks are at least as long as the main loop period P_{main}:

$$P_{main} \leq \min_{i=0}^{i=N-1}(D_i) \tag{14.5}$$

The main loop is run with period P_{main} (for example, $P_{main} = 100$ msec), so we can compute the amount of CPU time that will be spent processing interrupts in the worst case over that period:

$$C_{IsrTotal} \leq \sum_{i=N}^{i=N+M-1}\left(\left\lceil\frac{P_{main}}{P_i}\right\rceil C_i\right) \tag{14.6}$$

Note: " $\lceil \rceil$ " is a ceiling function, which rounds up to the next lowest integer, and should not be confused with brackets "[]", which just group elements of calculations.

This formula first determines the worst case (largest) number of times ISR T_i might be executed within period P_{main}, which is the ceiling of P_{main} divided by P_i. (The worst case is that all interrupts trigger right at the start of the main loop, then re-trigger as many times as possible for the main loop to finish just at the end of P_{main}.) Each interrupt executes that many times (potentially a different number of times for each ISR), consuming C_i of CPU time for each execution.

Now, we just need to make sure that the sum of the interrupt service times plus the sum of the main loop times is less than the available time:

$$\sum_{i=0}^{i=N-1} C_i + C_{IsrTotal} \leq P_{main} \tag{14.7}$$

which is equivalent to:

$$\sum_{i=0}^{i=N-1} C_i + \sum_{i=N}^{i=N+M-1} \left(\left\lceil \frac{P_{main}}{P_i} \right\rceil C_i \right) \leq P_{main} \tag{14.8}$$

Unfortunately, this is a recursive inequality because P_{main} appears on both sides. What is going on is that as the main loop increases in length, ISRs get a chance to run more times, increasing the required computation time for that main loop. This means you need to increase the length of the main loop, but that might let some ISRs run yet another time.

If you want the minimum possible P_{main}, the straightforward way to solve the inequality is to take a guess for P_{main} and see if it works. If the inequality is false, keep increasing P_{main} until the inequality is true. (A spreadsheet can help with this calculation.) Now you can see what we meant when we said the increased flexibility of using interrupts comes at the cost of increased complexity of analysis! If you have defined a fixed period such as 100 msec for P_{main}, then just plug that number into the equation and see if the inequality is true. If it isn't true, you need a bigger P_{main}.

> Using helper ISRs with a static schedule requires analysis to make sure that ISRs meet their deadlines and there is enough CPU capacity left over for the main loop.

To summarize, here is a complete set of equations for static scheduling with helper interrupts:

$$P_{main} \leq \min_{i=0}^{i=N-1}(D_i)$$

$$\sum_{i=N}^{i=N+M-1} C_i \le \min_{i=N}^{i=N+M-1}(D_i)$$

$$\sum_{i=0}^{i=N-1} C_i + \sum_{i=N}^{i=N+M-1}\left(\left\lceil \frac{P_{main}}{P_i} \right\rceil C_i\right) \le P_{main}$$

14.4.5. Pitfalls

There are ways to make this approach even fancier. However, attempting to get fancier with this approach is asking for trouble unless you have expertise in real time scheduling (and, you have the desire to deal with math even more complex than what we've already seen).

The use of interrupts greatly increases potential issues with concurrency and shared variables. For example, an interrupt might change a multi-byte value in the middle of the main program reading or writing that same value. Queues or other special techniques should be used to pass data to and from ISRs to avoid these problems (see *Chapter 20. Mutexes and Data Access Concurrency*). Masking interrupts in the main program is often used to avoid concurrency problems, but doing that for more than an instruction or two at a time is likely to invalidate the scheduling analysis by violating the assumption that interrupts are executed with no delay.

It might be tempting to look at interrupts as tasks in a rate monotonic system (see next section) and schedule that way. But this might not work. The reason is that rate monotonic scheduling assumes instant preemption of tasks. Most interrupts are not themselves interruptible, meaning you have to wait for any current interrupt to complete execution before a higher priority interrupt can start execution. Re-enabling interrupts during the execution of an ISR is a bad idea – doing that to try to get past this problem by making ISR-based routines preemptable is likely to make things worse instead of better.

14.5. Rate monotonic scheduling with harmonic periods

The most flexible, and most complex, scheduling technique we will discuss is Rate Monotonic Scheduling (RMS). In embedded systems a variant known as Deadline Monotonic Scheduling (DMS) is often used. We'll use RMS in this discussion since that is commonly used terminology, with the understanding that all discussions also apply to DMS unless otherwise noted. We'll talk about DMS in the embellishments section.

RMS is different than the scheduling methods already discussed because it supports task preemption. In a *preemptive* system, a high priority task can immediately suspend the execution of a lower priority task, with the high priority task

Tasks

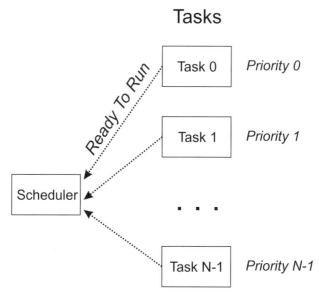

Figure 14.3. Preemptive scheduling (used with RMS).

running until completion or until it is itself preempted by an even higher priority task. Once a high priority task completes execution, the next lower priority suspended task resumes execution from where it left off.

In the other approaches, each task ran until it completed (with the exception of an interrupt preempting a main task, but after that, one interrupt couldn't preempt another interrupt). In RMS, we assume that every task has a priority, and that a high priority task can instantaneously preempt any executing lower priority task. Thus, the system looks like Figure 14.3.

Instead of a main loop as we saw previously, RMS uses a real time scheduler. That scheduler executes a pool of tasks, with each tasking having a fixed priority with Priority 0 being the highest, most urgent priority.

The job of the scheduler is to keep track of which tasks are ready to run. Any time a task becomes ready to run, it starts execution only if it is the highest priority task currently ready to run. If it isn't, it waits. If it is, the scheduler preempts whatever task is currently running and immediately starts running the new, higher priority task. Lower priority tasks wait until that highest priority task finishes. Whenever any task completes execution, the scheduler starts (or resumes) the highest priority task that is ready to run, if any. Thus far, this description applies to any preemptive tasking system with static (non-changing) task priorities.

RMS scheduling prioritizes preemptive tasks by period.

The essential feature of RMS is that priorities are assigned by the length of each task's period. Tasks are sorted in order of period (shortest to longest) and assigned priorities according to that order (shortest period gets highest priority; longest period gets lowest priority). There is no run-time computation necessary to ensure the schedule is met. It suffices to simply run the task with the highest priority that is ready to run at any given instant.

14.5.1. Strengths

There are two main strengths to using RMS: support for preemption, and a simple approach to scheduling.

- **RMS permits task prioritization and preemption.** This means tasks can have a very wide variety of periods and deadlines, without wasting a lot of CPU time. The advantage over pure static scheduling is that tasks which only need to run once in a long while don't have to be executed on every iteration of a main loop. Because RMS supports preemption, it is also possible to mix real time and non-real time tasks in the same system, so long as the real time tasks have higher priority.

- **The run-time scheduling system is quite simple.** You just run the highest priority task. Many other real time approaches attempt to modify priorities on-the-fly, which can be complex and consume a lot of CPU time just for the scheduling algorithm.

14.5.2. Weaknesses

There are three main weaknesses to RMS:

- **RMS requires a scheduler to manage the preemption.** This isn't a huge problem because you can buy a real time OS that does this for you. But, a scheduler adds complexity in the system. If you need the flexibility offered by preemption, it is well worth the cost.

- **RMS assumes no interrupts** (other than the ability to switch tasks, which is assumed to take zero time). RMS assumes zero-latency preemption. Any delay in preemption makes a big difference in available capacity. In particular, RMS assumes there are no interrupts in use. In practice, RMS really assumes that ISRs consume a minuscule amount of CPU power. In big 32-bit CPUs this may be a reasonable assumption; but in many lower-end CPUs this can be a problem. Analysis of a combined interrupt plus RMS task system is quite complex. If you leave some slack and make sure your interrupts themselves can meet deadlines (for example, using the approach in the previous section on static schedule for helper interrupts), you will probably be OK, but only if ISRs are very short compared to the main task computations.

- **General RMS scheduling can't use 100% of the CPU** and still guarantee deadlines are met. Moreover, it has a fairly complex theoretical background with accompanying math. We'll solve that by using the special case of harmonic task periods (see next section).

14.5.3. Scheduling analysis

Deriving the scheduling math for RMS is quite complex, and is covered in gory detail in any number of papers and books. So, rather than subjecting you to that, we'll just skip to the useful answers.

First, RMS scheduling only guarantees schedulability for 100% CPU usage if you use harmonic task periods. This means the period of each task must be an exact integer multiple of every shorter period in the system. It's OK to have multiple periods that are exactly the same. For example, the periods {2, 10, 20} are harmonic, because 2 divides both 10 and 20 evenly, and 10 divides 20 evenly. There might be many tasks with a 2 msec period, a few tasks with a 10 msec period, and a number of tasks with a 20 msec period, and such a system will satisfy the harmonic requirement. As another example the period set {2, 10, 25} is not harmonic, because 2 doesn't divide 25 evenly, nor does 10 divide 25 evenly. If you use non-harmonic task periods, you greatly reduce the amount of CPU you can use and still guarantee you meet deadlines.

> RMS guarantees schedulability for 100% CPU usage if you meet our general real time scheduling assumptions and use a task set with harmonic periods.

In practice, most embedded systems use harmonic periods to maximize CPU usage. In fact, they may run some tasks faster than they really need to, just so all periods are harmonic. For example, if tasks must be completed in 2, 11, and 21 msec, the corresponding deadlines might be set to 2, 10, and 20 msec respectively to make the task set harmonic while meeting all deadlines. Paradoxically, slightly speeding up task periods can actually reduce worst-case CPU loading for RMS by avoiding the possibility of some nasty task arrival patterns.

Once you have changed your task periods to be harmonic multiples, you just need to make sure the CPU isn't loaded to more than 100% (we'd recommend leaving some slack and not loading to 100%, because in the real world none of the assumptions made are perfectly true):

$$\sum_i \left(\frac{C_i}{P_i} \right) < 100\% \quad ; for\ harmonic\ P_i \tag{14.9}$$

which simply states that adding up the fraction of the CPU used per task (C_i/P_i) across all tasks gives total CPU utilization of less than 100%. Note that unlike periodic scheduling approaches we have discussed previously, there is no limit on how long or short a period can be, so long as periods are harmonic multiples and total CPU load doesn't exceed 100%.

14.5.4. Embellishments

A variant of RMS is *Deadline Monotonic Scheduling (DMS)*. The only difference is that with a DMS system deadlines can be shorter than periods. In DMS, a pseudo-period is created that is the lesser of the period and deadline. The pseudo-period is used for scheduling, assuming the task runs once every pseudo-period. For example, a task with a period of 10 msec and a deadline of 3 msec would have a pseudo-period of 3 msec. This would give it the same priority as all other 3 msec tasks. CPU usage calculations assume CPU time is consumed as if the task ran every 3 msec, even though it doesn't really execute that often. The task set would have to be harmonic with this 3 msec pseudo-period; the 10 msec real period would be irrelevant for scheduling purposes. This approach re-serves enough CPU time so that every task can meet its deadline even if all tasks happen to run with their short deadlines at the same time.

$$\sum_i \left(\frac{C_i}{\min(P_i, D_i)} \right) < 100\% \quad ; for\ harmonic\ min(P_i, D_i) \qquad (14.10)$$

Deadline Monotonic Scheduling is the same as RMS, but uses min(period, deadline) when scheduling each task.

If you go back and look at the definitions for this chapter, you'll see that we defined period for scheduling purposes as the minimum of period and deadline for a task. In effect, this makes RMS the same as DMS for our purposes.

If you get a handful of books on RMS, you can find techniques for relaxing some of the assumptions. For example, blocking can be accounted for in the math to handle situations in which one task blocks the execution of another task. But, once you use those embellishments, you're going down the path to becoming a real time scheduling expert yourself. (It can be a rewarding journey, but be sure to bring plenty of math skills!) If at all possible, it is best to keep your system simple enough that the math given here gets the job done. If you can't, then you or someone who helps you needs to get up to speed on real time scheduling theory.

14.5.5. RMS pitfalls

The main pitfall in RMS is trying to bend the rules without fully appreciating how much RMS depends on the rules being absolutely met. For example, if you have any delay at all in the ability to switch a task (blocking time), that time counts as if it were CPU time in the scheduling calculation. The math is beyond what we want to cover here, but suffice it to say things get fairly complex in a hurry as soon as you start bending rules. There are reasons static schedules are popular, and this creeping complexity of RMS analysis as rules need to be relaxed is one of those reasons.

> The biggest pitfall in using RMS is trying to bend the rules.
> Kids, don't try this at home.

Another potential problem with RMS is that it can be very difficult to create and test the worst case timing of the system. You have to have faith in the math. But, more importantly, you have to really be sure you haven't violated any of the assumptions behind the math (or, at least not violated them enough that there is a problem – which can be a fuzzy boundary).

A classical issue with RMS systems is that it is difficult to design a system with no interactions at all between tasks. But, as soon as you have dependencies between tasks, you can have problems with low priority tasks keeping high priority tasks from executing. Those problems arise when a low priority task has a resource locked, causing higher priority tasks to have to wait for that resource to become free even while other tasks with intermediate level priorities are allowed to execute. This is a situation generically known as *priority inversion*. Priority inversion causes serious problems from time to time, most famously causing disruption of the NASA Mars Pathfinder mission. This problem is commonly addressed with priority inheritance and priority ceilings, which both give low priority tasks temporary high priority whenever those low priority tasks hold a resource needed by a high priority task. These are the sort of techniques you can read about in real time scheduling books.

14.6. Overarching pitfalls

The biggest pitfall in real time scheduling is thinking you are so smart you can get away with making just a few changes that violate the assumptions behind the scheduling technique you are using. That's almost always a mistake. Until you've read a few books on scheduling theory (and understood the math!) you're not really ready to improvise on this topic. And, even then, doing so is asking for trouble.

14.6.1. Don't write your own RTOS

A related pitfall is writing your own preemptive operating system. Many companies have their own, home-made RTOS. While that used to be the only option, many inexpensive or free RTOS kernels are available. An RTOS is an extraordinarily subtle and complex piece of software. Almost nobody can get one perfectly right on their own. You're taking a big risk by trying to do that yourself instead of using one that lots of other people have helped ensure was done right. If you already have one that seems to work, then continuing to use it requires your team have someone with RTOS design expertise on staff. While many people do have good RTOS skills, this can be an issue when it's time for your RTOS expert to move on to another assignment and nobody is available to assume that role.

> Don't use a home-made RTOS in a production application.

14.6.2. Don't use EDF scheduling

Some designers use earliest deadline first (*EDF*) or least laxity (LL) scheduling. While it is intuitively appealing to run the task with the nearest deadline at the highest priority, in general you can't actually know whether such a system will meet its deadlines. There is a special case that works if all periods equal deadlines (which is almost the same as the requirement for RMS scheduling, except without needing harmonic task periods). However, system behavior is very bad if system load goes above 100%, whereas RMS is better behaved in overload conditions. Moreover, EDF as well as LL require run-time changes to priorities, which is more complex than the fixed priority approach used by RMS. We strongly recommend you always use RMS rather than EDF or LL.

> Stay away from EDF and Least Laxity – use RMS if you can.

14.6.3. Don't use big ISRs

Using large ISRs is a bad idea from two points of view. First, ISRs are places where bugs tend to hide. They are tricky to write, and are best kept as simple as possible. Second, doing timing analysis for ISRs is difficult because they are non-preemptive. RMS assumes that interrupts make no noticeable difference to task execution times. Large ISRs (more than a few dozen instructions) are best avoided entirely.

14.6.4. Don't just rely on testing to ensure deadlines are met

Depending entirely on running tests to determine if your real time deadlines will be met is never a good idea. Yes, you should test. But, you should also make sure you strictly follow one of the scheduling approaches outlined above (or have read enough books on scheduling theory that you can handle other embellishments and approaches). You should actually go through the worst case execution time analysis for each task, and the corresponding math to make sure you understand the worst case timing situation for your system.

14.7. Knowing when to get help

There are other, intermediate complexity scheduling techniques between a main loop and preemptive scheduling. For example, some embedded systems are best served by having a prioritized but non-preemptive tasking system, or a preemptive but non-prioritized tasking system. In our opinion you need to know more than we can tell you in a single chapter before you're ready to use such techniques, so we don't go into them in detail here.

The most important part of getting real time scheduling right is knowing when you're in over your head so that you can get help. Considerable expertise may be required to deal with real time situations that, at least at first, don't seem to be a big deal. Intuition is often misleading in this area.

> Real Time Scheduling is much harder than it looks.
> If you aren't 100% sure you're getting it right, get help.

If you can keep things very simple, then you can get by. If things get a little complex, you'll need help from someone with experience (and, you'll need to read up on the topic). Things are, by definition, complex as soon as you need to violate one of the assumptions stated in the analysis for your scheduling technique. If you have to do something at all difficult, your best bet is to get some expert help from someone who really knows this topic inside and out.

14.8. For more information

14.8.1. General topic search keywords
- Rate monotonic scheduling
- Deadline monotonic scheduling
- Cyclic executive
- Real time scheduling
- Priority inversion
- WCET
- Worst case execution time

14.8.2. Recommended reading

Kalinsky, D., "Context Switch," *Embedded Systems Programming*, February 2001, pp. 94-105.
Presents a different discussion of periodic and preemptive scheduling approaches.

Tindell, K., "Deadline monotonic analysis," *Embedded Systems Programming*, June 2000, pp. 20-38.
Walks through the math behind Deadline Monotonic Scheduling.

14.8.3. Additional reading

Jones, M., "What really happened on Mars Rover Pathfinder" *Risks Digest*, v. 19 n. 49, Dec 9, 1997.
A summary of the priority inversion problems on the Mars Pathfinder. This appeared in Risks Digest, which has many stories about computing risks, problems, and solutions. Archives of Risks Digest are available on the Web.

Chapter 15
User Interface Design

- Embedded systems must be easy to use even though they usually lack the niceties of full desktop-style user interface hardware.
- A methodical approach to creating user interfaces must consider the abilities of the user community and the tasks users must perform.
- Getting a user interface right requires both adhering to user-centric design principles and performing usability testing.

Contents:

15.1. Overview

Most embedded systems have some sort of user interface. It is the only part of the embedded system the user really sees, but too often it isn't designed as carefully and thoughtfully as it should be. There are some general principles that should be followed when creating a user interface, and some general design rules that should be taken into account to ensure your product is as easy as possible to use.

15.1.1. Importance of good usability

While everyone wants a user friendly design, it can be difficult to say exactly what that means in absolute terms. Nonetheless, usability can definitely be improved by following basic guidelines for good user interfaces. The result is more than just a product that people feel happier about using. A good user interface can reduce the number of mistakes people make when using the product, as well as increase user productivity.

15.1.2. Possible symptoms

While the details of any user interface are often as much a matter of art as engineering, there are some general rules that should be followed. Your user interface might have problems if:

✘ Users make many mistakes using the system. A poor user interface might make it difficult for users to successfully operate a system. If error rates using the system are high, then it is common to blame users for making mistakes, or attempt to train them so they will make fewer mistakes. A more enlightened approach is to attempt to reduce those error rates with better user interface design.

✘ Users complain the system is unfriendly. Most users aren't experts in user interfaces, so they may not be able to say why something is unfriendly – but that doesn't make their opinion valueless. If users hate your system, as a developer it is your job to fix the problem.

✘ The user interface is inconsistent. While there are a number of important principles for user interface design, the hallmark of a bad user interface is inconsistency. For example, if there are two buttons and one means yes while the other means no, the same button should mean yes every time, rather than having the meaning of the buttons switch back and forth. Consistency should also extend to visual layout on a screen and all other aspects of the system as much as possible.

✘ There is no section in the requirements defining user demographics. Requirements should mention what types of users the system must be designed for, with special attention to users with impaired abilities. Does the system have to work well with people who are color blind? Left-handed people? People who don't speak American English? People wearing gloves? And so on.

✘ There is no plan for user studies. At some point the only way to be sure you have the user interface right is to try it out on some typical users and see what they like, and what goes wrong. Skipping this step makes it more likely there will be unforeseen user interface problems. (Design engineers don't count as normal users for this purpose.)

15.1.3. Risks of a bad user interface

If you get the user interface wrong, you increase the risk of:

➤ Limiting the market. If your product is unusable by an important segment of the market, you reduce potential sales.

➤ Improper system operation, trouble reports, and product returns. Some systems are so difficult to use that people consider them defective, leading to increased costs for help calls and product returns.

15.2. User interface design process

User Interface (UI) design is a commonly used term to describe the design of the manner in which an embedded system interacts with humans. Other related terms are Human Computer Interaction (HCI) and User System Interface (USI).

The main point of user interface design is to use a methodical approach to designing the way an embedded system interacts with humans, which might include everyday users, maintenance personnel, and others. This area of design can be especially difficult in embedded systems because the resources available for interaction are often severely constrained. It's hard to make a great user interface when all you have to work with are a couple buttons and a few LEDs instead of a full keyboard, mouse, and graphical display as you would have on a desktop computer. But, while the hardware may be different than on a desktop computer, the general process and principles tend to be the same.

The general steps in designing a good user interface involve identifying the user population, proposing a design that follows good practices, testing that design, and iterating to improve the design.

15.2.1. Identifying the user population

Before you can create a good user interface, you need to understand what type of users you expect. Will they be ordinary people? Highly trained technicians? Children? Senior citizens? You also need to know what tasks will be performed by people who will be using the system.

To start, make a list of the characteristics of your typical users. It is important to include at least the following:

• Age and gender distribution

• Language spoken

• Location (for example, countries where the product will be sold)

• Any physical conditions that merit special attention (e.g., left-handed users and color blind users)

• Education and training level

For example, consider the contrast between the following two groups of potential users:

(a) 12-25 year olds; 95% male; speaking American English; living in the US; right-hand only use; red-green color blind friendly; users assumed to know how to navigate the Web on a PDA or cell phone, and significant experience with instant messaging

(b) 60-80 year olds; 70% female; speaking any one of: Continental English, Spanish, German, French, Mandarin Chinese; living anywhere in the world; configurable for left- or right-handed use; usable with moderate arthritis in finger joints; users have no particular computer or PDA experience.

It's likely that a good user interface would be quite different for these two user populations, even on systems that have the same basic purpose. Therefore, it's important that this type of information is fed into the requirements process, so that developers can make the right tradeoffs in user interface design.

Other aspects of the population may well be relevant, especially in the medical field where devices are designed specifically for user segments that have disabilities and other special conditions.

Identify the user population for your product.

15.2.2. Identifying the task

In addition to defining the user population, it's important to define the tasks that will be performed by users. In other words, how will users want to actually use the system? This is not a list of features (which is system-centric), but rather a set of goals the user wants to achieve using the system (which is user-centric).

One way to identify tasks is to create user stories. These are short descriptions of a typical motivation, goal, and interaction experience for a user, from the user's point of view. They can be used to feed system requirements as well as to create scenarios for usability testing.

Example: "Jane sees her young daughter taking her first steps. She wants to take a short video clip using her cell phone and send it to her husband to share the moment. She only has a few seconds to react, so she presses a single button to immediately start taking a video clip. When she is done capturing the clip, she plays it back on her cell phone to make sure the video and sound turned out OK. Then, she sends the video to her husband's cell phone using her stored phone number list."

The point of a user story is not to be an unambiguous set of requirements. Rather, it is to give designers a sense of the type of things users will want to do with the system. This will help them make sure the actual requirements don't miss required features, decide which features to make the easiest to access, and which features can better withstand being buried behind a few layers of menus. With this example, it is clear that taking video clips is an important feature that has to be readily and quickly accessible to the user so as to catch a spur-of-the-moment opportunity.

> **Identify the important tasks users will perform with your product from the user point of view.**

When all important tasks have been identified, they form a list of user stories. These can be the basis for creating technical requirements that provide all necessary product functions and features. They can also form a basis for acceptance testing. (If the product can't actually support all the required user stories, it can't be said to be completely working.)

15.3. Good user interface design

Once the users and tasks have been defined, developers can include those aspects in the software requirements and design. Beyond this, it is often very helpful to have specific design documents that relate to the human interface. In particular, since consistency across all the interfaces of a system is important, it is useful to have a design document describing the interface approach so that developers can refer to it to ensure consistency, and testers can refer to it to ensure adherence to those consistency principles.

15.3.1. User interface design principles.

There are a number of principles that make for a good user interface design. They include (adapted from Nielsen, 1993 and other sources):

- **Keep the interface consistent in all respects.** Everything   possible about the interface should be consistent, so the user doesn't have to stop and ask what a particular color means or a particular button does in a certain situation. Things to check for consistency include: colors, shapes, button functions, sounds, default to accept vs. default to reject for input confirmation, undo mechanism, and error handling.

- **Minimize the user's need to remember things.** It's difficult for users to keep track of hidden state inside a system. For example, if a digital watch might show an alarm time or time of day, it's important to have some indication of which is showing rather than expecting the user to remember which mode has been activated.

- **Give feedback for operations.** Make sure that a user knows an action was performed. While a beep emitted every time a button is pressed might be too annoying in everyday use, having no sign at all that a stop/go button was pressed might lead the user to pressing it more than once to make sure the system saw the button closure.

- **Use terminology and symbology that users understand.** With   the limited user interfaces available to embedded systems, it is important to be astute in selecting just the right abbreviations and symbols to use. There are international standard symbols for road signs and other similar standards that should be used when appropriate. Avoid obscure abbreviations or symbols that aren't immediately obvious to all users. When there is no other choice, try to make obscure symbols easy to look up. For example, three flashes of an LED might mean something important – but the user is more likely to know what it means if it is described in a label glued onto the unit than if it is buried in Annex W, page 972 of a user manual CD-ROM that was thrown out with the packing material.

- **Design to avoid or mitigate common errors.** People tend to make certain kinds of errors more frequently than others. User studies and general design rules should be employed to avoid the chance for users to make these errors, or make it easy to recover from them. For example, even a one-level undo or go back function can significantly reduce the impact of mistake that is caught almost immediately by the user (known as *slips*). Confirmation dialogs ("Are you sure you want to erase all your digital photos?") are useful to reduce the frequency of catastrophic user mistakes that can't be undone.

> Ensure that your user interface:
> is consistent,
> minimizes memory load,
> gives feedback,
> speaks the user's language, and
> helps users avoid making mistakes.

15.3.2. Testing the design for usability

You need some way to evaluate a user interface design. This involves a combination of subjective and objective measures. Subjective measures can include asking users what they like and don't like, asking users to compare the system's ease of operation to other similar systems, and so on.

Objective measures are also possible. Users can be monitored while using a system, and metrics can be taken to indicate how easy the system is to use. Possible metrics include:

- **Number of mistakes made.** This includes the number of times a user fails at a task, number of times a user has to employ an undo feature, and number of times a user has to restart a task from the beginning. A related metric can be the number of times a user is surprised by the system (meaning the system doesn't do what the user expected or intended).

- **Time to perform a task.** The faster a user can perform a work task involving a sequence of interactions with the embedded system, the better the user interface. Speed variations between users and speed attained through repetitive practice need to be accounted for in assessing results.

- **Number of times a user smashes a unit onto the floor.** We're only half joking with this one.

Test the design's usability with actual users.

15.3.3. Reviewing the design

Beyond testing, it is helpful to perform a design review to ensure that common user needs haven't been overlooked. Below is a starting point for a checklist that can help ensure relevant factors have been considered for users:

- Left-handed; 7-10% of population
- Color blind (especially red/green color blind); 7-10% of population
- Prescription glasses or contact lenses
- Sunglasses (some are vertically polarized, making it impossible to read horizontally polarized LCD displays)
- Gloves
- Hearing impaired (large fraction of older population), with or without hearing aid (which only passes limited sound frequencies)
- Sight impaired
- Arthritic (unable to manipulate small buttons or knobs)
- Different location (time zone; style of writing times and dates; differing seasons depending on northern or southern hemisphere)
- Different spoken language (including country-specific variants)
- Different written language, including non-Roman character sets
- High noise environment
- Hands free operation (such as used while driving)
- Child operator (smaller body size)
- Child-proof and pet-proof tamper resistance
- Female vs. male operator (body size and strength differences)

Perform a design review concentrating just on usability.

15.3.4. Iterated design efforts

A really good user interface comes from following good design practices, doing some testing with representative users, and fixing problems that show up during tests. Expecting to get the user interface perfect the first time on a new type of product is unrealistic. Creating a good user interface takes significant effort and iteration until the interface performs well with user tests.

15.4. Pitfalls

The main pitfall in user interface design is having developers that implicitly or explicitly think that they are representative of the users, and are therefore fully qualified to evaluate the suitability of the user interface. Developers are among the worst possible subjects for user interface testing. This is because they know what the system is supposed to do; they know how it is supposed to work; they are demographically not as diverse as the general population; and they have a particular way of thinking (a quantitative, analytic approach) that is relatively uncommon in the general population.

Having developers propose user interface approaches and catch easy things such as red/green color blind display issues is fine. But they shouldn't be used as stand-ins for the user when performing user interface testing.

> **Developers don't count as users for usability tests.**

15.5. For more information

15.5.1. General topic search keywords
- User interface design
- Usability

15.5.2. Recommended reading

Murphy, "Safe systems through better user interfaces," *Embedded Systems Programming*, August 1998, pp. 32-46
  This discusses the role of user interfaces in general, and specifically their importance in critical systems (such as, for example, the pitfalls of high false alarm rates).

NUREG-0700, *Human-System Interface Design Review Guidelines*, US Nuclear Regulatory Commission, Ref. 2, May 2002.
  This is a comprehensive guide to user interfaces. While it is tailored to nuclear power plant control rooms, it is full of specifics, and available for free on the Web.

15.5.3. References

Nielsen, J, *Usability Engineering*, AP Professional, Boston, 1993.
  This is a classic book on usability.

IMPLEMENTATION

Chapter 16
How Much Assembly Language Is Enough?

- Better compilers and larger memories are eliminating the traditional need for assembly language in embedded systems.
- Assembly language should be used sparingly, or not at all.
- Knowing assembly language is still helpful for tuning high level language source code so compilers can generate more efficient executables.

Contents:

16.1. Overview

While learning assembly language has always been a rite of passage for embedded developers, the days of writing extensive assembly language programs for embedded systems are largely over. It is unusual to really need more than a few dozen instructions in assembly language. In most cases, there is no need to write in assembly language at all.

> **No source code should be in assembly language**
> **(or, perhaps, very little).**

The main exceptions to this rule are for very small microcontrollers with extremely limited memory, wholly inadequate compiler support, specialized hardware, and huge production volumes. But even in these cases, it's smarter to get a microcontroller with more memory and better tool support than to embark upon writing a lot of assembly language source code.

16.1.1. Importance of avoiding assembly language

Assembly language programs cost more to develop, are more bug prone, and are not necessarily any faster than high level language programs. Assembly language should be used sparingly, and every use of assembly language should be scrutinized very closely to see if it is absolutely necessary.

However, this doesn't mean that knowledge of assembly language is obsolete. As we'll explain, it is still valuable to know assembly language to understand what your compiler is doing to your source code. But understanding assembly language isn't the same as writing all your programs in it.

16.1.2. Possible symptoms

You are using more assembly language than you should if any of the following symptoms is true:

✘ The whole program is in assembly language for speed. It is never appropriate to code an entire program in assembly language just for speed. Most often, there are only a few time-critical routines, and if anything these are what should be coded in assembly language.

✘ The compiler is too inefficient, so assembly language must be used extensively. It is true that some compilers are pretty bad. But, most widely used chips have reasonable compilers for C or other programming languages. If a compiler is having trouble generating efficient code, it is better to modify the source code so the compiler understands it better, not just abandon the compiler. For example, if a compiler can't optimize indexed arrays, switching to pointer notation in C might result in much better generated code without needing to go all the way to assembly language. If a compiler is uniformly horrible, you should get a different chip that has a good compiler.

✖ Assembly language is the way you've always done it, so you keep writing in assembly language. Embedded compilers were mostly bad a decade or two ago. Times have changed. So should your development practices.

16.1.3. Risks of too much assembly language

➤ Increased development time and cost. In general, cost per line of code tends to be the same regardless of programming language. If assembly language takes 4 times more lines of code to get the job done, then you can expect it to cost 4 times more to develop compared to the same program in a language such as C.

➤ Increased defect rates. More lines of code means more bugs. Trickier code (because you're trying to optimize) also means more bugs, and often nastier ones too.

➤ Decreased maintainability. High level languages provide support for better control flow structures, data typing, and more methodical approaches to software. While it is possible to write highly structured assembly language, that isn't what happens in practice.

If the main reason developers give for using assembly language is that they don't have a fast enough CPU or don't have enough memory, you are also exposed to the risks inherent with too-full resources (see *Chapter 18. The Cost of Nearly Full Resources*).

16.2. Why avoid using assembly language?

It used to be that most embedded software was in assembly language. You still need to know assembly language to be an effective embedded system developer. What has changed is how you use that knowledge. Using assembly language has always been painful, and that pain is no longer justified by the gains it brings. The biggest problems are high development cost and lack of portability.

16.2.1. Higher cost and longer development time

The cost of writing a line of code is in many cases approximately the same regardless of the programming language. Therefore, if one line of C code, such as:

```
VarA = VarB + VarC;
```

requires three lines of assembly language (depending on the instruction set being used):

```
LDA VarB   ; load VarB into accumulator
ADD VarC   ; add VarC into accumulator
STA VarA   ; store accumulator into VarA
```

then the assembly language version will, all things being equal, cost three times as much to develop.

Over large programs, it is common for each line of C code to correspond to perhaps 3 to 5 lines of assembly language. That means something that would be a

1000 line program in C would be a 3000-5000 line program in assembly language. The assembly language program would therefore cost 3 to 5 times as much to create (or more), and have 3 to 5 times as many bugs (or, likely, even more bugs than that).

Moreover, assembly language has poor support for modern software practices such as well structured control flow, variable type checking, and object oriented design. This makes it more difficult to write good code.

> Using assembly language increases costs and number of bugs.

16.2.2. Poor portability

Assembly language is the least portable programming language. If you are trying to port software written in assembly language from one CPU to a different CPU with a different instruction set, your best bet is to just throw the code away and start over with an entirely new implementation.

Economics, politics, and business concerns have a strong influence on which CPU you use. And all those factors can change. Writing in assembly language is painting yourself into a corner with a single instruction set. Why lock yourself in to a particular CPU by writing all your software in assembly language? (This argument isn't as true in the Intel-dominated desktop computing market, but we're talking about embedded systems here.)

It's true that porting code from one CPU to another in a high level language can run into problems. But at least if you write in a high level language you have much less to worry about, and it is feasible to do a porting without redeveloping everything.

16.3. Techniques for avoiding assembly language

If writing in assembly language should be avoided, how do we still get the speed and efficiency we need? Sometimes just throwing a little money at the hardware to get a faster CPU is the right solution. But, an alternative is to help the compiler be effective at optimizing your software.

16.3.1. Buying a bigger, faster CPU

If your system is so stretched for speed and memory that you are considering using assembly language, you should first consider getting a bigger or faster CPU. Unless your program is very small, your production volume very large, and your developers severely underpaid, it's cheaper to buy a better CPU than spend lots more money developing your software. (See *Chapter 18. The Cost of Nearly Full Resources.*)

> Buy a more capable CPU
> to minimize the need for assembly language.

But, if for whatever reason buying a bigger, faster CPU won't work, there are several approaches to optimization that work well with high level languages.

16.3.2. Profiling and optimizing

If you must optimize, with or without assembly language, there is no point optimizing the whole program. In typical programs, most of the time in a computation is spent in a handful of subroutines or inside a few inner loops. You should spend most of your effort making that part of the code run faster, and not waste your time optimizing code that spends very little time running.

> Only write the most time-critical parts in assembly language.

Fortunately, many systems have a profiling tool that can help identify the hot spots your software. You run your program with the profiler, and it either keeps track of everything that gets executed, or randomly samples the location of the program counter at various times. In either case, you can get an idea of where the majority of time is being spent in your program and just optimize those sections. If you have to, turn a hot spot into a subroutine and write that subroutine in assembly language, with the rest of the program in a high level language. But, even better, use the results of profiling techniques below to tune your source code instead.

16.3.3. Tuning source code for the compiler

Tuning source code involves looking at the output of your compiler and, potentially, changing the source code so the compiler can do a better job of optimizing it. The reason this can be effective is that compilers often aren't quite as smart as developers at seeing optimization opportunities. Or, they do see them, but language rules make automatic optimizations unsafe. By unsafe, we mean that there might be obscure situations in which the optimization would give an incorrect result, even though most of the time the optimization would work perfectly fine. Compilers have to be right all the time, not just most of the time, so they aren't allowed to make unsafe optimizations on their own. But you can help if you know the optimization is safe for your particular situation.

> Helping the compiler is better than writing in assembly language.

Helping the compiler work better can be done using the following steps:
1. Create the code in a high level language, such as C.
2. Make sure the optimization flag is turned on for your compiler. If you don't turn on the optimizer, you won't get optimized code! There are often many different optimization options, and you might need to do some research on compiler technology to understand all of them. To start, turn on global

optimization to the default level of optimizing compilation (often this is the run-time flag "-O") and see what happens.

3. Compile the code, and find hot spots using profiling.

4. Look at the assembly language output of the compiler for a hot spot. (For C compilers, often the "-S" flag will produce an assembly language listing as part of the compilation process.)

5. See if the assembly language looks good, or if the optimizer has done a poor job on this particular code.

6. Try modifying the high level language code to see if the compiler does a better job. After a few experiments, you'll get a feel for what the compiler does well and what it does poorly.

7. Go back to step 3 and repeat for the most important hot spots until you have optimized the code or decided it is hopeless. If it's hopeless, then you should buy a faster processor (preferred), get a better compiler (preferred), or use assembly language to code the hot spots (if there is no alternative).

In some cases tuning is performed by giving more information to the compiler. In other cases it is rewriting the code into a format that the compiler can optimize more easily. And in still other cases, it is performing an optimization by hand that the compiler just isn't smart enough to do. The following sections have examples of all three approaches.

16.3.4. Giving more information to the compiler

Sometimes all the compiler needs is to know a little more about your program to make sure an optimization is safe. Or, it needs some hints to let it know how you want it to do things.

Here's an example of giving more information to the compiler with a good optimizer.

Original code:
```
short int x;      // 8 bit integer
...
x = x / 2;
```

If x has a non-negative value, you'd expect a good compiler to replace the division by 2 with a shift-right by one bit (an optimization called strength reduction). But, if the compiler did that, it would generate incorrect code! The problem is that shifting right divides an integer by two for non-negative integers, but can give an incorrect answer for negative integers.

Instead, many compilers will use a slow signed integer division instruction instead of a shift. But if you have a really good compiler, it might generate something like this instead (in 68HC12 assembly language):

Compiler output:
```
    LDAA   X      ; load x
```

```
        ANDA   #128  ; test hi bit
        BEQ    Lpos  ; no correction if non-negative
        INC    X     ; increment if negative
Lpos:   LDAA   X     ; load x
        ASRA         ; shift x right one bit
        STAA   X     ; store result = x/2
```

This code is complex because the shift-right trick only works on non-negative numbers. For shifting to work properly on signed numbers, you need to first increment any negative number before the shift. So, if you find a compiler that optimizes division by 2 to a shift right for signed numbers, you've found a buggy optimizer (this is worth checking on your compiler, just to be sure).

But, if you know that you are only interested in positive numbers, you can help the compiler out by telling it this information.

Improved code:
```
unsigned short int x;    // 8-bit unsigned integer
...
x = x / 2;
```

Compiler output:
```
    LDAA   X     ; load x
    LSRA         ; logical shift x right one bit
    STAA   X     ; store result = x/2
```

The compiler can safely do this now because it knows shifting right works properly to divide unsigned numbers by two. In this case the problem wasn't that the compiler was dumb so much as that the programmer needed to provide information about a special case (unsigned integers) that enabled the compiler to do a better job of optimizing.

16.3.5. Rewriting code to make optimization easier

Sometimes compilers aren't smart enough to perform optimizations that are difficult for them, but possibly easy for a person to do. A common example is code hoisting, in which an expression is evaluated once before a loop is entered rather than every time a loop is executed.

Example code:
```
for (I = 0; I < b; I++)
{ t = z + k/q;
  x[i] = x[i] + y[t];
}
```

For any number of reasons the compiler might generate code to recompute t every time through the loop. But, you can help the compiler out by doing this optimization manually:

Improved code:

```
t = z + k/q;
for (I = 0; I < b; I++)
{  x[i] = x[i] + y[t];
}
```

Because t only depends on values that aren't changed within the loop, this optimization is safe, and avoids recalculating t every time through the loop. But, before you do this optimization yourself, see if your compiler is smart enough to do it for you (some are; some aren't; and some can only do it for easy situations and not difficult ones).

Another classic example of rewriting code to make the compiler's job easier is accessing arrays via indexing (e.g., "x[i]") vs. via pointers (e.g., "*x"). Some compilers can optimize index approaches, some can optimize pointer approaches, and a few can optimize both. It's worth experimenting with your compiler to see which approach works better before writing a lot of code. Note that both indexing and pointers will work properly regardless of the compiler or CPU you use. But, it is common for one to be much faster than the other based on how the compiler optimizes code.

16.4. When is it OK to use assembly language?

Sometimes using assembly language is the right thing to do. This happens in four circumstances: a tiny processor, a very small routine that is run very frequently, performing extended precision math calculations, and special purpose hardware.

> Sometimes assembly language is the right thing to use.
> But it's a lot less often than you'd think.

16.4.1. Really tiny processors

Some processors just aren't good compilation targets for a C compiler. The problem comes in when the processor has only a few bytes of RAM, and can't support a large C stack to hold temporary variables. While compilers continually get better, it might be that no compiler is available that can effectively deal with a super-tiny chip.

If you can, get a bigger processor that has a decent C compiler. But if you can't, then assembly language may be your only choice. The only consolation is that any chip this small only has a few hundred bytes of program memory, so the program will be relatively small. Before you commit to this path, be sure that you take into account the cost of software development compared to the money being saved on a super-tiny chip.

16.4.2. Small, frequently used routine

Sometimes there is a very small, very frequently used routine with extremely tight real time performance requirements. Often it is an interrupt service routine. But, sometimes, it is a handful of instructions inside a loop.

Tuning the source code will make this small routine fast enough. But, on rare occasion, assembly language is called for if you aren't able to simply get a faster processor. Take care to make sure that the routine really is called frequently, or that it really does have a very tight deadline before indulging in assembly language.

16.4.3. Extended precision math

Extended precision math is the one place where assembly language is necessary on many processors. For example, if you need 128-bit integer arithmetic on an 8-bit processor, that probably isn't built into your programming language, and you'll need to write the math routines yourself.

The issue with extended precision math is addition, subtraction, multiplication, and division are all much more efficient if you have access to a carry bit, and high level programming languages don't give you access to the carry bit. So, at times, it makes sense to write portions of a math library in assembly language if speed is crucial.

16.4.4. Specialized hardware resources

Some processors have specialized hardware resources that aren't supported by compilers or aren't a good match to programming language abstractions. If you can, it's better to find a processor which has good compiler support for its specialized hardware. But if there is no choice, some assembly language might be required to get good performance.

As with other situations, it's important to take into account the true cost of this approach (including software development costs and risks) compared to the cost of simply buying a more powerful CPU that can be programmed entirely in a high level language.

16.5. Pitfalls

On a good day, a really good programmer can create assembly language programs that are better than what a compiler can produce. But, that same programmer can more easily, and more consistently, get the compiler to produce code just as good (or almost as good), simply by tuning the high level language source code. Tuning code takes time, but it takes less time and involves less risk than programming a large section of a system in assembly language.

16.6. For more information

16.6.1. General topic search keywords

- Code optimization
- Optimizing compiler

16.6.2. Recommended reading

Kraeling, M., "Optimizing C code in a real-time environment," *Embedded Systems Programming*, January 1996, pp. 66-74.
An overview of code optimization techniques.

16.6.3. Additional reading

Warren, H., *Hackers Delight*, Addison-Wesley, 2002.
A rich collection of programming speed optimizations, mostly involving integer manipulation and arithmetic.

Chapter 17
Coding Style

- Software is much easier to read and maintain if a consistent style is used throughout all the code in a project.
- Which coding style you use isn't as important as just having a consistent style and corresponding written set of style guidelines.
- Coding style encompasses not only code mechanics such as indentation, but also commenting styles, naming conventions, and language usage rules.

Contents:

Style guidelines should specify required information for each file, such as comment header block contents. Style guidelines should express a philosophy for commenting.

Style guidelines should include language rules to improve code quality and reduce the risk of bugs. MISRA C is a good starting point for ideas on language usage rules.

Style guidelines should include naming conventions for variables, subroutines, and other entities

Self-documenting code isn't.

17.1. Overview

Coding style refers to the general format and stylistic approach of your source code. It is easy to get bogged down in religious wars about what makes for good style. We take a more pragmatic approach – good style is what works for your situation. The important part is to have *some* style that is followed consistently throughout your project.

17.1.1. Importance of a consistent coding style

A consistent coding style makes it easier for someone other than the original programmer to see what is going on in a piece of code. Making style consistent makes it easier to concentrate on things that really matter – such as whether the code is actually correct or not.

It's important to remember that a piece of code can have several readers. Those readers include other developers trying to interface to the code, design reviewers, testers, and downstream code maintainers. Thus, it is worth spending a little extra time to make the code easy to read for others.

17.1.2. Possible symptoms

Any of the following is a sign that it would be worthwhile improving coding style:

✘ There is no written coding style guideline. While it is possible to have verbal consensus on coding style for a small programming team, the absence of a written guideline indicates a problem. If there is no written guideline, you will often find many of the other symptoms true as well.

✘ There is no standard header block comment style. Coding styles mandate specific information at the beginning of every file, including file name, a summary of file contents, and so on. If every file has a much different set of beginning lines, then probably other aspects of the file's style vary too.

✘ The degree of commenting varies dramatically. The degree of commenting can vary within reason. We're talking about systems in which some files have no comments at all and others have more comments than code.

✘ Variable naming conventions vary dramatically. Some parts of a program might capitalize variables names while others don't. Some might use conventions to indicate data type within the variable name, and some might not.

17.1.3. Risks of not having a written coding style guideline

Inconsistent coding style can lead to risks such as:

➤ Increased time to hand off code to a new developer. Code that is consistent in style is easier to learn than code that varies wildly in style.

➤ Increased defect rates. Good, consistent style helps in reducing stupid mistakes.

➤ Increased inspection costs. Good, consistent style makes the code easier to understand for reviews.

17.2. Good coding style

Every project should have a written coding style guide. There are as many coding preferences as there are programmers, so looking for the One True Coding Style Sheet is an exercise in futility. However, good developers have somewhat similar ideas of what types of things matter, and often have only a small set of choices they find acceptable on any given point. So, as a practical matter, within any particular development project or small company it is reasonable to adopt a single style for a particular project.

Every project should have a brief coding style guide.

17.2.1. Style issues

Coding style sheets address more than just style. They cover the following aspects of the implementation:

- Required elements of every source code file, sometimes in the form of a template that is followed for all files.

- Commenting guidelines, such as where comments should appear and how detailed they should be.

- Language usage rules, including desirable and undesirable use of language.

- Naming conventions for variables, subroutines, and elements of the program.

We discuss each type of style issue in turn.

17.2.2. Source file templates

Source file templates should mandate that certain types of information be included in each source code file, both at the beginning of the file and as part of each major file section (for example, information required at the start of each subroutine). Typical elements in a source file template include:

- **Title block.** Includes the project name; file name; CPU type (if relevant); tool chain (*e.g.*, compiler); overview of purpose and contents of file; copyright statement; and revision history.

- **External Interface.** A summary of externally visible aspects of the file, including subroutine declarations and globally visible variables. In some cases this information is kept in a separate header file, such as a ".h" file in C.

- **Data type declarations.** Data type definitions used by multiple routines in the file. This might also be in a header file.

- **Global variables,** if any.

- **Procedures, methods, or other code definitions.** Often there is a specific set of information that must be provided with each procedure, including things such as: description of function, description of inputs, description of outputs, and summary of global variables affected by the routine.

> Style guidelines should specify required information for each file, such as comment header block contents.

17.2.3. Commenting guidelines

Commenting rules are the most subjective part of a coding guideline. At a minimum, they should provide guidance as to how many comments should be put in the code, and at what level they should be written. For example, there might be a guideline such as: every loop should have a comment explaining the purpose of the loop and loop invariants.

Often there is a philosophy component to commenting guidelines. For example, comments might serve to describe the *why* of an operation, rather than the *how*, because how should be obvious just from looking at the code.

> Style guidelines should express a philosophy for commenting.

17.2.3.1. Traceability comments

Another commenting guideline that can prove useful is providing a standardized way to trace the implementation back to the design. For example, there might be a required comment that points out where every arc and state in a statechart shows up in the code, or where every box in a flowchart shows up in the code.

17.2.3.2. Assertions

A different kind of comment that can help with debugging is the use of *assertions* (executable statements that check conditions and generate an error if the condition is true). These are comments in the sense that they are a way for the programmer to convey information about how the program is supposed to execute. As an example:

```
assert(x<0);
```

would compile a statement that checks for x<0 and generates an error if that condition is false, otherwise continuing execution. Asserts are often set up as macros that are enabled during debugging and might be disabled (turned into comments rather than executable code automatically) for system integration and deployment. In C, a simplistic assert implementation looks something like:

```
#define assert(CND) if(!(CND))PrintError("assert fail-
ure");
```

When assertions are no longer desired, the macro can be redefined to do nothing.

17.3. Language usage rules

Language usage rules come in two flavors: formatting guidelines and language structure guidelines.

17.3.1. Formatting guidelines

Formatting guidelines cover topics such as how many spaces to indent for each level of nesting, how to align end-of-line comments, whether a brace after a conditional evaluation is on the same line or a new line, and so on. These items are largely a matter of taste, but consistency across a software system is very useful. In other words, we don't care how you indent your curly braces. But we'd like to see all the code within a project look the same.

One way to improve formatting consistency is to use a *pretty printer*, which is a program that reformats source code to be consistent.

17.3.2. Language usage rules

Language structure rules are created to reduce the chance of making errors, increase software robustness, and otherwise improve code quality. Often they are tailored to cover the types of errors that have proven common in the particular application area of the project. Some example language structure rules include:

- All case or switch statements shall have a default case, which generates an error message if otherwise unused.

- An assignment shall not be used in a conditional evaluation, even if the language permits it. This is designed to reduce inadvertent errors that are common in the C programming language, such as:

    if (x = y) { ... }

    when what was meant was:

    if (x == y) { ... }

- All pointers passed into a subroutine shall be checked for null before first use.

- Defined constants should be used instead of numeric constants wherever practicable (for example, if an array is size 14, you should define a constant to be 14 in one place rather than use the number 14 directly in the code everywhere the array size is needed).

There many possible rules of this type. Some might be checkable by compilers (see *Chapter 21. Static Checking and Compiler Warnings*), but many are not. Which rules are used is in part a matter of taste, but there is general consensus on many of these rules.

> Style guidelines should include language rules to improve code quality and reduce the risk of bugs.

For projects written in C++, it is common to have some rules that prohibit using language constructs that are expensive at run time (such as anything with the keyword *virtual*). This is done not to prevent outright bugs, but rather to ensure that the generated code is efficient.

17.3.3. MISRA C

MISRA C is a language standard for the C programming language that was created for safety critical automotive embedded systems. The overarching philosophy is to ban language structures that are likely to result in bugs. As such, it provides excellent source material for developers programming in C who are looking for language use guideline suggestions. Here are some representative examples:

- All object and function identifiers shall be declared before use.
- Non-constant pointers to functions shall not be used.
- (Advisory): Tests of a value against zero should be made explicit, unless the operand is effectively Boolean.

Some of the rules are quite widely used, even in non-critical systems. Some are just a good idea and are optional or advisory in MISRA. Some rules outlaw otherwise useful techniques because they are judged too easy to get wrong. Not every rule will appeal to every developer, but some very serious effort over many years has gone into creating this list of rules. It is a list worth considering.

The MISRA C standard can be purchased from the Motor Industry Software Reliability Association (MISRA). There is a C++ version as well.

17.4. Naming conventions

It is common for style guidelines to standardize naming conventions for variables, methods, and other entities. Often, naming conventions define how names should appear (*e.g.*, capitalization), how names should be assigned as parts of speech, and how names should be related to data type information. The possible conventions are many and have different advantages. The question is which ones suit you best.

Capitalization of names varies by language and software culture. For example, some programmers make macro definitions all capitals ("MACRO(x)"), and use underscores to separate words in all-lower-case names ("get_next_char()"). Others prefer capitalizing words (often called CamelCase) instead of underscores ("GetNextChar()"). Commonly, style guidelines will outlaw practices likely to lead to errors, such as having two names which differ only in their capitalization.

Assigning names to parts of speech can significantly affect how well code reads and how easy it is to understand. For example, in C one might have a convention that all procedures are verb phrases and all variables are noun phrases. For example "ComputeAverage()" would be a procedure, and GradesList[] would be a variable. In C++ one might similarly require that all objects be noun phrases and all methods be verb phrases. There is a tradeoff to be made between very long descriptive names and shorter, more cryptic, names that are easier to type and take less space on a printed line. Again, most of this is a matter of taste, although attempting to assign parts of speech to different types of labels in a program can be an enlightening exercise that improves code readability significantly.

Some developers like to include data type information in a variable name so it is more difficult to confuse what type of data is being handled. This dates back to early programming days when, for example, in FORTRAN the first letter of a variable determined its type. Variables beginning with the letters I through N were integers, and everything else was a floating point number (back then they didn't really have character or string data types the way we think of them). This practice continues to this day, with some programmers prefixing every integer variable with the letter I or perhaps N.

More sophisticated and comprehensive approaches exist, such as Hungarian Notation, which might, for example, prefix an array of unsigned 8-bit integers with the letters arru8 (for example, arru8GradesList[]). Use of a naming convention can have its advantages, although with compilers that have good data type warning capabilities the importance is somewhat reduced. It is a matter of taste and what works best for your application area. But, consistency within a body of code is highly desirable.

> Style guidelines should include naming conventions for variables, subroutines, and other entities.

17.5. Pitfalls

The worst mistake that can be made with respect to coding style is not actually having a defined style (preferably written down). Styles vary between development groups, but should be as consistent as is practicable within a particular project or group.

An additional significant pitfall is spending too much time arguing about which style to use. There will be differences among developers. If you hit an area in which developers can't agree, reach a compromise and move on. Flip a coin if you have to, or take turns setting one rule each. It doesn't really matter which style you use within reason – consistency is the important part. It's fine to take someone else's style guideline as a starting point and modify it to suite your purposes.

There is no need to reinvent everything yourself. A web search will reveal many coding style guidelines you can use as a starting point.

17.5.1. So-called self-documenting code

Self documenting code is a term that is bandied about to defend the use of code with no comments, no design, and no architectural descriptions. It is true that some code is practically poetry, and really doesn't need comments. Some code isn't quite poetry, but is really well written prose, replete with expert factoring and procedure names that use just the right words to convey the narrative of the story being told. But, few of us are natural poets or excellent literary authors in our native spoken language. Fewer are the equivalent of poets or literary authors in programming languages. You might be one of them, but not everyone is.

Self-documenting code usually isn't.

Write the best code you can. Tell the best story you can. But don't use that as a pretext for skipping comments and ignoring the other parts of the design package.

17.6. For more information

17.6.1. General topic search keywords
- Coding standard
- Coding style
- Pretty printer

17.6.2. Recommended reading

Ganssle, J, "Firmware Development Standards," *Embedded Systems Programming.* Part 1: March 1998, pp. 129-132. Part 2: April 1998, pp. 117-121.
This is an overview of topics that should be included in a comprehensive firmware development standard. Jack has also made a starting point standard available on his web site: http://www.ganssle.com

Ganssle, J., "MISRA minimizes mishaps," *Embedded System Design*, November 2006, pp. 67-70.
This article summarizes the MISRA C coding standard, which gives rules for writing code that is less likely to be buggy. Some static analysis tools automatically check MISRA C rules.

Chapter 18
The Cost of Nearly Full Resources

- Having nearly full hardware resources can dramatically increase software development costs, and often increases total system cost compared to buying more capable hardware.
- As a general rule of thumb, systems should avoid using more than about 75-85% of any resource (memory, CPU, network bandwidth).

Contents:

18.1. Overview

Most embedded systems have severe constraints on cost, making it attractive to use the least expensive memory, CPU, and network connection possible. But, as hardware resources become full it becomes more difficult, expensive, and time-consuming to create software that can fit within those constrained hardware resources. Understanding how expensive it can be to squeeze software into constrained hardware resources is a key to making intelligent hardware/software cost tradeoffs.

18.1.1. Importance of having slack in resources

An obvious reason to have unused resources is to leave room for expansion. There always seems to be another feature to add, another piece of data that needs to be stored in memory, and another message to be added to the network, so some extra capacity needs to be designed into the system to handle changes and functionality growth that occur during initial design and during subsequent revisions.

An additional consideration is that as resources near 100% usage, it becomes much more difficult to change or add features to software. While we know that making changes to highly optimized code is difficult, we don't often express that difficulty in terms of a cost tradeoff against using more capable (and more expensive) hardware.

In general, if any hardware resource is too full, it is better to invest in more capable hardware than to try to squeeze software to make it fit in tight resources. How full is too full depends on the situation. But, we shall make a case that anything above about 75% to 85% full is risky.

18.1.2. Possible symptoms

✘ Measurements of memory, CPU, network bandwidth, or other hardware capacities are above 75% to 85% full. (The number depends on your situation; in some cases above 50% full can be an issue for an especially long-lived and change-prone system.)

✘ The system sometimes misses real time deadlines or runs out of memory at run time.

✘ Some combinations of features can't be turned on at the same time due to insufficient computing power, memory, or network bandwidth.

✘ Developers are spending a significant amount of time optimizing the system to meet resource constraints. Examples include making code faster, making code smaller, compacting data structures (e.g., using bit fields instead of bytes to store Boolean variables), or combining network messages to reduce bandwidth use. A particularly risky manifestation of this is when an ad hoc, complex real time schedule is created to compensate for lack of processing power (see *Chapter 14. Real Time*).

✖ Design guidelines are being violated for the sake of speed or size optimization (*e.g.*, goto statements or jumps are used solely to reduce code size).

✖ Assembly language is being used instead of a higher level language such as C or C++.

Many of these symptoms are not black-and-white indicators of a problem. Squeezing software to make it fit into small microcontrollers is a time-honored embedded system tradition. But, it is far too common to squeeze more than is appropriate and end up making the overall lifecycle cost more expensive instead of less expensive. Thus, when any of the above symptoms show up, it is important to ask whether or not the right hardware vs. software cost tradeoff is being made.

18.1.3. Risks of too-full resources

The risks of over-optimizing systems can permeate the entire system lifecycle. Highly optimized systems tend to be brittle, meaning they break easily and are difficult to maintain. Specific risks that are incurred if a system is too close to being full include:

➤ Inability to upgrade or modify the system later, because there is no capacity left for new functions.

➤ High defect rate in released products due to excessively optimized, tricky software.

➤ High defect rate with upgrades or modifications. Highly optimized code is notoriously difficult to change.

➤ Schedule and cost overruns for software development and testing due to the added expense of optimization and debugging of optimization mistakes.

➤ Increased product returns due to software that operates too close to the edge, sometimes missing deadlines or running out of memory.

➤ Faster product obsolescence due to software wearout (software becomes so complex and buggy that it has to be thrown away and redone from scratch).

18.2. How full is too full?

There is, of course, a counterbalancing risk of not doing any optimization. A completely unoptimized system may have such high hardware costs that it is too expensive to sell profitably. Therefore, the question to be asking is how much optimization is the right amount.

Unfortunately, there is very little scientific data on the cost of over-filling hardware resources in an embedded system. However, there is one study based on a survey of many military embedded systems that tends to ring true in light of the experience of many embedded system developers. Figure 18.1 shows the results of that study.

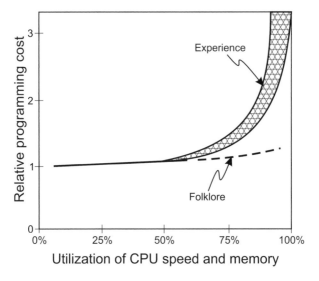

Figure 18.1. Effect of high hardware resource usage on programming cost. Based on Boehm, 1975.

The exact numbers from that graph are unlikely to apply to every possible situation. Rather, the important thing to take away from the graph is the general shape – software costs rise dramatically as resources become full.

> Software costs rise dramatically when system resources are more than 75% to 85% full.

As you can see from the figure, the cost of software development goes through the roof above 75% to 85% capacity usage. The reasons for this are varied, but can include the following direct and indirect costs:

- Extra effort must be spent on optimization.
- More defects end up in the tricky, optimized code that need to be fixed.
- Extra effort must be spent on debugging and correcting optimized code for every defect found.
- There is less room available in the system for development aids. For example, in a full system there is no room for extra code to help with debugging.

The additional costs incurred by having to throw software away and create a new product from scratch when the code wears out early due to excessive complexity is an additional cost not accounted for in the figure.

There are some hardware fixes that can help. Sometimes there is a bigger CPU within a product family that can be used for prototyping to provide extra resources. Virtual memory (if available) can be used to reduce the effects of limited memory size. But these hardware tricks just take the edge off the problem – they don't really solve it.

18.3. An example of hardware/software cost tradeoffs

The cost graph we looked at suggests that full resources can greatly increase software costs. That, combined with the fact that software tends to be more expensive than our intuition wants to believe, can result in engineering tradeoffs that increase total system cost by trying to cut corners on hardware capability. The best way to understand this is to work through an example.

Consider a mid-range 16-bit microcontroller. (What mid-range is depends on the context and what year it is, but this is just an example to illustrate the point – changing technology won't change the underlying truth of full resources being the wrong choice in some situations.) Let's assume the microcontroller comes in two sizes which have following costs:

- Small controller: 128 KB Flash Memory, $9.13 apiece

- Large controller: 256 KB Flash Memory, $11.88 apiece

- Development cost per byte of code: $5 if resources aren't full (assume $30/line of source code; 6 bytes of code per line of source code)

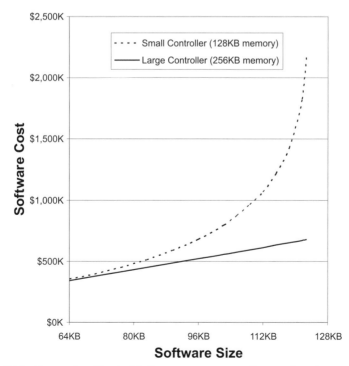

Figure 18.2. Example effect of full resources on software development cost.

The above numbers are reasonably representative at the time of this writing, and the costs are based on a real automotive microcontroller. We'll also assume that the curves shown in Fig. 18.1 are representative for our purposes.

Total software costs accounting for the effects of resources becoming full are shown in Figure 18.2. In this figure, we keep the size of memory fixed (128K or 256K depending on the hardware) and see what happens as the program put onto that platform gets bigger.

Clearly, squeezing software into a smaller CPU costs a lot more as the size of the software approaches the smaller CPU flash memory capacity of 128 KB. The larger CPU costs more money, so the lowest total system cost will be determined by how many units are produced.

We've used the above assumptions and software costs to plot the costs of producing four different size production runs: 1000 units (1K), 10K units, 100K units and 1 million (1M) units in Figures 18.3 and 18.4.

Fig. 18.3 shows that, for this example system, it is always cheaper to use the small CPU for a very large production run of 1M units. This isn't much of a surprise, because increasing software costs by even a factor of two or three doesn't equal the cost savings of using less expensive hardware when multiplied by a million units. This is the scenario that many managers have in mind when deciding to use less expensive hardware to reduce product costs.

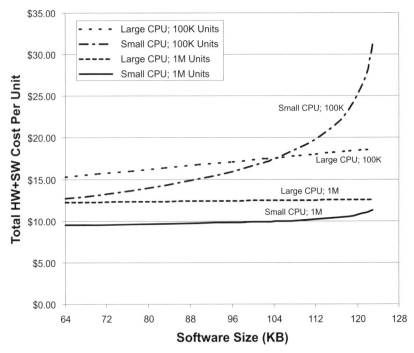

Figure 18.3. Example per unit total cost taking into account hardware and software costs for large production runs.

The more interesting question is, what happens if you aren't actually making a million or more units of something?

Look at the curves for 100K units. This is still a large production run by the standards of many industries. Because there is only one tenth the number of units over which to amortize software costs, it is less expensive in total to use the larger CPU if memory is more than about 82% full (the crossover point of the Large CPU and Small CPU 100K curves). At that crossover point, both approaches result in a per-unit cost of $17.58. This is a much lower percentage than you might have expected. After all, 82% full is not all that full in many everyday situations. Nonetheless, it turns out to be pretty full for CPU speed or memory consumption. To be clear: for this example, if you fill memory on the small CPU up to more than 82%, overall it's cheaper to switch to the bigger CPU even though you are going to have to pay additional hardware costs for 100,000 of those more expensive CPUs.

Figure 18.4 shows that even for moderately large production batches, the crossover point for when it is better overall to use a large processor can come surprisingly soon. For 50K units, the crossover point comes at 73% full (a per-unit cost of $22.02). For 10K units, the crossover point comes at only 57% full (a per-unit cost of $51.15).

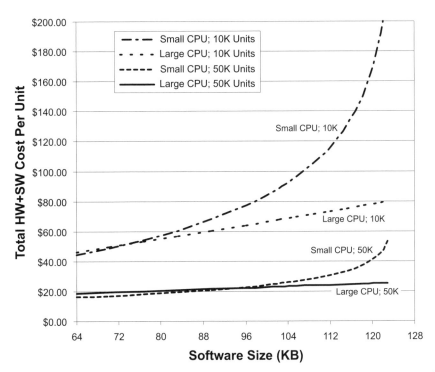

Figure 18.4. Example per unit total cost taking into account hardware and software costs for medium and small production runs.

What happens at even smaller run sizes? For runs of less than approximately 4750 units, it is always less expensive to use the large CPU, even for programs of only 64KB in size. It might be obvious to use over-kill on hardware when you are making only ten or a hundred units. But in this example, the crossover point is way up in the thousands of units!

The above are based on a particular set of models with a particular set of assumptions, and on cost multiplier data which might not be the same as what you'll see. So the precise crossover values and so on aren't really the point here. The main point is that anything other than extremely high volume production resulted in crossover values of 70%-85% or lower in resource usage, which many might find surprising.

It is important to note that while our example deals with memory capacity, similar arguments (and math) apply to other types of capacity within a system, including: CPU usage, network bandwidth, number of I/O pins used, and so on. The break-even point for going to a larger system will vary depending on the particular resource, but having any resource completely full is both costly and risky.

Based on this and our experience, we propose the following guidance:

> **You should get bigger hardware if**
> **your production run size is less than one million units, and**
> **your resources are more than 80% full.**

> **If your production run is less than 10K units, oversize your**
> **hardware by a factor of two.**

These ideas may sound quite aggressive in terms of demanding more slack hardware resources than are typically used. But, if it were possible to get much more real data from real projects, it wouldn't surprise us at all if it turns out they aren't aggressive enough.

While every situation is somewhat different, these rules will help keep you thinking the right way about the tradeoff between hardware and software costs. Having a significant amount of slack resources (20%-50% unused resources) will provide significant benefits beyond reducing the overall need for optimization. These can include:

- Eliminating the need for assembly language in all but the most time-critical operations, thus reducing development cost and risk.
- Reducing the risk of missing deadlines due to small timing variations not accounted for in real time scheduling calculations.
- Leaving resources for debug and instrumentation code to ease development.
- Increasing flexibility for post-release bug fixes and upgrades.

18.4. Fixing overly full resources

The best way to fix overly full resources is to buy more resources, even if it means increasing hardware costs on every unit produced. Unless you are producing truly huge quantities of products (100,000s or millions of units), it is better to spend more money on hardware than to make life difficult for software developers.

Resources aren't just memory and CPU cycles. Every project should consider whether it has adequate spare resources in at least the following areas:

- Flash memory
- RAM (including heap, stack, and static variable space)
- EEPROM
- Other memory types
- FPGA gates
- I/O pins
- Network bandwidth
- CPU cycles (CPU processing power)
- External memory bus bandwidth
- A/D channels
- Counter/timers

While the graph and multipliers discussed in this chapter tend to apply more to memory and CPU cycles, we'd expect a similar effect to occur any time resources are nearly or completely consumed. In short, if you start jumping through hoops to conserve a scarce resource, you're increasing development costs to save hardware costs. Far more often than we'd like to believe, that's the wrong path to take.

18.5. Pitfalls

Every time a numeric target is introduced, it's possible that this target will produce dysfunctional behavior. Having slack capacity is no exception. Here are some pitfalls to avoid when planning slack capacity. (No doubt there are others as well that we just aren't creative enough to think of!)

18.5.1. Optimizing to increase slack capacity

The point of examining slack capacity numbers is to get a feel for the system. Spending a lot of time optimizing to make the slack values look better is counter-productive. For example, rewriting an entire C program in hand-tuned assembly language might reduce CPU usage from 90% to 50%. But arguing that resultant system should cost only half as much total (because it has a lower multiplier) is not appropriate – it almost certainly will cost a lot more! The curve showing cost multipliers is mostly driven by developers spending more effort doing time and space optimization as resources become full (not much effort for 50% full systems; lots of effort for 95% full systems). So the multipliers should be used based on non-optimized, straightforward code size estimates.

18.5.2. Over-zealous avoidance of optimization

Clearly optimization is appropriate in embedded systems in many situations. For example, if writing a 25-byte assembly language subroutine lets you cut CPU usage in half, that is often a good idea. The cost multiplier data involves assumptions about optimization across an entire set of code. Good performance tuning that focuses a very modest amount of effort on a tiny fraction of the code is often OK, especially if care is taken to do a good job of design, implementation, documentation, and testing. However, wholesale optimization of a large amount of code is a bad idea unless truly huge numbers of systems are being manufactured or there is just no other way to meet performance criteria given limits to size, power, weight, and so on.

18.6. For more information

It is unusual to find a discussion of this topic. This is because in the desktop computing world it is common practice to simply buy a bigger or more powerful computer when needed. But, in the embedded world it is still typical for hardware costs to dominate product decisions.

18.6.1. General topic search keywords
• COCOMO

18.6.2. References

Boehm, B., "The high cost of software," in: Ellis Horowitz (Ed.), *Practical Strategies for Developing Large Software Systems*, Addison-Wesley, Reading MA, 1975, pp. 3-14.
A first step toward models of software costs, including many sources based on empirical data.

COCOMO II web site:
http://sunset.usc.edu/csse/research/COCOMOII/cocomo_main.html
The COCOMO approaches estimate software costs by taking into account various factors, including resource usage, and have evolved over time from Boehm's work. As with the discussion in this chapter, be careful not to take the numeric estimates too literally – they have a lot of assumptions built in.

Chapter 19
Global Variables Are Evil

- Global variables are memory locations that are directly visible to an entire software system.
- The problem with using globals is that different parts of the software are coupled in ways that increase complexity and can lead to subtle bugs.
- Avoid globals whenever possible, and at most use only a handful of globals in any system.

Contents:

19.1. Overview

"Global Variables Are Evil" is a pretty strong statement! Especially for something that is so prevalent in older embedded system software. But, if you can build your system without using global variables, you'll be a lot better off.

Global variables (called *globals* for short) can be accessed from any part of a software system, and have a globally visible scope. In its plainest form, a global variable is accessed directly by name rather than being passed as a parameter. By way of contrast, non-global variables can only be seen from a particular module or set of related methods. We'll show how to recognize global variables in detail in the following sections.

19.1.1. Importance of avoiding globals

The typical motivation for using global variables is efficiency. But sometimes globals are used simply because a programmer learned his trade with a non-scoped language (for example, classical BASIC doesn't support variable scoping – all variables are globals). Programmers moving to scoped languages such as C need to learn new approaches to take full advantage of the scoping and parameter passing mechanisms available.

The main problem with using global variables is that they create implicit couplings among various pieces of the program (various routines might set or modify a variable, while several more routines might read it). Those couplings are not well represented in the software design, and are not explicitly represented in the implementation language. This type of opaque data coupling among modules results in difficult to find and hard to understand bugs.

Global variables are evil.

19.1.2. Possible symptoms

You may have problems with global variable use if you observe any of the following when reviewing your implementation:

✘ More than a handful of variables are defined as globally visible (ideally, there are none). In C or C++, they are defined outside the scope of any procedure, so they are visible to all procedures. An indicator is the use of the keyword extern to access global variables defined outside the scope of your compiled module.

✘ Variables are used in a routine that are neither defined locally, nor passed as parameters. (This is just another way of saying they are global.)

✘ In assembly language, variables are accessed by label from subroutines or modules rather than via being passed on the stack as a parameter value. Any access to a labeled memory location (other than in a single module that has exclusive access to that location) is using a global.

The use of global variables is sometimes defensible. But their usage should be for a very few, special values, and not a matter of routine. Consider their occasional use a necessary evil.

19.1.3. Risks of using globals

The problem with global variables is that they make programs unnecessarily complex. That can lead to:

➤ Bugs caused by hidden coupling between modules. For example, misbehaving code in one place breaks things in another place.

➤ Bugs created in one module due to a change in a seemingly unrelated second module. For example, a change to a program that writes a global variable might break the behavior of code that reads that variable.

It may be necessary to have variables that are global, or at least serve a similar purpose as global variables. The risk comes from using global variables too freely, and not using mitigation strategies that are available.

> **A few globals might be worth the risk if used carefully.**

19.2. Why are global variables evil?

Global variables should be avoided to the maximum extent possible. At a high level, you can think of global variables as analogous to GOTO statements in programming languages (this idea dates back at least as far as Wulf (1973)). Most of us reflexively avoid GOTO statements. It's odd that we still think globals are OK.

First, let's discuss what globals are, then talk about why they should be avoided.

19.2.1. Definition of global variables

The strict definition of a global variable is a variable that has global scope – meaning it can be seen everywhere in the entire program. As a practical matter, a global variable is one that can be accessed outside the scope of the routine that defines it or accepts it as a parameter. In other words, a global variable seems to appear out of thin air when reading a particular piece of code. It isn't defined; it isn't in the input parameter list; the reference to it is just there, with no easy way (other than a text search) of finding out what is going on with it. We will call non-global variables *locals* for convenience.

Global variables are defined in a variety of ways depending on the programming language. Here are some examples:

• **Assembly:** any variable accessed via a label is a global. For example,
   LDA MyVar
loads the accumulator from MyVar – and MyVar is a global variable. This

means that in assembler programs pretty much anything that isn't a reference to the stack or a register value is a global.

- **Classical BASIC:** all variables are global variables. They can be read or written from anywhere within a program. You may be using a version of BASIC which supports local variables, but that is a comparatively recent addition to the language.

- **C and C++:** all variables defined outside the scope of a procedure: For example:

```
int GlobVar;          /* this is a global variable */
void MyFunc(void)
{  GlobVar = 5; }
```

- **Java:** variables aren't normally global unless you use a trick, such as declaring variables public static to make them visible outside the declaring object.

It is common to confuse the distinction between dynamic *vs.* static variables compared to local *vs.* global variables. A dynamic variable is one that is automatically created on the stack at run-time, especially in a scoped language such as C or Java. In these languages, temporary variable storage space is created on the stack every time a subroutine or method is called, and released when a return operation is performed. When dynamically allocated variables are released (for example, when you do a return from the subroutine that defined them), their value becomes undefined. Static variables, on the other hand, are given a permanent address and can be counted upon to retain their values indefinitely without being thrown away. In C, all variables defined within a routine are dynamic (unless the static keyword is used), and all variables defined outside any routine are static.

A static variable is not necessarily a global variable. Its memory address alone doesn't determine which other modules can see it. A dynamic variable is not necessarily local either, if a pointer to it is passed around. Thus, while it is most common in C that global variables are also static variables, it is not accurate to say all static variables are global. Here is an example in C of a variable that is static, but not global:

```
int IncrErrCount (void)
{ static int ErrCount = 0; // zeroed at startup
  ErrCount += 1;          // tally another error
  return(ErrCount);       // return error count to date
}
```

The variable ErrCount is permanently allocated, but is local to the subroutine. No other routine can see (know the address of) that variable. This use of a static variable is not a problem, because it is only visible inside the defining routine.

19.2.2. Quasi-global variables

In languages that support separate compilation of source code files, there are *quasi-global* variables which are visible everywhere inside a single source code file, but not visible to code in other source code files. In C code this is accomplished by using the keyword *static* with a top-level variable, as in this example:

```
static int GlobVar;    /* a quasi-global variable */
void MyFunc(void)
{ GlobVar = 5;
}
```

The static keyword in this example hides the variable from other compiled modules, keeping it hidden from most of the system if we assume there are a large number of different source code files compiled to make the entire system. A quasi-global variable is better than a completely global variable, because at least you know that it can't be accessed from outside the code in the file you're looking at. But it still has all the other disadvantages of a global variable, especially if the file it is used in has a lot of code that references that variable.

> **Quasi-globals are better than full globals.**

Quasi-globals are better than regular globals because their scope (code that can see them as a variable) is restricted to a single compiled file. But, the bigger that file is, the more code can see the variable, and thus the higher the risk.

19.2.3. Global variable problem: implicit coupling

Why are globals such a big deal? The main issue is that global variables cause implicit coupling between potentially far-flung pieces of code. Consider, for example, a C program that has perhaps 30 different ".c" files written by a half-dozen different programmers. You have this situation:

```
file:   GlobalDefs.c
...
int TurboFlag = 0; //defined as a global
...

file:   PerformanceMonitor.c
...
if(somecondition){TurboFlag=1;} //turbo mode on
...

file:   UserInterface.c
...
if(somecondition){TurboFlag=0;} //turbo mode off
...
```

```
file:    Compute.c
...
// use TurboFlag to choose fast vs. accurate
if(TurboFlag) { SomethingFast; }
else    { SomethingSlow; }
...
```

In this example, which is representative of how many programs use global operating mode variables, the global variable is defined in one place, changed in two other places, and used to control program flow in a fourth. For all we know, there are other places it can be changed too. (A global text search might reveal those other places, but how can you keep that type of information in your head for more than one or two global variables in a program?)

Here are some example situations where this approach can get you into trouble:

- You want to know what a global does, or even just its data type. You have to search for the definition, which could be anywhere. If you are lucky it is in a file named something like GlobalsDefs.c instead of tucked away someplace obscure.

- You need to change how the variable works, but have trouble finding all the places the variable is used. A text search will find all the places in the code it is used unless there are pointers to it. If you use pointers you're in for a tough time, because a text search won't be enough to find everywhere the variable is accessed.

- At run-time, something is changing the variable in an unexpected way, and you don't know how that is happening. Because the variable could be changed from anywhere, there is no way to look for routines that have the variable in their parameter list or otherwise isolate the problem. Solving this requires a debugger with watchpoint capability, which interrupts execution when a particular memory address is accessed. But, you have to reproduce the problem during debugging for this to work, which isn't always easy to do.

In other words, the fact that you can access the global from anywhere makes it difficult to isolate or identify the places where you actually do access it.

A related issue is the spreading of bugs via implicit links through global variables. If you change code at one place, you have no easy way of knowing what other parts of the code will be affected. Yes, you can do a text search of everywhere the global is accessed, and hope that no pointers or difficult-to-search-for references exist. But it is all too easy to get that wrong.

19.2.4. Global variable problem: bugs due to interference

In some small processors where global variables are used for speed, there isn't enough RAM for every routine to have its own independent variable space. This means that programmers map several global variables onto the same RAM space, and try to keep straight which values are being used at any given time. Such an approach is just begging to have very nasty bugs, and should be avoided.

If you don't have a lot of RAM and need to re-use it from one routine to the next, the stack mechanism built in to many programming languages, such as C, is a much less risky way to do the same thing. If you only have 128 bits of RAM to work with, there might not be much you can do. But, if this is the case, see *Chapter 18. The Cost of Nearly Full Resources*, because what you are doing is increasing your software development cost (and risk) to save hardware costs, which is very often the wrong tradeoff to be making.

19.2.5. Global variable problem: lack of mutex

Another popular use for global variables is as a mechanism to pass values from one process to another. For example, a global variable might be used as a place for an interrupt service routine to store an input byte until a processing routine can retrieve it. The reason a global is used is convenience, since an ISR doesn't accept parameters. One problem with this approach is that you can't actually be sure that the only code that sets the variable is the ISR unless you search the entire code base and verify no other routines do that. A way to mitigate this risk is to use a quasi-global variable in a file which defines only the ISR and the routine to which the ISR passes data, restricting the global variable visibility to be within that file and nowhere else.

More generally, it is common for global variables used to communicate between processes to have concurrency issues. Using a fully global variable for communication can almost always be avoided. When it must be done, it is important to protect that global variable with a mutex to ensure no strange and elusive bugs appear due to concurrency problems. (See *Chapter 20. Mutexes and Data Access Concurrency*.)

19.2.6. Pointers to globals

Sometimes you need to find all references to a global to understand or modify a program. A text search will find all references to a global – but only if there are no pointers to it. If there are pointers to a global variable passed around, then it is even more difficult to figure out where the global might be read or written. Forbidding pointers to globals is the best way to avoid such problems.

Pointers to globals are even more evil.

19.3. Ways to avoid or reduce the risk of globals

Fortunately, there are ways to avoid globals, or at least make them more manageable if they simply must be used. Below are some typical approaches. Not all of these techniques are mutually compatible. So, this should be considered a bag of tricks that can be used, rather than a list of good practices that should all be followed. Most programs will need more than one of these techniques, depending on the situation.

19.3.1. Get a more capable processor

In some cases, the reason global variables are used is to speed up program execution. For example, some processors have page zero operations that provide shorter instructions and faster access to the first 256 bytes of RAM. Yes, there are some cases where this savings in speed or size is worth doing. But such situations are fewer than there used to be. You should consider that using globals in the first 256 bytes to exploit this feature is likely to significantly increase your software development costs, just as any other optimization technique that involves exploiting limited hardware resources will. *Chapter 18. The Cost of Nearly Full Resources* discusses this in more detail. This technique should be used only on very large production runs (millions of hardware units manufactured).

> **If optimization forces you to use globals,**
> **get a better compiler or a faster processor.**

Note that if a compiler is smart enough to map variables into page zero for you, *and* that complexity is completely hidden from the programmer, *and* the compiler doesn't have bugs that get this mapping wrong, *then* it is perfectly fine to use this optimization. We have no problem with using smaller instructions that run faster! The problem comes when programmers have to spend a lot of extra effort to do this. This puts them at increased risk of bugs because the optimization requires using risky data structures (globals) instead of less risky data structures (locals) in source code.

19.3.2. Move the global inside the procedure that needs it

Some globals are created not because they truly need to be global, but because they need to retain their values across multiple invocations of the procedure that uses them (in other words, they need to be static). In C++ it is common to use constructors and destructors to do this sort of thing. But, in C it is a little trickier to do. One approach in C is to simply move the definition of the global into the highest level routine that needs it, then pass references to it down into subroutines.

> **Use a static local variable instead of a global when possible.**

Here's an example routine that uses a global:

```
int ErrCount = 0;   // initialized to zero at startup
```

```
int IncrErrCount (void)
{ ErrCount += 1;      // tally another error
  return(ErrCount);   // accumulated error count
}
```

But, there is no need to make ErrCount a global if IncrErrCount() is the only procedure that needs to modify it. Instead, it could be rewritten as:

```
int IncrErrCount (void)
{ static int ErrCount = 0; // initialized at startup
  ErrCount += 1;          // tally another error
  return(ErrCount);       // accumulated error count
}
```

In this example, ErrCount is only visible to the routine that needs it, so it is no longer a global variable. The C keyword static is used to tell the compiler to allocate a variable in memory that retains its values between calls to the procedure rather than making the variable temporary and placing it on the stack. (Note that in C, the initialization of a static variable happens only once when the program is first run, not every time the routine is called.)

If IncrErrCount called other routines that needed to know what the value of ErrCount was, it could pass the value or a pointer to that value down to the called routines.

19.3.3. Make a shared variable quasi-global instead of global.

If you must use a global variable to share a value across several routines, then a way to contain the spread of problems is to put only the routines that access that value into a single source code file, and declare the variable as a quasi-global using the static keyword. For example:

```
static int ErrCount = 0; // initialized at startup

int IncrErrCount (void)
{ ErrCount += 1;      // tally another error
  return(ErrCount);   // return error count to date
}

int GetErrCount(void)
{ return(ErrCount); // return error count to date
}

void ClearErrCount(void)
{ ErrCount = 0;  // reset error count to zero
}
```

In this case of defining a top-level global variable (one that is not inside a procedure), the static keyword means "not visible outside this program file." So that guarantees the variable ErrCount can't be accessed outside the file it is included in. This limits the damage, and in C is often a necessary evil.

C++ has the concept of a friend to document what is going on with such shared variables, and provide stricter control over who sees and who doesn't see a shared variable. While using friends involves some of the risks of globals, it's far better to use a friend than a fully global variable. You can think of friends as a more sophisticated version of quasi-globals.

19.3.4. Make the global an object, and provide access methods

If a global variable must be accessed in many places, and there is just no way around it, then making it a globally visible object rather than an ordinary global variable may have several advantages.

> **Make globals into objects rather than directly accessible variables.**

If you are using an object oriented language such as C++, then this is relatively easy. But even in a non-OO language such as C, this can be done without too much trouble. For example, let's say you want to create a global error counter along the lines of previous examples. You could do the following:

- Create a separate .c file that only contains one related set of globally visible data objects and their access routines.

- For each object, use a static definition at the top level. This makes it visible to all procedures in that .c file, but nowhere else in the program (in other words, it makes it quasi-global).

- Provide procedure calls to read, write, or otherwise operate on the data.

The net result is that you have a variable that can't be accessed except via the access methods you've provided. This is a close approximation to how C++ handles objects in many respects. For example, a global count of errors encountered might have this code in the separate global variables .c file:

```
static int ErrCount = 0;  // initialized at startup

inline int IncrErrCount (void)
{ ErrCount += 1;     // tally another error
  return(ErrCount);  // return error count to date
}

inline int GetErrCount(void)
{ return(ErrCount); // return error count to date
}

inline void ClearErrCount(void)
{ ErrCount = 0;   // reset error count to zero
}
```

The **inline** keyword is used to encourage the compiler to put the code to access the variable in-line with other code, eliminating the overhead of a procedure call. With a good optimizing compiler, this code will compile with the same runtime speed as an ordinary global variable. (This can also be true for C++ approaches that put the global variable into an object with access methods.)

While not as syntactically clean as it would be in C++, the above code gets the job done. A more C++-like notation might be to call the procedures: ErrCount_Incr, ErrCount_Get, and ErrCount_Clear, but the naming is a matter of choice for your style guidelines.

The obvious question is, why would we want to go to all the trouble of defining the access routines when we could have just defined a global and been done with it? Here are some reasons. You may or may not find them compelling, but they are worth considering.

- **It makes it impossible to get a pointer to the variable.** Because the pointer is hidden behind the access functions (it is declared static at the top level), it is impossible for any module outside the definition file to see it. Thus, it is impossible to point to. This could be helpful, because it makes it much more difficult for a developer to violate a no pointer to globals rule. With this approach, identifying places in the code that access the variable still requires a text search for the name of the access method. But, at least there are no pointers to worry about.

- **It provides debugging hooks.** Debugging of problems with globals can be difficult because they can be accessed from anywhere. Debugging via address matching on loads and stores for globals (watch-point debugging based on the global variable address) isn't always possible, and needs on-CPU hardware support or an emulator to work well. With the access methods we've described, it's impossible to access the variable without going through a defined access method. The access routines can therefore be instrumented to show what is happening. Debugging via breakpoints based on program counter values (with a breakpoint at the start of an access routine) is a universal debugger capability. If you don't have a debugger at all, you can at least put print statements in the access methods to see what's happening with the variable by modifying only one spot in the software system.

- **It simplifies concurrency management.** A tricky part of globals is making sure that multiple concurrent tasks accessing them don't have problems with sharing. A mutex or other locking mechanism is used (see *Chapter 20. Mutexes and Data Access Concurrency*). With this method you only need to put the mutex logic in one place – the access procedure. With other methods, you need to make sure you get the mutex right every place the variable is touched, which gives many more places to verify, and many more chances to make a mistake (most commonly, the mistake of forgetting to use the mutex).

19.3.5. If you must use a global, document it well

For whatever reason, you might find you still must have a global variable in your program. Hopefully you won't need many! But for those you need, here are some things you can do to reduce the chance of having problems.

- Use a naming convention to make it easier to recognize all globals in a text search.

- If the global is shared by concurrent tasks, use a naming convention to remind developers that it must be protected by a mutex or lock.

- Don't allow taking a pointer to a global.

- Use comments where a global is defined to keep an up-to-date list of everywhere it is used, and any rules for manipulating the variable. It shouldn't be too hard to have automated tools generate this list dynamically, if you have access to all the source code.

> If you still have to use a global, spend a lot of effort making it as clean and well documented as possible.

19.4. Pitfalls

Globals are evil, and it's better to avoid using them. As with any idea, avoiding globals can be carried to absurd extremes, but the usual pitfall is using too many globals instead of too few.

19.5. For more information

19.5.1. General topic search keywords

- Global variable
- Scoping

19.5.2. Recommended reading

Ganssle, J., "A pox on globals," *Embedded System Design,* October 2006, pp. 57-60.
Jack hates globals about as much as we do. Here's another take on the same topic.

Jones, N., "Efficient C code for eight-bit MCUs," *Embedded Systems Programming,* November 1998, pp. 66-83.
This article discusses a number of efficiency techniques, including using static non-global variables instead of globals.

19.5.3. Additional reading

Wulf, W. & Shaw, M., "Global variables considered harmful," *ACM SIGPLAN Notices,* February 1973, pp. 28-34
An early paper explaining why global variables are bad.

Chapter 20
Mutexes and Data Access Concurrency

- Variables that are shared between tasks need special protection to avoid data concurrency bugs.
- Typical hazards include multi-byte data values that are updated in mid-read, hardware registers that change while being read, and multiple writers for a particular data value
- Access mechanisms include using the volatile keyword, atomic modifications via interrupt masking, data queues, and mutexes.
- Special care must be taken to ensure that code is reentrant if it can be in use concurrently by multiple threads.

Contents:

20.1. Overview

Two tasks are *concurrent* if they can both be active simultaneously at any point in time. (Even if one task is suspended while another executes, they are concurrent because the first task didn't complete its computation before the second task started). It is common for embedded system software to execute control algorithms endlessly while the system is in operation, so most embedded systems have some level of concurrency issues.

Any time a piece of data or a memory location is shared between tasks in an embedded system, it is possible to have problems due to sharing. In brief, concurrency problems occur when one task accesses a data structure and incorrectly assumes it won't be changed by some other task. Looked at another way, concurrency problems come when two tasks fail to cooperate when sharing a data resource. A particularly common problem in embedded systems is when an ISR modifies a data value in a way that causes main routines accessing that data value to fail. A related problem is ensuring software reloads data that may have been changed by some other process (or hardware) since the last access.

There are two general solutions for concurrency problems with shared data. One is to lock or otherwise protect the data so it can only be modified or read in situations when doing so won't cause the system to fail. The other is to use approaches that aren't susceptible to data concurrency problems, such as passing data between tasks via queues, and making shared code segments reentrant.

20.1.1. Importance of using data access concurrency techniques

Most embedded systems have data concurrency issues in one form or another. As soon as you have more than one task, access the same piece of data from different parts of your software system, or use interrupts, you are at risk of having data concurrency problems.

Knowing whether you are suffering from a data concurrency bug can be difficult, because symptoms often depend on the exact timing of different parts of the system. It's important to be thorough and proactive in eliminating concurrency problems. If concurrency bugs make it into code you are trying to test or deploy, it is very difficult and expensive to locate and correct them.

20.1.2. Possible symptoms

At a high level, problems with shared data tend to show up as infrequent failures that can't be tracked down to defects in any particular line of code (because the problem is the interaction of multiple parts of the code):

✘ Occasional bugs occur that seem to happen at random, but which might occur more frequently in particular system operating modes.

By looking at the source code, you might also find the following symptoms which are often indicative of this type of problem:

✖ ISRs update variables or memory locations, and non-ISR routines accessing those locations don't disable interrupts while using them.

✖ Global variables are accessed by multiple tasks, and don't have mutexes or other locking mechanisms protecting them.

✖ Hardware resources are shared by multiple tasks, but aren't protected by a mutex or other locking mechanism.

✖ Variables can be changed by another task or hardware, but software accessing those variables doesn't force a reload of the value when a change might have taken place.

✖ There are shared code segments (for example, math libraries) that use static, global, or other non-reentrant data structures.

20.1.3. Risks of incorrect concurrency management

➤ Intermittent bugs that are difficult to reproduce, and may appear only after the system has been shipped to the field.

➤ Data that has impossible or invalid values due to data changes that occur partway through access to the data structure. This can cause incorrect operation, system errors, or system crashes depending on the situation and whether data values are checked for validity before being used.

20.2. Data sharing hazards

Data sharing problems typically come about when it is possible for one task in a system to preempt another task. This situation includes not only task switching, but also ISRs. Because ISRs are the more common problem, we'll use them as examples in this discussion. But, realize that this problem can happen any time two tasks (ISR or otherwise) share a data value. It can even happen with non-preemptive task switching, although this is much less frequently a problem than with preemptive task switching.

20.2.1. Data updated in mid-read

Perhaps the most common bug resulting from data sharing problems occurs when a data value that is multiple machine words in size is read by a task, and is changed by some other task partway through the reading process. The classical case in which this occurs is a program that reads a time of day value while that value is being updated by a hardware timer ISR.

Consider what happens if you have a time-of day field that has the following: a 16-bit day (with day zero being, for example, January 1, 2000), 8-bit hours, 8-bit minutes, and 8-bit seconds. This is a five-byte date/time field. Now consider a task that wishes to write a date-stamped log of events. It will call a routine that assembles the current time and date into a data structure. For example:

```
void GetDateTime (DateTimeType *DT)
{ DT->day = TimerVal.day;    // copy current day to DT
  DT->hour = TimerVal.hour; // copy time fields to DT
  DT->minute = TimerVal.minute;
  DT->second = TimerVal.second;
}
```

Let's assume TimerVal is a data structure defined elsewhere that is updated by an ISR several times a second based on a hardware counter/timer rollover. (The ISR also keeps track of fractions of a second, but assume we don't care about that information.) Calling this routine returns a date/time tuple of bytes that snapshots the time of day and puts it into a variable owned by the calling routine (called DT in the subroutine).

But, what happens if the ISR happens to trigger partway through running this routine? You could get an old day and hour copied into DT, the ISR could trigger, and then you could get the new minute and second values. If there happens to be a value rollover when the ISR executes, you could get weird results. For example, let's say you are running on an 8-bit processor and the date/time is currently the following:

```
Day = 255; Hour = 23; Minute = 59; Second = 59
```

If the ISR were to increment the time by one second in normal operation, you would get:

```
Day = 256; Hour = 00; Minute = 00; Second = 00
```

But, what if the ISR were to increment the time by one second part-way through execution of GetDateTime? You could get any one of the following depending on where that happened:

```
Day = 00; Hour = 00; Minute = 00; Second = 00
```
if the ISR happened between reading the high and low bytes of Day (this is the worst case – your answer is wrong by 256 days on an 8-bit CPU.)

```
Day = 255; Hour = 00; Minute = 00; Second = 00
```
if the ISR happened between reading Day and Hour

```
Day = 255; Hour = 59; Minute = 00; Second = 00
```
if the ISR happened between reading Hour and Minute

```
Day = 255; Hour = 59; Minute = 59; Second = 00
```
if the ISR happened between reading Minute and Second.

There are two really nasty issues with this bug. The first is that it won't even be seen at all unless the ISR happens right when the time is being read and a value rollover happens to take place. This bug can easily be a one-in-a-million problem. But the second issue is that the bigger problems happen even less often than small problems. You might not catch a problem with an incorrect seconds value, especially if you are only logging events once every few minutes or hours. It might not cause enough of a disruption in the system to get your attention.

But a really big problem – say being off by an hour or a day, might happen only once in a great while. You might not see it at all until you've deployed thousands of units to the field (but by then fixing bugs is a lot more painful!). Depending on your application, this might or might not be a huge problem with your business and customers. But, if you don't realize you have a data sharing issue, it could be extremely difficult to duplicate, track, down, and resolve.

Watch out for rollovers while reading a multi-byte timer value.

20.2.2. Updates of data held in registers

A related, but more subtle, problem is when a programmer or compiler reads a value and then keeps it in a CPU register while the value changes. For example, if you wanted to take a thousand samples of data and associate them with a counter/timer value, you might write code like this:

```
// Caution – this code has a problem!
inline unsigned int GetTimer(void)
{ // define address of 16-bit counter/timer
  unsigned int * TimerAddr = 0xE42D;
  int RetVal;

  // read counter/timer value and return
  RetVal = *TimerAddr;

  return(RetVal);
}

...


for (I = 0; I < 1000; I++)   // capture 1000 data points
{ Data[i].value = A2D();      // value from A/D converter
  Data[i].time = GetTimer();  // timestamp the value
}
```

In this code, a memory-mapped timer value is read and put into the time position of the Data array. The GetTimer routine is inlined for speed (an optimizing compiler might well do this even without being asked). So, what's the problem?

Unfortunately, a really good optimizing compiler might take the following steps to optimize your code:

1. In-line GetTimer to avoid the overhead of a subroutine call (this doesn't really hurt anything).

2. Notice that TimerAddr always points to the same location, so just do a direct load instead of going through a pointer (this doesn't really hurt anything, and is in fact a desirable optimization).
3. Notice that the same address is being loaded each time GetTimer is called, and so just load it once before the loop starts to avoid wasted effort (this is a problem!).

In effect, the compiler will generate this code after optimization:

```
RetVal = *TimerAddr;
for (I = 0; I < 1000; I++)
{ Data.value[i] = A2D();
  Data.time[i] = RetVal;
}
```

Clearly this is wrong – the same time stamp is applied every time through the loop!

Fortunately the solution for this problem is relatively easy. We should have forced the compiler to read the value from the timer every time the source code asked for it to be read. In C, this is done by using the keyword *volatile*:

```
volatile unsigned int * TimerAddr = 0xE42D;
```

instead of the non-volatile code in the above example. This forces the timer to be read every time RetVal is needed.

The volatile keyword should be put in place for you in the header files provided with your compiler, but it's important to know about this if you are trying to use hardware that isn't standard with your microcontroller.

A similar problem can occur if the value being accessed is a variable read by one task and written by another. It's important to make sure that the programmer or the compiler doesn't keep the value around long after it has been updated by the other task (the volatile keyword works for this too). The volatile keyword is discussed further in following sections.

20.2.3. Multiple writers

The most difficult problems occur when multiple tasks are trying to modify a memory value concurrently, trying to write data to an output device, or otherwise trying to gain write access to a shared resource. Coordinating multiple writers is more difficult than ensuring a reader doesn't get corrupted data. There must be a fool-proof mechanism for taking turns among multiple writers, and this is a very difficult thing to get right unless you use a standard strategy such as one of those discussed in the next section.

As an example, consider a system event or error log. Any task in the system might need to write to that log. But, only one task at a time should have access to it to avoid scrambled fields resulting from multiple tasks over-writing parts of each other's data in the log. This is similar in nature to the problems we saw with the time stamp example above, except now you have multiple tasks trying to write instead of one task trying to read while another writes. Solving problems of this type require a heavy-duty mechanism, typically a mutex (discussed below).

20.3. Data protection strategies

There are a number of data protection strategies of increasing capability and complexity. Each one is useful in specific situations, and it is important to understand the strengths and weaknesses of each. It is also desirable to use the lightest weight approach that is sufficient for the situation so as to keep things simple and efficient.

> All data structures shared by multiple tasks (including ISR tasks)
> should use some form of concurrency protection.

> The lightest weight concurrency protection mechanism practical for
> the situation should be used.

20.3.1. Volatile keyword

The lightest-weight way to deal with concurrency issues is to force a compiler to read or write a memory location every time it is referenced in the source code. In C and C++, this is done using the keyword volatile. For example:

```
volatile int X;
…
Y = X + X;   // read X twice and add those values
```

In this example, X would be loaded twice and those two values would be added together, even with an optimizing compiler. If X changed between times it was read, the value of Y would reflect the sum of those two different values. The volatile keyword is telling the compiler that every time X is read (or written) it might have a different value, so optimizations to reduce how many times it is read or written aren't allowed.

> Use the volatile keyword in C or C++ if data can be
> changed between times it is read.

The most important use of volatile is to ensure the compiler properly reads or writes streams of bytes to a memory-mapped I/O port. Every memory-mapped I/O address should be declared volatile to make sure the hardware interface works as intended.

An additional use for the volatile keyword is to ensure that changes to a memory location made by one task are seen by other tasks as soon as those changes take place. For example, if a variable value is updated periodically by an ISR, the task reading that value should declare it volatile to make sure it always uses the latest value.

Use the volatile keyword in C or C++ if data is being produced by another task or hardware device.

The volatile keyword should be used for tasks that write values as well as read them to ensure that values are updated as soon as possible, and the latest value is always used.

Example code with a problem:

```
volatile static int LatestValue;

TASK 1:
...
while()
{ LatestValue = ReadIO(); // continuously update
   ... wait until IO ready with next data value ...
}

TASK 2:
...
for (I = 0; I < MaxSample; I++)
{ X[i] = LatestValue;   // take a sample to process
   ... wait for next time point to take next sample ...
}
```

This example code depends upon the volatile keyword in the following ways. If Task 1, which polls an input port, didn't use volatile, then LatestValue might never be written. The optimizer might just read I/O bytes, place them in a register, and then forget about them until the last time through the loop (which never comes), because it would think that only the final value needs to be written.

If Task 2 didn't use volatile, then it might read LatestValue once, put it in a register, and just assign the same value to all elements of X[i], mistaking the loop for a loop that initializes all elements in an array to the same value (which is certainly a common use for a loop like this in many other programs).

There are two main limitations to the volatile keyword approach:

(1) It doesn't provide protection if multiple tasks want to change the value.

(2) It doesn't provide protection for data values that take more than one instruction to read or write, if a task switch could happen partway through the read or write.

Values with more than one byte or word of data require a heavier weight data locking approach to avoid changes during the process of reading the set of data words, depending on the system and the instructions being used to write the data.

20.3.2. Atomic modifications and disabling interrupts

An *atomic* operation is one which can't be interrupted once it is started. In particular, an atomic operation assures you that once the operation starts, there can be no task switch, interrupt, or other disruption of the process until after it completes. In systems we're interested in, a single ordinary machine instruction is atomic, but most sets of two or more instructions aren't unless you take special precautions.

20.3.2.1. Atomic operations for multiple threads

Any time more than one word of data is being written, even by a single task, it is possible to have concurrency problems if there is a task switch or interrupt partway through the writing process. Consider something as simple as incrementing a variable:

```
volatile int X;
...
X = X + 1;
```

Could this lead to concurrency problems? Yes – depending on the CPU's instruction set and compiler, it could. For example, a microcontroller that has some 16-bit instructions, but only an 8-bit instruction for incrementing a memory location might compile this C code as:

(1) Load X into a 16-bit register A

(2) Add 1 to register A

(3) Store register A back into X using a single instruction (16-bit store)

This case would work properly so long as other tasks could read X but not write it. But, the compiler might try this approach instead because it generated smaller code or faster code (or just because the optimizer wasn't turned on):

(1) Increment the low byte of X, generating a carry-out flag

(2) Add with carry the value 0 to the high byte of X

This results in the same output, but with the drawback that the value modification to X is done in two steps – first the low byte, then the high byte. If another task (ISR, or full task) happens to execute between operations (1) and (2), X will have the wrong value for a while. This is similar to what could happen in the date/time rollover problem discussed previously.

The solution is to disable interrupts during the increment operation. For example:

```
volatile int X;
...
DisableInterrupts();
X = X + 1;
EnableInterrupts();
```

In most embedded systems, disabling and enabling interrupts is done with an in-lined procedure that just compiles into a one byte instruction, so the overhead is minimal. This way, you know you are covered regardless of how the code is generated. To be safe, you should do this any time you are writing to a shared variable that is bigger than one byte in size. In some systems it is OK to assume that data accesses of one word in size are safe; but be sure your compiler doesn't generate byte-based instructions for word-sized data before you assume this!

Disable interrupts when modifying a multi-byte shared variable that isn't protected by a mutex.
Re-enable interrupts as soon as possible!

In some situations interrupts may already be disabled before the atomic operation is performed. If this is the case, the current interrupt masking state (often called the interrupt mask) should be saved before disabling interrupts. Then, instead of re-enabling interrupts, the previous interrupt masking state should be restored. This way interrupts that are disabled before the atomic operation will remain disabled after the atomic operation. This advice applies everywhere else we discuss disabling and enabling interrupts as well.

20.3.2.2. Atomic operations for hardware access

The above situation is also a problem if X is a memory-mapped hardware address, even though the volatile keyword is used. But disabling interrupts won't be enough if hardware operates on the data independently of the CPU.

Hardware should be designed so that if a multi-byte update must be made, the hardware doesn't act on the new information until all the bytes have been changed. In some designs, the hardware might actually wait until all bytes have been modified before reading data, in which case there is no problem. But in other designs the hardware might just freeze for a few clock cycles to give time to do the update – and if a task switch hits at just the wrong time, the hardware will resume operation with partially changed results. Ensuring that all hardware bytes are updated atomically is always a good idea, and may require disabling interrupts while hardware is being updated to ensure that all updates are made quickly enough.

20.3.2.3. Atomic operations within ISRs

There is an additional special case within an ISR. Unless you have re-enabled interrupts during an ISR (which is a bad idea), interrupts are already disabled by default while you are in an ISR. Thus, you can be sure that any updates an ISR makes to a shared variable is atomic without taking any additional steps.

20.3.3. Queues

Queues are used when one task might need to write multiple values of data faster than another task can consume those values. A single shared variable won't work because it will get over-written and some of the values will be lost. So instead a *queue*, also known as a First-In First-Out (*FIFO*) buffer, is used to temporarily store data until it can be consumed by the receiving task.

The important thing to keep in mind when dealing with queue concurrency issues is that every item in the queue (including head and tail pointers) must have only one writer. As soon as any item within the queue data structure has multiple writers, managing concurrency gets more difficult. But, the good news is that a simple queue can be built in which the head pointer (the next element to be read) is only modified by the consuming task, and the tail pointer (the next element to be written) is only modified by the producing task. It's important to both use the volatile keyword and disable interrupts to ensure that modifying the head and tail pointers doesn't cause concurrency issues.

> Use a queue for single-reader/single-writer
> sharing of streams of data.

20.3.3.1. Queues to avoid concurrency problems

Here is some example C code for a queue. Note that we use the notion of pointer loosely in this code – the pointers are actually indices into an array in this particular implementation.

```c
// Note: put this and the corresponding remove routine
//   inside a single separate .C file to hide variables
//   from other routines
#define FIFOSIZE 10
#define PASS 1
#define FAIL 0

static int fifo[FIFOSIZE]; // one per queue element
static short unsigned int head=0, tail=0; // init empty

// insert element onto queue
// return PASS if success; otherwise return FAIL
bool insert(int x)
{ int newtail;
  // access next free element
  newtail = tail+1;

  // wrap around to beginning if needed
  if (newtail >= FIFOSIZE) { newtail = 0; }

  // if head and tail are equal, fifo is full
  if (newtail == head) {return(FAIL)};

  // write data before updating pointer
  fifo[newtail] = x;
  tail = newtail;
```

```
    return(PASS);
}
```

The key idea of proper queue operation is making sure that the reader and writer don't attempt to access the same piece of data at the same time. You have to assume that as soon as pointers have been updated, the other task will be there to read the data or re-use the queue entry for the next piece of data.

The way this code works is that the data is written into the queue before the tail pointer is modified. Updating the tail pointer is the very last thing that is done. That way if the consuming task needs an element from the queue, it can't access the element being written until after all the data is in place. It's important that writing the new value of the tail pointer is done atomically, so that the consuming task can't get a partially changed multi-byte value. We solve that problem here by using a short integer, which is a single byte or word. Removing elements from the queue at the consuming task is done in a similar manner, with the head pointer being changed only after all relevant data has been read from the queue.

The limitation to a queue is that it assumes there can only be exactly one reader and exactly one writer. If more than one task can read a piece of data or write a piece of data, a heavier weight protection mechanism has to be used, such as a mutex.

20.3.3.2. Double buffering

The technique of double buffering is a special case of using queues. In a *double-buffered* system the queue contains exactly two entries. Furthermore, one entry is in use by the reader and one entry is in use by the writer at all times. When both the reader and writer are ready, they swap ownership of the two buffers. Double buffering is commonly used in large data structures, such as video frame buffers. But, it can be used anywhere a simpler version of a FIFO queue is desired.

20.3.4. Mutexes

A *mutex* is a way to assert exclusive ownership over a shared resource, and ensure that the ownership stays in place even if there are task switches. Mutex stands for MUTual EXclusion, and means that only one task out of however many are executing is allowed to access a shared variable or other resource at a time. (A *semaphore* is a more general mechanism that permits multiple tasks to have access to limited resource at one time, but works in roughly the same way.)

The idea behind a mutex is that there is a variable which indicates whether any task is using the resource. When a task is using the resource, the mutex is said to be locked, and all other tasks are prevented from using the resource. When no task is using the resource, the mutex is unlocked. We'll give a simple implementation to show how it works.

> Use a mutex for any shared data that can't be protected with a
> simpler locking mechanism.

First, we need to define two shared variables – one that is the data we want to
share, and one that is the mutex lock. The data being shared could be anything –
multiple bytes, a large data structure, a hardware resource, or whatever. Once
you use a mutex there are no restrictions on what is being shared. But, a mutex is
a heavyweight protection mechanism, so you should only use it when
lighter-weight mechanisms won't get the job done.

The following code interwoven with discussion that follows is a classical way
to implement a mutex:

```
// This is the shared data structure
// It could be a struct or anything you want it to be.
volatile int SharedData;

// This is the mutex
// 0 is unlocked; 1 is locked; initialize to unlocked
#define UNLOCKED 0
#define LOCKED   1
volatile unsigned short int SharedDataMutex = UNLOCKED;
```

The shared data and mutex should be visible only to those parts of the software that need to see them. Often they are global variables, but that need not be
the case. In C++, these variables could be hidden inside an object, and the procedures for getting and releasing the mutex defined below would be methods to
access that object (See *Chapter 19. Global Variables Are Evil*).

When the system starts running, SharedDataMutex is 0, meaning the shared
resource is unlocked. If a task wants to acquire the resource, there are two sharing situations it has to deal with: the resource might already be in use, or another
task might be trying to acquire the resource at the same time. If two tasks are
competing for the resource, a task switch might take place during the middle of
the competition, resulting in a concurrency problem such as both tasks accidentally being granted access (thinking they own the lock) concurrently. These problems can be overcome by using the following code, which is an implementation
of a technique known as a spinlock (also called a test and set lock):

```
// attempt to acquire the lock
void GetMutex(volatile unsigned short int *Mutex)
{ unsigned short int InitialValue;

// This while loop iterates until the initial
//   value is unlocked (meaning this task has
//   successfully captured the Mutex and locked it)
do
{ DisableInterrupts();    // ensure atomic access
  InitialValue = *Mutex;  // get current value
  *Mutex = LOCKED;        // attempt to get a lock
  EnableInterrupts();
} while (InitialValue == LOCKED);
// loop while failed to acquire the lock

// exit loop when lock acquired; Mutex left LOCKED
}

// release lock when done with associated data
void ReleaseMutex(volatile unsigned short int *Mutex)
{ *Mutex = UNLOCKED;   // release the lock
}
```

A program that uses these routines would do this:

```
GetMutex(&SharedDataMutex);
// now we own the lock
 … use SharedData as much as we like …
ReleaseMutex(&SharedDataMutex);
// now someone else can use the data
```

Executing GetMutex with a parameter that points to SharedDataMutex will eventually obtain a lock on SharedData to ensure exclusive access. The way GetMutex works is a bit tricky. First, let's assume that no other task owns the shared resource yet, meaning Mutex is 0 (UNLOCKED). Strictly speaking, it is the value pointed to by the parameter Mutex, which is SharedDataMutex in this case, but we'll just call it Mutex to keep things simple. In this case, the value of UNLOCKED is put into InitialValue, Mutex is set to LOCKED, and the while loop terminates. Now this task owns the lock on the data, and other tasks are prevented from using the shared value until the lock is released.

If the shared resource is already in use, what happens is that Mutex is already 1 (LOCKED) upon entering the while loop. This means InitialValue is set to LOCKED. Mutex is set to LOCKED, but this has no effect, because it was already LOCKED. In other words, an attempt to lock a locked variable keeps it locked, and lets the routine know it was previously locked (via InitialValue). The currently running routine knows it failed to actually obtain the lock, because InitialValue indicates some other routine got there first. The loop continues until another task releases the lock (setting Mutex to UNLOCKED), letting the newly running task finally see InitialValue come back as UNLOCKED, meaning it has successfully acquired the lock on the resource. We assume this is a system with preemptive task switching, so that other tasks can run while execution of the while loop is suspended.

The DisableInterrupts() and EnableInterrupts() calls are there because the read of Mutex followed by setting it to LOCKED must be atomic. If multiple tasks are attempting to acquire a lock to the same shared resource, an interrupt could happen partway through this code sequence and result in two tasks thinking they had the lock. The way to prevent this is to make that two-line segment of code atomic.

This is a lot of work to access a shared variable! But, the payoff is that interrupts have to be disabled for only a short period of time in the while loop. At all other times, interrupts are enabled, even while the winning task has exclusive access to the shared resource. This can make a big difference in response times and real time schedulability. (Speaking of response times, if you are on a single-CPU system it makes sense to give up execution to the scheduler (e.g., invoke the yield function) if you fail to get a mutex. This will let other tasks run sooner than they otherwise would, eventually freeing up the mutex so you can use the shared resource. There is no point retrying the mutex if you are the only task that is allowed to run.)

Every separate shared resource needs to have its own mutex.

It's important to realize that using a mutex brings into play a number of heavyweight concurrency issues. These include:

- **Priority inversion:** This happens when some high priority task has to wait for a mutex that is locked by a low priority task. This can happen even with lighter weight mechanisms, such as having to wait for space to open up on a queue that is full. But the problem is likely to be more difficult to debug with a mutex in use.

- **Deadlock:** Two tasks are competing for multiple mutex locks, and each task ends up with a mutex lock needed by the other task. Unless countermeasures are taken, both tasks will wait forever to get all the mutex locks they need.

20.4. Reentrant code

A module is *reentrant* if it can be used concurrently by more than one task without a data sharing error. Concurrent execution can easily happen in subroutines shared by multiple tasks such as math libraries, I/O drivers, and error handlers. The usual way to make a module reentrant is by making sure all variables are in registers or on the stack. In C, this is done by avoiding use of global variables, avoiding the keyword static applied to variables, and making sure there are no pointers to potentially shared memory locations. The default location for non-global variables is on the stack, so procedures are reentrant unless you try to make them otherwise.

> **At a minimum, reentrant C and C++ procedures should not use the static keyword and should not reference global variables.**

In assembly language, this is trickier, because it is easiest to define variables in fixed memory locations (often called direct or extended memory addresses) rather than stack locations.

If you absolutely must reference a global or static value in a reentrant procedure, you must protect it from other concurrent threads executing that routine using one of the techniques we've described. Doing this creates problems with performance, so it's better just to avoid global and static variables.

> **Any procedure that might be called by more than one active task should be reentrant.**

20.5. Pitfall

The main pitfall is in not having enough respect for the difficulty of concurrency problems. Getting concurrency right is extremely difficult. It is all too easy to fool yourself into thinking you have a better approach than everyone else, or that you can bend the rules in using a particular lightweight concurrency mechanism. Most of the time, you'll be wrong. Worse, you might not find out the special case that doesn't work with your technique until you've done a lot of testing, or units have already been shipped to the field. If you aren't an expert, use the tried and true approaches. Even if you are an expert, you should still use them.

20.6. For more information

20.6.1. General topic search keywords
- Data queue
- Mutex
- Semaphore
- Reentrant code
- Thread safe

20.6.2. Recommended reading

Gannsle, J., "Reentrancy," *Embedded Systems Programming*, April 2001, pp. 183-184.
  A brief look at practicalities of creating reentrant code.

Beatty, S., "Where testing fails," *Embedded Systems Programming,* August 2003, pp. 36-41.
    Discusses concurrency issues from a testing and troubleshooting point of view.

VERIFICATION & VALIDATION

Chapter 21

Static Checking and Compiler Warnings

- Static checkers produce warnings when they see something suspicious looking in source code.
- Every program should be run through a good static checker to find and resolve potential bugs.
- Programs should compile clean, with no warnings, to ensure that no potential bugs slip through.

Contents:

21.1. Overview

Compilers produce two kinds of messages when they encounter something they don't like in source code: warnings and errors. Errors are caused by defects in the source code that make it impossible to compile, and must be fixed for the program to run at all. Warnings, on the other hand, are things the compiler finds questionable, but which don't prevent it from creating an executable program.

21.1.1. Importance of performing static checks

Unfortunately, a program that has produced warnings often doesn't run the way you expect. Ignoring compiler warnings puts you at increased risk of having bugs in your software that you could have avoided if you had dug deeper into the cause of the warning.

Not all compilers are good at generating warnings. Compilers for desktop systems are often quite thorough in their warnings. But, compilers for small microcontrollers are often not as robust, and might miss many potential warnings that correspond to software bugs in your source code. Fortunately, there are tools created to fill this gap, called static checkers (sometimes called *lint* tools, named after a famous of this sort), or more generically called static analysis tools. A good compiler or static checker should be run on all programs you write, and all sources of warnings should be eliminated to help reduce bugs.

21.1.2. Possible symptoms

✘ There are warnings generated when compiling your code. Any warnings at all. Even ones that seem OK because you think they are false alarms.

✘ Compiler warnings have been turned off because they are seen as being useless or annoying.

✘ A robust desktop compiler, a Lint-like tool, or other static checker has not been run on the program to look for additional warning messages.
AND
No special effort has been spent to see whether the embedded compiler being used is good at generating warning messages.

21.1.3. Risks of omitting static checks

Failing to find and fix as many warning situations as possible puts you at risk of missing defects you might otherwise have found:

➤ Missed bugs caused by "stupid" mistakes that a good compiler could have found.

➤ Missed bugs that stem from ambiguities in the language specification. These tend to cause programs to vary in operation from platform to platform and compiler to compiler. Code that works properly on one version of a particular compiler might stop working on a different version, different compiler, or different CPU.

➤ Missed bugs arising from risky use of language features, which might (or might not) indicate the presence of a bug.

➤ So many warnings which are thought to be OK that a new, important, warning is missed in the flood of compiler warning messages.

In other words, if you don't pay attention to and avoid warning messages, you are ignoring an important source of free help in avoiding bugs.

21.2. The role of compiler warnings

The difference between compiler errors and warnings is this: when a compiler generates an error, it is saying "This program has a defect that is severe enough that I don't know how to generate code." And so it doesn't – you don't get a compiled executable program. On the other hand, with a warning you do get running code, even though the compiler is trying to tell you something like one of the following:

- I can compile this code, but it most likely isn't going to do what you thought it was going to do.
- I can compile this code, but I'm just winging it in terms of what it is actually supposed to do; the language standard doesn't completely define what to do in this situation.
- I can compile this code, and the language precisely defines what it does, but probably this is a bug.
- The language used to work this way, but you're not supposed to do it this way any more (it's a deprecated language feature).

21.2.1. Example warnings

Here are some simple example snippets of C code that often generate warnings:

21.2.1.1. Uninitialized variable

```
int X, MyVar;
X = MyVar;    // MyVar doesn't have an initial value
```

The problem here is that the variable MyVar isn't assigned an initial value, so the value that will be put into X is undefined. Often this warning refers to an uninitialized variable or says something like: "variable used before it has been assigned a value." This warning is almost always an indication of a bug.

21.2.1.2. Suspicious language use

```
if (x = y) { ...do this... }
```

In C, this is a classic bug. The meaning of "x=y" in an assignment is that the variable *x* is assigned the value in *y*, and then that value is tested for true/false and used in the condition evaluation. It is equivalent to the code:

```
x = y;
if (x) { ...do this...}
```

In most cases, what was meant was really:

```
if (x == y) { ...do this...}
```

which is a comparison, not an assignment, and leaves the value of x unchanged after testing to see if it was equal to y.

There are occasionally situations in which the "(x=y)" clause would make sense and actually be useful. But, it isn't much more useful than putting the assignment in a separate statement. More importantly, having a firm rule against assignments within condition evaluations makes it easy to detect and remove bugs in which a "==" should have been used. Thus, it is common for C coding guidelines to prohibit assignments within conditionals.

21.2.1.3. Risky type conversions

Mixing different data types in an equation often leads to problems, and those problems can vary considerably depending on the language, the processor, and the compiler. For example, consider this line of code:

```
C = A / B;    // assume that A is 3 and B is 4
```

If A, B, and C are all floating point numbers, the result of this computation will be 0.75. If A, B, and C are all integers, the result will be 0. But, what if A is an integer, while B and C are floating point numbers? Will the result be computed as 0.75 and then rounded up to 1? Or will it be computed as an integer division, resulting in zero? It all depends on the details of the language. This is a notorious source of errors, and your compiler might generate a warning for this situation. If the language has rules for how to handle this situation that are unambiguous, it might not. (But it still might not be what you expected!)

A related warning is when the result of 32-bit arithmetic is put into an 8-bit variable (in the same division example, if A and B are 32-bit numbers and C is an 8-bit number, the compiler might generate a warning).

There are many possible warnings. Take a look at the warning options or flags for your compiler and (if you have a good compiler) you'll find the list to be extensive. Some compilers enable you to turn on and off individual classes of warnings to suit your preferences. We recommend turning on as many warnings as is practical for your situation in the compiler, and making sure your code compiles clean – without warnings.

```
Turn on all compiler warnings.
Fix code so it doesn't generate warnings.
```

21.3. Lint and static analysis tools

Some compilers aren't very good at finding warning situations. In fact, the earliest compilers really didn't generate many warnings at all, mostly to simplify the compiler and speed up its operation. So, back then, a separate program was created with just the job of finding warnings, and was called Lint. (A more modern descendent is called Splint.) The term lint has become something of a generic term for a program designed to find suspicious constructs within code. A more precise generic term is *static code analysis tool*.

Static code analysis tools work by implementing the front end of a compiler, which analyzes the program but doesn't worry about actually generating an executable program. Such tools can check a wide variety of properties, and flag potential problems as warnings. Typical properties that can be checked for include:

- **Uninitialized variables:** variables that are used before being set to a value.

- **Unreachable code (dead code):** code that can't be reached by any flow of execution, such as code in an if statement in which the condition tested always evaluates to false.

- **Suspicious language usage:** for example, using "=" instead of "==" inside a condition evaluation in C.

- **Type checking:** ensuring that the data types of parameters to a function call or components of an equation are compatible.

- **Use of variables and procedures before definition.** In many languages, variables take on a default type if used before they are defined, but this is now considered poor practice. It can lead to bugs if that default isn't the intended data type. A common warning of this type is caused by classical C programs defaulting to an int return value if a procedure is referred to before a function prototype is declared.

- **Non-standard language features** that will reduce portability.

```
If your compiler doesn't have robust warnings, use another
compiler or static checker to find potential problems.
```

More exotic static analysis approaches exist, but the above features (and others like them) are the basics that everyone should be trying to use. Some additional aids that you might find useful include tools to check memory allocation (ensuring that all memory allocated is eventually freed), arrays bound checkers (ensuring no accesses are made beyond the end of an array), and buffer overrun checkers. For more critical systems, model checking is used, which involves creating a mathematically rigorous formal model of the program and testing to see if it is possible to violate any important behavioral requirements.

A really good compiler will have many warnings built in based on static analysis techniques. But, since compilers vary, it's worth taking your code and either running it through a different compiler or – better yet – a static analysis tool such as Splint to see what your compiler might have missed.

21.4. Pitfalls – working around warnings

There are times when a piece of code generates a warning, but the code is doing what it should. For example, you might have a coding style requirement that all case statements have a default clause, even if that default clause can never be reached. Depending on the cleverness of your static checker and the actual code, the checker may figure out the default clause can't be reached and flag with an unreachable code warning. Now you have to decide what to do, and there is no hard-and-fast answer.

21.4.1. Warning pragmas

One way to handle this situation, if your compiler supports it, is to insert a pragma into the code saying, more or less, don't worry about the following type of warning here – we know what we're doing. (A *pragma* is a directive to the compiler that conveys programmer intent, without necessarily generating any code.) The availability and use of pragmas is compiler dependent, non-portable, and can be quite clunky. An additional limitation to this approach is that it tempts programmers to get sloppy and use such pragmas to get rid of warnings without really taking a careful look at what is going on. It is important in design reviews to make sure that all such pragmas are correct, and compellingly necessary.

21.4.2. Switch statement default cases

In some cases, you may wish to create a standard coding practice that sidesteps the warning (basically, fool the static checker). If the practice is standard and obvious, this might be OK, and is our favorite way to handle some situations if done with reasonable thought. For example, consider that you have a switch statement on an enumerated type, as might be the case if you are implementing a statechart with a switch statement. If the enumerated values are {on, off, starting, stopping}, your switch statement will have four cases – one per value. But, if you provide a default case in a switch statement (which is good practice to catch run-time errors), the static type checker might be clever enough to spot that the default case can never run. It *can* run if the value used for the switch is corrupted somehow, which is the point of having a default case. But a compiler assumes fault-free program execution, so it can't envision how a corrupted value might happen and thus generates a warning for code it thinks can never be executed.

You could simply turn off all warnings about unreachable default clauses in switch statements, if your compiler has an option that specific. But, turning off all unreachable code warnings is risky – there are many places where unreachable code is a pretty sure sign of an error. So instead, you might need to trick the analyzer into thinking the default clause is there to catch an enumeration value that isn't otherwise used. You can do this easily with most compilers by including an unused or undefined value in all your enumerations, such as: {on, off, starting, stopping, undefined}. Note that undefined isn't a language keyword – it could be anything so long as it makes sense to the programmer. This will result in a compiler having to assume that the default clause is there to handle the undefined value, which in a very real sense is true. Executing the default clause or having a value of undefined are both errors that should be caught at run-time.

21.5. For more information

21.5.1. General topic search keywords

• Static code analysis

21.5.2. Recommended reading

Schilling, W., & Mansoor, A., "Integrate static analysis into a software development process," *Embedded System Design*, November 2006, pp. 57-66.
This article surveys static analysis tool capabilities and lists several readily available tools.

Ganssle, J., "MISRA minimizes mishaps," *Embedded System Design*, November 2006, pp. 67-70.
This article summarizes the MISRA C coding standard, which gives rules for writing code that is less likely to be buggy. Some static analysis tools automatically check MISRA C rules.

Chapter 22
Peer Reviews

- Peer reviews are the most cost-effective method available for reducing software defects and improving software quality.
- While informal peer reviews are better than no reviews, reasonably formal reviews are well worth the effort.
- Every written document that is part of the system design package should be reviewed, including not only implementation, but also requirements, architecture, designs, test plans, and so on.
- It is important to create a supportive, non-judgmental social environment for the review process.

Contents:

Problems found late in the development cycle cost more to fix than problems found early. The best way to find problems early is with peer reviews.
Every item in the design package should be peer reviewed. Peer reviews have a defined set of steps and participants. Some important rules for peer reviews are: inspect the item, not the author; don't get defensive; don't fix problems in the meeting; limit meeting scope to 2 hours; keep a reasonable pace; and avoid debates.

22.1. Overview

Peer reviews involve having developers other than the author perform a methodical reading to look for bugs, ambiguities, and other issues. While informal reviews can have some value, the most valuable reviews are those in which multiple participants pre-read, physically meet, and discuss the item being reviewed during the meeting.

22.1.1. Importance of doing peer reviews

Because reviews are very effective at finding defects in written documents, skipping reviews lets defects slip through to later phases of the design process. The earlier a defect is found, the less it costs to fix. Conversely, letting defects slip through to later development phases increases the effort, cost, and disruption involved in fixing problems.

It is well worth the time and effort involved to have every single written artifact in a design process peer reviewed. This includes not only code implementations, but also requirements, architectural descriptions, designs, and test cases. Performing good peer reviews requires a bit of training and discipline, but easily repays the effort involved.

22.1.2. Possible symptoms

✘ Peer reviews aren't being held.

✘ No documentation of peer review outcomes exists, suggesting they are informal or irregular.

✘ Significant numbers of bugs are discovered during system integration. Many of these bugs are relatively simple, and could have been caught earlier with an independent review.

✘ Bugs found in the system are largely discovered in the testing phase. Most other bugs are discovered after the first product shipment date.

22.1.3. Risks of not doing peer reviews

The risk of not doing peer reviews is one of missed opportunities to detect defects. The possible consequences of omitting peer reviews include:

➤ Discovery of defects late in the development cycle, when correcting them requires significant rework, time, and expense.

➤ Defects escaping into released products, because testing isn't thorough enough to find defects that might have been caught easily in a peer review.

22.2. Peer review effectiveness

The traditional approach to discovering defects – testing – has the disadvantage of not being possible until code has been written. This means that problems in-

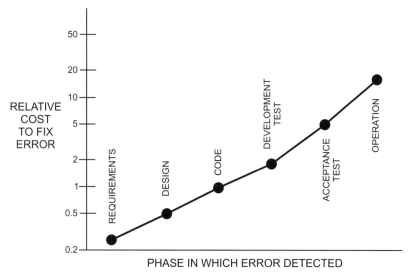

Figure 22.1. Relative cost to fix errors based on phase in which detected. (Source: Boehm 1976)

troduced early in the design process, such as incorrect requirements, can't be found until relatively late in the development cycle.

Peer reviews, on the other hand, are based on a person looking at a written document and trying to find problems with it. The nice part about peer reviews is that they can occur at any place in the development cycle, on any written document.

The most compelling motivation for peer reviews is that they are effective at catching defects early, when it is still cheap to fix them.

Figure 22.1 shows a typical graph of the cost to fix a requirements defect compared to how late in the development cycle the defect is found. The idea is that the further along in the development a process a problem is found, the more expensive it is to go back and fix it. Fixing an incorrect requirement during a requirement peer review involves a little time and changing a document. But, fixing that same requirement defect in thousands of systems that have already been shipped to customers is a much more significant expense!

> **Problems found late in the development cycle
> cost more to fix than problems found early.**

Testing can't find a defect until near the end of the development cycle, when it is expensive to fix. That's because you can't really test something until it is built, and by the time it is built most of the development costs have already been incurred. The beauty of peer reviews is that they can be conducted after each life cycle phase, starting well before the system is ready for testing. Good peer re-

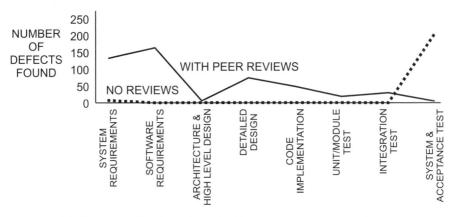

Figure 22.2. Number of defects found with and without peer reviews from two example projects.

views help catch defects in the same stage they were created in, dramatically reducing the time and effort required to fix them.

The effectiveness of peer reviews is widely acknowledged. But, most experience is with desktop and enterprise computing applications. Figure 22.2 shows some data from a company that produces safety critical embedded systems of moderate complexity.

The two lines represent the same software development team on two roughly comparable projects five years apart. In the first project, no formal reviews were done. In the second project, the team had instituted peer reviews on all written documents (and, in addition, had made significant improvements in all areas of their software process). The difference is striking. For the no-review project a few defects were found during informal system requirements reviews, but essentially all defects were found during system test, when they are expensive to detect and correct. In the second project, most defects were found much earlier – before a lot of effort had been spent testing software based in incorrect requirements, design, or implementation.

> Peer reviews help find problems early in the development cycle.

22.3. Conducting peer reviews

22.3.1. What can be reviewed?

There is value in reviewing just about anything that can be written down on paper as a part of the design package. This includes the basic documents that should be created as part of any design package (see *Chapter 3. How Much Paper Is Enough?*), such as :

  • Customer requirements

- Engineering requirements
- Architecture
- Design
- Implementation
- Test plan
- Test results
- Bug list
- User guide
- Marketing materials
- Schedule and staffing plan
- Software development plan

Other items can also benefit from being reviewed. In general, if it is worth writing down and keeping, it is worth reviewing.

> **Every item in the design package should be peer reviewed.**

22.3.2. How do you perform peer reviews?

Effective peer reviews vary in how they are organized, but all have some common traits. The grand-daddy of peer review techniques is the Fagan-style review, called an *inspection* (Fagan, 1986). The general framework it follows is still the best starting point for creating your own review process. A review progresses through a variety of stages, including:

- **Planning.** Make materials available, arrange the right people and meeting place.

- **Overview.** Assign roles and inform participants of expectations.

- **Preparation.** Study the material to be reviewed before the actual review meeting.

- **Inspection.** Find the defects in a meeting. A reader goes through the item to be inspected a line or section at a time, summarizing what is there. Others on the inspection team look for problems as items are discussed.

- **Rework.** Fix the defects (done by the author after the inspection meeting has concluded, not during the meeting).

- **Follow-up.** Re-inspect as appropriate to ensure defects have been fixed and there are no unintended side effects.

One fairly common addition to this method is to have each reviewer look at the item to be inspected before the meeting and create an issue log of problems found. This is especially relevant for external reviews (3rd parties not part of the development team doing a review) who have only a limited time on site for a review meeting. This lets the reviewers during the actual inspection meeting skip the easy-to-find issues that have already been spotted and concentrate on deeper issues.

Inspections work best if the participants assume particular roles. Typical roles are:

- **Moderator.** In charge of organizing and running the inspection. Some experience and interpersonal skills training is required for moderators to be successful.

- **Recorder.** Records defects found. Sometimes the moderator performs this role.

- **Reader.** Someone who paraphrases the item being inspected to focus attention for the discussion.

- **Inspector(s).** Participants who look for problems. Everyone in the review, except the author, can be an inspector.

- **Author.** The creator of the item to be inspected. The author is there to answer questions, and should not perform other functions.

Other specialized roles are possible. In particular, the concept of perspective-based reviews involves different readers emphasizing particular aspects of the system. For example, Fagan defined the role of a tester, who is an inspector assigned to look for testability issues. Other roles are possible too, such as someone who looks for maintainability or user interaction issues.

There are some basic principles that must be followed to have successful inspections. Some general rules are:

- **Inspectors: Inspect the item, not the author.** Criticism is difficult for everyone to take. The focus needs to be on the item being inspected, and not upon the author's technical skill.

- **Authors: Don't get defensive.** You're there to answer questions, not defend the product.

- **Don't fix problems, just find them.** Engineers and designers love to figure out how to fix problems. Fixing problems is the author's job. The reviewers' job is just identifying them. Avoiding discussions of fixes will keep the review process moving smoothly, and lessen the defensiveness of the author.

- **Limit meeting scope.** Meetings should last 1-2 hours. After that amount of time everyone will get burned out.

- **Keep a reasonable pace.** Meetings should cover 100-200 lines of code per hour (or lines of text for dense items such as requirements documents). Going too fast means the inspectors will miss things.

- **Avoid debates.** Issues such as conformance to style guidelines can be noted briefly, but issues that are a matter of personal preference should not be debated during the inspection.

Inspect the item, not the author;
don't get defensive;
don't fix problems in the meeting;
limit meeting scope to 2 hours;
keep a reasonable pace;
avoid debates.

It is helpful to have an idea of the aspects of an item that should be considered when performing a review. Often it is useful to have brief checklists defined for each type of item being reviewed so nothing is forgotten. Typical general areas considered are: completeness, correctness, adherence to style requirements, adherence to higher level system design documents, traceability to other design documents, and exceptions (for example, null pointer handling or numeric overflows).

22.3.3. Review productivity

Reviews might seem like a huge effort, and in many ways they are. But, they are so effective they are worth it so long as the number of people on the inspection team stays moderate (4 to 6 people as a guideline).

As an example, consider five people reviewing 150 lines of code per hour. This is an aggregate review rate of 30 lines of code per person-hour. Compared to typical programmer productivity over the life of a project of 1 to 2 lines of code per person-hour, this is a small fraction of the total cost of the code. Other things get reviewed as well, but it should still be practical to keep review costs to about 10% of total costs, in exchange for finding perhaps half of all defects in reviews when they are relatively less expensive to fix. It doesn't take many problems found by reviewers to get a substantial payback on the investment in reviews.

Reports on the effectiveness of reviews vary, but are overall quite positive. For example Boehm (2001) reports that peer reviews catch 60% of defects. That is a significant number of defects found before testing. Also important is the general experience that reviews find some defects that were likely to be missed by testing. So, the combination of reviews and testing provides more thorough coverage of potential problems than testing alone. Boehm (2001) also says that perspective-based reviews are 35% more effective than reviews without individual emphasis roles defined for the inspectors.

Not every review has to be a formal inspection. Informal reviews, hallway discussions, e-mail based checks, online review collaboration tools, pair programming, and other methods of having a second person look things over are all worth doing, even if inspections are being performed. But, only formalized inspections have the full extent of benefits described. Give them a try and see if they find problems earlier in your projects.

22.4. Pitfalls

The biggest pitfalls in reviews come from trying to take shortcuts. Reviews can seem like a lot of effort because they are a group activity, but no other approach really gets the benefits of a group inspection. Pitfalls include:

- **Trying to review too much or too quickly.** Going faster than 100-200 lines per hour of code or equivalent for other documents results in a superficial inspection and missed defects. Reviewing for more than an hour or two at a time results in burnout. It may be appropriate to hold an all-day review if an external consultant is only on-site for one day. But, such a review is really just an overall check of the project, and cannot replace continual peer reviews.

- **Trying to use less formal approaches.** Having someone take a look at a piece of code via e-mail provides value, but is not a replacement for formal peer reviews. Informal approaches have value, but just aren't as effective. They can supplement formal peer reviews, but they can't replace them.

- **Using on-line code review tools.** These tools are good in that they make it easier for teams to do code reviews who would otherwise not do reviews at all. However, they are still an informal approach that probably misses out on the full benefits possible with formal in-person reviews. Using them is better than having no reviews, and they definitely provide value. But using them is not the same as actually having face to face peer reviews.

- **Violating the rules for good reviews.** Nothing will kill the review process at an organization faster than having authors feel personally attacked. (Or, worse, find their paycheck affected by peer review results.)

22.5. For more information

22.5.1. General topic search keywords
- Fagan inspection
- Peer review

22.5.2. Recommended reading

Boehm, B. & Basili, V., "Software defect reduction top 10 list," *IEEE Computer*, January 2001, pp. 135-137.
    Summarizes ten key points about software defect reduction, including several relevant to peer reviews.

Wiegers, K., *Peer Reviews in Software: a practical guide*, Addison-Wesley, Boston, 2001.
A practical book on how to conduct reviews. While written for general software development situations, it is well suited to embedded systems.

22.5.3. References

Fagan, M., "Advances in software inspections," *IEEE Trans. Software Engineering,* v. SE-12, n. 7, July 1986, pp. 744-751.
Describes Fagan-style reviews.

Boehm, B., "Software Engineering," *IEEE Trans. Computers*, C-25, no. 12, December 1976, pp. 1226-1241
Solidifies the meaning of the term software engineering, and gives a state-of-the-practice overview that is still worth reading today.

Chapter 23
Testing and Test Plans

- Testing involves execution of software to see if it performs correctly.
- Styles of testing include exploratory, black box, white box, and smoke testing.
- Different types of typical test situations include unit test, subsystem test, integration test, acceptance test, beta test, regression test, and self test.
- Testing should attain a defined level of coverage (test thoroughness) for the aspects of the system you care about the most.
- While the goal of testing is to find bugs, there can be two quite different motivations for finding them: (1) fixing the software bug itself, or (2) detecting and fixing process problems that result in the bug.

Contents:

23.1. Overview

A key aspect of ensuring embedded software is of reasonably good quality is thorough testing. The best way ensure you get thorough testing is by starting with a written test plan. A test plan includes a list of tests to be performed, expected results of those tests (in other words, what result means the test has passed?), and traceability information so that it is clear what requirement or other part of the design package is verified or validated by running the test.

23.1.1. Importance of testing and test plans

In embedded systems, lack of a written test plan means that testing won't be thorough enough to catch important problems before products are shipped. A key reason for this is that customers have a higher standard of quality for embedded systems than for desktop software.

We know that desktop software is often horribly complex and we are willing to tolerate occasional bugs and system crashes to get all the latest and greatest features. However, we are much less tolerant of a car that needs to be rebooted while on a highway, or a water heater that gives us a cold shower in the morning because we haven't patched its software. While in time people's forgiveness of buggy desktop software may fully transfer forgiveness of bugs to embedded systems, at least for now the expectations for embedded software quality are much higher than expectations for desktop software. Software good enough to *mostly* work isn't the usual goal for embedded systems; the goal is embedded systems that *really* work all the time, in a dependable manner.

Just as skipping the design documents when creating software is a bad idea, so is skipping the written test plan when creating tests.

23.1.2. Possible symptoms

✘ There is no written test plan.

✘ The test plan isn't traceable to the system requirements. This means, for example, that you haven't documented in writing which requirements are covered by each test in the test plan.

✘ The time to execute tests isn't given a reasonable portion of the development cycle, or is cut short due to schedule overruns.

✘ Testers aren't involved in the product design until after implementation is completed. This makes it likely that some code will be difficult or impossible to test well.

23.1.3. Risks of inadequate test efforts

➤ Discovery of defects late in the development cycle due to inadequate early testing. Late discovery increases rework time and expense.

➤ Defects escaping into released products because testing isn't thorough enough.

➤ Premature product release or inadequate testing, because there is no written test plan to help testers defend the position that more time is needed to get adequate test coverage.

➤ Wasted effort in testing because of duplication in testing or uncertainty over which tests have been run.

23.2. Overview of testing

Testing involves the actual execution of a piece of software to see whether its behavior conforms to requirements, designed behavior, and other expectations. It is distinct from other forms of verification and validation in that it is actually based on what the code does, as opposed to what reviewers think the code might do. For this reason, testing is often given heavy emphasis in embedded system development.

Beyond testing, *validation* is a generic term for any activity that ensures the result of a design process was what was desired. Typically validation helps with ensuring forward traceability (knowing what you produced is what you meant to produce). In contrast, *verification* is ensuring that design steps are being followed properly, and roughly corresponds to the notion of backward traceability (knowing you are adhering to the outputs of the previous design step). The blanket term *V&V* (Verification and Validation) is often used to describe any activity that falls in the general arena of making sure the design process is on track.

Testing is important. But many times it would be even better to spread efforts among testing, reviews, and other types of assurance activities to achieve a balanced mix of approaches. In other words, it is the total effectiveness of V&V that matters, not just testing.

23.2.1. When can we test?

Testing can be used at any of the later phases of the development cycle. Any time code has been written, it can be tested. Typical points at the development process where testing takes place are:

- **Unit testing:** testing an individual module in isolation. These tests are often performed by the developers who wrote the module.

- **Subsystem testing:** testing a set of related modules to see if they interact properly, with simulated or scripted inputs from other, missing, subsystems used to exercise the subsystem being tested. These tests can be run by developers, independent testers, or both.

- **System integration test:** a test of the entire system to ensure that various subsystems interact properly. Often these tests have an engineering rather than product user focus, and concentrate on specific software requirements. This test is often performed by an in-house but separate test group to ensure objectivity in testing.

- **Acceptance test:** a test of the entire system that concentrates on whether the overall system requirements are met, especially non-functional system requirements such as performance and reliability. These tests have a user focus, and must be run by someone other than the developers. A representative customer might participate in, observe, or even perform this testing.

- **Beta test:** a controlled release of finished products to carefully selected customers, who exercise the system under realistic operating conditions. Beta testers report bugs that have escaped past the acceptance test into a supposedly finished product. The primary rationale for beta testing is that customers might have novel ways of using the system that developers and in-house testers didn't consider.

- **Regression test:** a set of tests, usually automated, that are run on a system or subsystem after a bug fix or revision has been made. The goal of a regression test is to catch situations in which fixing one bug creates or reactivates another bug.

- **Self test:** a set of tests to check whether the embedded system is operating properly. This type of test is significantly different than the other tests in that it is looking for hardware defects in deployed systems rather than software design defects. It is run periodically or upon power-up.

> Different types of testing include:
> unit, subsystem, system integration, acceptance,
> beta, regression, and self tests.

Each phase of testing concentrates on a different scope of potential defect, and may use one or more of the types of testing discussed in the next section (smoke, exploratory, white box, or black box testing). If all these phases of testing are used, most bugs will be caught before development has been completed, and can be corrected with less disruption than finding and fixing bugs later.

23.2.2. What styles of testing can be used?

There are four typical styles of testing, each with a different role to play.

- **Smoke testing.** This is a quick and dirty exercise of the system to see if it is obviously broken, or seems to be operating well enough that it is worth investing time in more rigorous testing. A typical smoke test might pass if code can be compiled and loaded; the system can be powered on; and a few non-trivial system functions can be exercised. If all this works, the system is worth testing in more detail. If something obviously wrong happens, such as a system crash during power up, then there isn't much point in doing detailed testing – something major is clearly wrong. This term stems from hardware testing in which an initial test is to turn power on, and look for smoke pouring out of hardware components that are faulty or aren't connected properly. If no smoke pours out that's good news, but hardly an indication that the hardware is working perfectly. Software smoke testing might not be as dramatic, but it similarly is a useful quick check.

- **Exploratory testing.** This is testing in which a skilled tester explores the function of the system. The emphasis is on using experience, system operating context, and judgment in finding the most important bugs as quickly as possible. A really good tester can locate and isolate many bugs quickly, and is likely to find bugs the developers never thought to look for. Exploratory testing can be very efficient, but is subjective, with abilities varying considerably among testers. As such, it is difficult to know what coverage has been achieved by a particular testing session. Doing exploratory testing is worthwhile in moderation. Find someone who has a knack for breaking things, and see what they turn up. (You will get better results if the exploratory tester is experienced in this type of testing.) But for embedded systems this shouldn't be the only style of testing used. A good practical use for exploratory testing is checking to see if a bug fix seems to be behaving properly before invoking an expensive, comprehensive test on the entire system.

- **White box testing.** This uses the architecture, design, and structure of the system to guide testing. For example, for a conditional branch, white box testing makes sure there is a test case for each of the two paths through the branch (branch taken; branch not taken). For a statechart, white box testing makes sure that every state in the statechart is visited, and every arc between states is traversed by at least one test. White box approaches are a good way to make sure all the code has been tested with at least one test case.

- **Black box testing.** This testing uses behaviors as a guide to creating tests. For example, every written requirement might be used as the basis for creating one or more tests to ensure that the requirement has been fulfilled. Black box testing is a good way to make sure you haven't missed any requirements. However, black box testing isn't necessarily good at uncovering special cases caused by implementation details (white box testing is usually better at that).

Different styles of testing include:
smoke, exploratory, white box, and black box testing.

All four forms of testing are important for every system. White box and black box testing form complementary sets of tests to make sure you both exercise all the code that has been written, and check to see that the code actually does everything it is supposed to do. Exploratory testing is a valuable addition to these techniques which can potentially find problems that otherwise would be missed. Smoke testing is useful to decide if a major mistake has been made in a software revision, but doesn't ordinarily take the place of the other styles of testing.

23.2.3. How much testing is enough?

The point of testing is to attempt to find bugs (defects). But, saying you want to test until you've found all the bugs is unrealistic. It is impossible to know whether testing has found all the bugs or not in any real-world piece of software, because there are just too many possible bugs in even relatively simple code. Let's say you find a few bugs, fix them, and then don't find any more bugs after a bit more testing. Does that mean there are no bugs left? Probably not. It just means you just haven't been clever enough at testing to find them.

Just because it is impossible to be perfect at testing doesn't mean we don't need some sort of answer as to how much testing is enough. At some point you need some way to know how effective your testing is, even if you don't get a precise answer.

A key idea in testing is understanding your test *coverage*, which is the thoroughness with which you have tested. Ideally, you'd like coverage to tell you the percentage of all possible bugs that you have tested for. But, this is impossible, because for practical purposes there are an infinite number of possible bugs, and it is difficult to know how many bugs any particular test will or won't find. So instead, coverage is defined in terms of different aspects that are more readily measurable. Some examples of coverage are given below.

- White box testing coverage:
  - Fraction of source code statements executed at least once
  - Fraction of statechart states visited and statechart arcs traversed at least once
  - Fraction of I/O ports or devices exercised
  - Fraction of interrupt service routines tested
  - Fraction of memory locations checked for hardware defects
  - Fraction of modules covered by unit testing
- Black box testing coverage:
  - Fraction of system requirements tested by acceptance test
  - Fraction of interfaces tested for robustness (measuring response to erroneous inputs – human inputs, network messages, and sensors)
  - Fraction of modules tested according to behavioral specifications
- Exploratory testing coverage:

○ Fraction of typical problems in systems checked for according to checklist or developer experience

○ Fraction of interfaces (user interfaces, I/O interfaces, network connections) checked for problems at some tester-determined level of thoroughness.

There are a great many possible coverage metrics for both black box and white box testing – the above are only a few suggestions. It's difficult or impossible to get perfect coverage in all dimensions, and even thinking up all possible dimensions is no small thing. But, getting very high coverage (perhaps 95% or higher) along a few basic dimensions should be a minimum goal for any test plan.

> A test plan should specify both coverage measures and
> percent coverage for each relevant measure.

23.3. Why do we test?

There are two completely different reasons to do testing: to eliminate bugs, and to be reassured you don't have any bugs. How you test and how long you test critically hinges upon which reason is more important to you. In both cases testing is an attempt to find bugs. But your motivation for finding them results in very different outcomes for each bug found, depending on the situation.

> Testing attempts to find bugs. But, what you do about the
> bugs found depends on your situation.

23.3.1. Testing to fix bugs (debug-oriented testing)

The most common motivation for testing is to find and fix bugs. Some people even use the terms testing and debugging more or less interchangeably for this reason. But, it is better to be precise with these terms. *Testing* is the act of determining if a bug is present, and *debugging* is the process of localizing and correcting a bug.

When you test to fix bugs, you run a set of tests, note the bugs found, fix the bugs, and test some more. Hopefully there is a reasonable set of black box and white box tests in place, often in the form of a regression test suite. Exploratory testing can be used to exercise the system beyond the white box and black box tests to look for more defects.

The response to finding a defect is simply to fix the defect, get reasonable assurance that the fix worked (and didn't break something else), then test some more. You keep testing until you run out of time (the usual case). Sometimes, you have the luxury of testing until you've attained a desired level of test coverage, or you haven't found an additional bug in so long it isn't worth performing further testing.

If you have software that is particularly buggy, it might be that using only exploratory testing is the most efficient way to reduce the number of bugs, especially if you have too little time to do a thorough testing job. For example, if the test group isn't able to start testing until two days before product shipment, then exploratory testing may be the only realistic option. That's not a good situation, but if you are stuck with it and have skillful testers, then exploratory testing may be your best bet.

In the happier case that you actually have enough time to test your system thoroughly, you should continue testing and debugging until you meet an exit criterion for the test phase. Some common exit criteria are:

- **You run out of time allocated to testing.** Using this as the sole criterion is not the best idea!

- **You have achieved your coverage goals.** As a simple example, you might have a goal of 100% black box testing of requirements in addition to 95% white box testing of code branches.

- **You can't find any more bugs,** or it isn't cost-effective to keep looking for them because you are finding so few bugs. This doesn't mean there aren't any bugs left, but rather that the testing techniques you are using aren't going to find enough bugs fast enough for it to be worth the effort. As a simple example, you might terminate testing when no high priority bugs have been found in the past two weeks of testing and no medium priority bugs have been found in the past one week of testing.

- **You meet your acceptance test criteria for software quality.** For example, you might have an acceptance test of the system running for two weeks without a crash under heavy load.

Combinations of the above and other criteria are possible and in many cases desirable.

> If you are trying to make your application less buggy,
> then test and debug until
> it isn't cost effective to look for the remaining bugs.

To many people, this entire section is obviously what testing is always about – finding bugs and fixing them. But, in fact, there is a completely different way to look at testing that is relevant for embedded systems.

23.3.2. Testing to verify development process quality

Let's say you have spent a lot of time creating truly excellent software. You've been careful to do a thorough design, and have done unit, subsystem, and some system integration tests. You've done peer reviews. You've done everything you can reasonably do to get it right. And, you have a customer who expects their system to really work, not just mostly work. For such a project, finding bugs in testing so you can fix them isn't good enough. You can only find a fraction of the bugs via testing, and it's nowhere near 100%. It's extremely unlikely you'll find all residual bugs just by testing. If you have a lot of bugs going into testing, you'll still have plenty of bugs left after testing.

> **If you have high quality (relatively bug-free) software,**
> **removing bugs is the wrong reason to do testing.**

Instead, you should look at testing in the following manner. Consider the classical scientific method (in brief, a repeated cycle of: observation, hypothesis, experiment, conclusion). In this context, testing maps onto the scientific method as follows:

(1) Observation: "We've used a really good software process that should result in high quality code."

(2) Hypothesis: "Our process is so good, it will result in bug-free code." (We know better – our code isn't perfectly bug-free. But we think we are so close that this goal that it is true for practical purposes.)

(3) Experiment: Run tests to look for bugs.

(4) Conclusions:

(a) If bug is found – the hypothesis is falsified. In other words, our process must have a problem, because a bug was there. If we want higher quality software, we need to fix the process because *the quality of the process is what our hypothesis was based on.*

(b) If bug is **not** found – the hypothesis is not falsified. In other words, as far as we can tell it's true – our process is so good the code is bug-free for practical purposes. We haven't proven the hypothesis true, mind you, but we tried our best and didn't prove it false either. Might as well ship the software.

In other words, if you've really worked hard on making your software high quality, you expect that your software is as close to defect-free as you can make it. Therefore, any bug found should be a bit of a surprise, which disproves your hypothesis of a high quality software process.

> **For high quality software and processes,**
> **finding a bug means your *process* is broken and needs to be fixed.**

Thus, if you find a bug in really high quality software, you should respond much more vigorously than just saying "oh, here's another bug; let's fix it." Instead, you should treat every bug found as a symptom of some problem in your development process, and correct not just the bug, but also the weaknesses in your process that let it slip through into testing.

Let's use an example to illustrate this point. Suppose that during acceptance testing, you uncover a defect that ultimately turns out to be caused by a null pointer value being passed as an input parameter when a valid pointer should have been used instead. Let's say a little debugging indicates this null pointer was created as an error return code from a function, and that error code was never checked for, so the null pointer propagated and later caused a bug. If your goal was merely debugging, you'd fix the problem and move on. If your code is of medium or low quality, this can be a rational approach, since you can argue that other null pointer problems might be there, but they aren't that big a deal if you don't see failures caused by them during testing. You hope that your experience during testing will be representative of most of your users' experiences. In other words, you have bigger fish to fry than checking every pointer in your entire program, especially since many (not all, but many or even most) similar bugs might turn out to be benign in most situations.

But, if you are striving for truly excellent code, there is a much deeper problem here. You thought you were getting things right. If something as obvious as an unchecked null pointer got past your unit tests, subsystem tests, peer reviews, static checkers, and so on, what else might have gotten through? It wouldn't be much of a surprise if there are other unchecked null pointers somewhere. Can you even be sure that the checks were done properly if they missed something like this? In other words, a bug found during testing of high quality code is much more than just a bug – it is an indication that something is broken in your process!

Here is the type of response you might make in this null pointer bug example to fix the problem in the larger sense. You'd do some or more of the following (and possibly other things as well):

- Fix the defect (of course).

- Locate all other instances in which the function that returned the null value is used, and make sure that those other places don't have a similar bug.

- Possibly, look at all functions that can return an error code value, and see if errors are checked for there.

- Possibly, look at all pointer uses and check to see if null pointers could cause a problem (this is going to be a lot of work).

- Add tests to the test plan to check for proper null pointer handling.

This is a start, although it just looks for similar problems in the code. If you made a mistake once that you know of, likely you've made it elsewhere too.

But, these steps don't answer the question of *why* you made the mistake. Sure, it could have just been a "stupid" mistake originally. But, why did it get past all the checks and balances that are in place? Conceivably, everyone involved just kept happening to make their one stupid mistake of the day on that same bug, and did everything perfectly except for that one bug. (Sure, it could happen. But it doesn't seem likely that things will happen this way every time, or even most of the time. Something else is going on.)

Most likely the checks and balances currently in place just weren't designed to help prevent this type of problem. So, let's see what we can look at to help prevent the problem from happening again. First, look at the process itself:

- Update or add a rule to coding guidelines requiring that error codes be checked for as the output of routines.
- Update or add a rule to coding guidelines requiring that null pointers be checked for when a subroutine accepts or uses parameters.
- Ensure that design review checklists look at handling of error return codes and look for appropriate null pointer checks.
- Ensure that unit test guidelines suggest testing for null pointer parameter value handling.
- Ensure that error logging software detects and records null pointer generated exceptions in the run-time error log, so other problems of this sort that are missed by reviews can be found via testing, even if they didn't cause an overt system crash.

Next, look at whether the development process was actually followed for this module. If it wasn't, then perhaps it wasn't followed for other modules, and other bugs remain undiscovered that slipped through those other missed checks:

- Check to see whether the module(s) causing this bug were created according to relevant development processes, including a look at their architecture, design, implementation, and test written materials. (Are the materials there? Are they up to date? Should they have made the bug easier to find than they did?)
- Check to see whether appropriate peer reviews were conducted on the modules responsible for the defects.
- If problems in following the process are found, perhaps audit to see if the process wasn't followed in other modules.

Wow, that's quite a commotion to cause every time a bug is found! But, if you have extremely high quality software, it is the way to get code quality even higher.

There is one very important thing you should **not** do under any circumstance. Don't punish the developer who wrote the code with the bug! (Similarly, don't punish people involved in reviews and testing.) If you are creating really good code with a really good process, slip-ups will still happen. Punishing people for making mistakes when they aren't being intentionally negligent will kill morale, and possibly the effectiveness of your entire software process. It only takes one management mistake to undermine trust for a very long time.

> If you find a bug, fix your process.
> But don't punish the developers!

What you should really do depends on your situation. If you are finding 100 bugs a day, it's pretty clear you have code that has plenty of bugs, and you are testing just to remove bugs. Identifying the types of bugs that keep coming up over and over and trying to improve your process to deal with those makes a lot of sense. But creating a huge process correction exercise dozens of times a day just isn't realistic.

On the other hand, if your code has very few bugs, then you'll get some benefit by tracking down what is really going on in the process and fixing that as well as the bugs.

23.3.3. The spectrum of testing goals

In real projects, there is a continuum of positions that are reasonable to take between pure bug-removal testing and pure development process quality assurance testing. They include:

- Testing as debugging.
  - Testing approach: mostly exploratory testing.
  - Bug response: figure out a bug fix or workaround to cure the symptoms, and move on.
- Testing as bug reduction.
  - Testing approach: black box, white box, and exploratory testing.
  - Bug response: track bug to technical root cause, then fix the root cause.
- Testing as code quality improvement.
  - Testing approach: high coverage black box, moderate coverage white box, and some exploratory testing.
  - Bug response: fix bug, look for and fix similar bugs elsewhere, update regression test suite to make sure bug doesn't reappear later.
- Testing as process quality improvement.
  - Testing approach: 100% black box coverage to requirements, as high as possible white box coverage of design structures and code structures, some exploratory testing.
  - Bug response: fix bug, look for and fix similar bugs elsewhere, look for and fix process problems contributing to the bug, look for and fix areas in which the process wasn't followed.

In general, the buggier your code, the closer to the beginning of the list you will tend to operate. The cleaner your code, the closer to the end of the list you can operate if you wish.

> **Measure testing effectiveness by whether you found the number of bugs you expected to find.**

Based on this list, it should be clear that the success of testing can't necessarily be measured by how many bugs are found. How many you find depends not only on the thoroughness of the testing, but also on how many bugs are there in the first place. Rather, the success of testing has to be judged based on the relative importance of finding defects to be fixed, finding process problems to be fixed, finding lapses in adhering to the process, and the degree of testing coverage achieved for both black box and white box testing.

23.4. Test plans

Now that we have a broad view of testing, we can talk about what goes into a test plan. A good test plan answers at least the following questions: what will you test? How will you test it? How thoroughly will you test (or, alternately, how will you know you have done enough testing)?

We think that a written test plan is the best approach. First and foremost, a written plan ensures that testers know what to do and have a way to remind themselves of scope and purpose to keep them on track during testing. Additionally, a test plan helps others understand how thoroughly the system will be tested. A particularly important point of a test plan is that it is a way to determine what level of testing is necessary up front – before the heat is on and the product ship date is upon the team. (That doesn't mean things won't change when the shipping date looms close. But it does provide an anchor to help people understand what they are sacrificing by skipping parts of the test plan.)

23.4.1. What to test

You'd always like to run more tests than you have time and budget for. That's just a fact of life you have to deal with. Test planning is all about minimizing risk and maximizing efficiency. The risk you are attempting to minimize is that a serious bug or development process defect makes it past testing and results in an unacceptably defective product. The efficiency you are trying to maximize depends on your testing goal, but in general the idea is to get the best coverage for the lowest cost.

A test plan should set forth which types of tests should be performed during the development process. For example, you might want all modules to undergo some level of unit testing, and the system to undergo acceptance testing. A general list of what to test should include:

- What levels of tests are desired (unit test to system-level tests)

- What types of testing or combinations of testing are desired (white box, black box, exploratory) for each level of testing

- What the basis for testing coverage is (for example, coverage for white box unit tests might be fraction of lines of code in the module that are executed by one or more tests)

Keep in mind that the earlier testing is done, the easier it will be to isolate and correct any defects found.

Testing may be different for bug fixes and minor updates compared to major changes in functionality. It might not be cost effective to perform a complete system acceptance test after a very minor bug fix. (There is always the risk that even a minor bug fix will break something unexpected elsewhere in the program. So skipping complete testing is a decision that should be made with care.)

23.4.2. How to test

Actually doing the testing can be a significant undertaking. For example, in unit tests you often have to create scaffolding code to provide inputs to a module that you want to test, and building this scaffolding can be a significant development task in its own right. So can an extensive regression test suite, which might have to include automation for testing. Additionally, testing a system that involves sensors and actuators means having real I/O hardware that operates in a representative environment, or creating emulations of that I/O hardware and the environment for testing.

Sometimes the difficulties in creating scaffolding and simulated I/O are so severe that testing is only done on the completed code. But, more often, it is cost effective to do some limited testing before the system is integrated into a working first version. For example, if a particular module has a calculation error, catching that problem in unit test leaves no question as to which module is the problem (since only one module is being tested during its unit test). But, that same calculation error might take days to track down if it is only seen in an integrated system which depends upon many modules to function properly.

Thus, your testing strategy involves a tradeoff between early testing to reap the benefits of early detection *vs.* delaying testing to minimize the effort required to develop test scaffolding. There is no single right answer, but good answers involve some mix of testing across the spectrum.

Typical test techniques that have proven helpful in testing include:

- Isolate I/O operations to separate modules, so that the rest of the modules can be tested without requiring I/O hardware. For example, call a procedure to read a data point rather than reading hardware directly. That way during unit testing a scaffolding subroutine that replaces the hardware read procedures can be used to provide test data.

- Use a good simulator to test software to the degree practical (some microcontroller development systems come with an ability to simulate the CPU and provide simulated I/O values)

- Instrument an existing, similar system to capture data that can be used as input to test a new system.

- Use standard test support tools to help provide test infrastructure. (There are many, many test support tools available for free on the Internet.)

For each test, a good test plan will specify the following:

- What is to be tested? (A module? A subsystem? The ability to read or write an I/O port? A safety response?)

- Traceability to other parts of the design to understand the test and results. (Which system requirement are we testing? Or, which statechart are we verifying is correct?)

- Test input, sequence of inputs, or procedure for human testers to follow.

- Expected test output to consider the test a pass vs. a fail.

23.4.3. How thoroughly do you test?

As mentioned in the discussion on coverage above, understanding how thorough testing is can be a difficult problem. Therefore, there is no single way to say how much of a system you have tested, and little way to predict the chance of a big system bug making it past testing. But, you can expect a better outcome if you test the system more thoroughly based on reasonable coverage metrics. Your test plan should pick the coverage metrics you care about and define the level of coverage desired. Even something as simple as saying "at least 95% of all lines of code shall be executed at least once during testing" is a reasonable way to proceed, although the percentage number will vary a bit depending on the situation and the system.

> **Test until you achieve a predefined level of test coverage.**

Additionally, a test plan should set forth criteria that define when testing is done. It might only be after all the defined coverage levels have been reached. It might be after some bug-finding metric is reached (*e.g.,* test until we go a full week without finding a bug). But, it is nice to define the completion criteria as early as possible in the project, before deadline pressures force compromises of the amount of testing that will be done.

23.4.4. Test automation

Should you automate testing? This question stirs up heated debates, and the best answer depends on your situation. Automating exploratory tests might not make sense, because the point of that kind of testing is to be a lightweight way to look around for things not covered by other forms of testing.

On the other hand, if you expect many releases of different product versions that all have to be tested to a high level of coverage, then an automated test suite might well make sense. The way to look at it is that automated testing saves labor while doing the testing, but costs significant resources to develop. Creating a set of automated tests is a software development project in its own right. Therefore, you want to focus automation efforts on tests that will be run many times over and over during the life of the product, so that you are likely to recoup the effort that went into creating the automated tests. Creating software tests is a software development effort. Don't automate one-time tests.

There are commercial automated testing frameworks, and even some non-commercial ones, such as GNU Expect. Use a testing framework tool if at all possible to save some effort.

23.4.5. Test result reporting

Test results should be recorded. This avoids having to re-do tests when people forget which tests they have done and which they haven't. The most common way to do this is to use a spreadsheet to list the test plan, and then annotate results cells in the spreadsheet with the test results.

A test has passed when the system responded as expected, and has failed when the system failed to respond as expected. This is the obvious situation, but there are some special cases that must be kept in mind. For example, if a system shuts down during a test of the shutdown function, then that test has passed even though the result was a system shutdown. Similarly, if you are testing an error reporting function, a reported error might be a pass so long as it is the error you expected to see reported. Be careful that your test framework doesn't assume all error reports indicate a failed test.

23.5. Pitfalls

The biggest pitfall in testing is not having (and not following) a test plan, and in particular treating testing as a semi-optional phase that gets done to the degree there is time left to do it. Only by having concrete coverage goals and a methodical test approach can you have some confidence that you have tested your system enough to suit your needs.

It's important to realize that testing alone isn't enough to create truly high quality software. While you can spend huge amounts of time and effort attempting to test software to reduce bugs, doing so is more expensive and risky than taking the time to do careful design and using a more comprehensive approach to V&V that includes peer reviews and other techniques. Testing is a valuable tool to ensure your software is good. But it shouldn't be the only tool.

23.6. For more information

23.6.1. General topic search keywords

- Software testing
- Software testing FAQ
  A few versions of the software testing FAQ are available in various places on the Web. The FAQ includes a wealth of useful information, including book recommendations and explanations for many testing terms and concepts. It moves from time to time, so we just give the search term instead of a direct pointer.

23.6.2. Recommended reading

http://www.stickyminds.com
>
> This is a web site devoted to software testing, which includes white papers and discussion groups.

Whittaker, J., "What is software testing? And why is it so hard?", *IEEE Software*, January/February 2000, pp. 70-79.
>
> Discusses the state of the art in desktop software testing, giving a good background in software testing philosophy overall.

Beatty, S., "Sensible software testing", *Embedded Systems Programming*, August 2000, pp. 98-121.
>
> This is an intro level discussion of software testing, and it focuses mostly on module/small program testing practice.

Beatty, S., "Where Testing Fails," *Embedded Systems Programming*, part 1: August 2003, pp. 36-41; (web supplement part 2: August 2003, pp. 4-7).
>
> Covers aspects of software that aren't found by traditional black box or white box testing techniques, such as timing, processor loading, schedulability, and deadlocks.

Chapter 24

Issue Tracking & Analysis

- Keeping track of defects is essential for improving both the software product you are creating and the process you use to create it.
- Written issue lists should record all defects found, their root cause, and their resolution status.
- Defect analysis can help find areas in which both products and the development process can be improved overall.

Contents:

24.1. Overview

Defects are problems with your software development results that cause it to fail to perform as desired. We'll use the terms *bug* and defect interchangeably. We'll also use the more generic term *issue* as a way to talk about all items that should be tracked, as explained later.

Some people use the term defect more narrowly, to mean a situation in which a software implementation deviates from its requirements, but that use is too limiting for our purposes. Defects can be caused by a variety of sources, including problems with requirements, architecture, design, and implementation. It doesn't matter where the problem comes from – either your product does what the customer needs it to do, or it doesn't. Once you find a problem, you should track the process of resolving it.

24.1.1. Importance of tracking issues

Keeping track of issues can help with understanding whether your system is as dependable as you need it to be in both direct and indirect ways. Beyond the obvious approach of providing a to do list for bug fixes, a defect tracking database can also give insight into which pieces of the system need to be reworked because they are *bug farms* – small sections of the code responsible for a disproportionately high fraction of problems with the system.

24.1.2. Possible symptoms

You aren't doing sufficient issue tracking if:

✘ There is no single list of bugs which are awaiting fixes.

✘ There is no single list of fixed bugs with annotations of root cause.

✘ There is no analysis of bug causes, minimally by code module and preferably including source of defect (requirements, design, coding, etc.).

✘ There is no single source for non-defect issues that need to be addressed in current or future versions of the software.

An issue database need not be fancy. A simple text file might suffice, although spreadsheets are more common and often more useful. But, if no record is being made of defects as they are discovered and fixed, you are missing opportunities to improve your system and your software development process.

24.1.3. Risks of not tracking issues

➤ Letting important bugs go un-fixed, either due to losing track of which bugs are still outstanding, or improperly prioritizing bug fixes.

➤ Wasting resources trying to fix bug farms one defect at a time instead of re-engineering the entire defective module.

➤ Wasting resources trying to fix bugs caused by requirements or architecture problems via modifying the implementation or using workarounds that don't really address the root cause of the problem.

24.2. Issue tracking

Issue tracking involves recording information discovered about a bug or other issue throughout the bug's lifecycle – from discovery through resolution, and keeping that data even after the bug has been fixed for analysis purposes. From this point on, we're going call it *issue tracking* for reasons discussed below.

24.2.1. Why track issues?

Issue data should be in a central location or list to provide more useful information than is available with just a set of distributed bug fix lists kept by individual developers. Uses for a centralized issue list include:

• Providing a to do list of which issues are unresolved.

• Supporting prioritization of issues across all outstanding defect and non-defect issues (which issues are most important to fix first?).

• Providing data for analysis to support both product and process improvement (discussed in the next section on analysis).

> **Track all issues found
> after a defined point in the development process.**

24.2.2. What information should be tracked?

Many bug, defect and issue tracking database tools are available. Similarly, the type and amount of information that can be tracked varies tremendously. But, even something as simple as a spreadsheet with a few columns of data can suffice for systems with few issues and simple needs. We suggest if you're not already doing issue tracking, you should start simple, and just use a spreadsheet. You can always progress to fancier tools and more thorough data collection as you decide they will provide value.

The basic information important to any defect tracking list includes the following:

• **Tracking ID number.** This can be an integer number or alphanumeric identifier that is only a few characters, to make it easy to do text searches for it in documents. It is also quite helpful to have a short text name so people know which issue you're talking about in a discussion. For example: "#1034 Crash when pressing two input buttons"

• **Priority.** How important is this issue? Often it suffices to rank each issue as one of: critical, high, medium, or low. Priority ranking is used to indicate how urgent it is to fix this particular issue. This is not quite the same as the severity of the symptom of a bug. For example, it may be critical to fix an otherwise minor run-time problem that severely annoys every user, but perhaps only medium priority to fix a software crash that happens only rarely in a way that is easily recoverable and minimally affects only a few users.

- **Status.** This indicates where the issue is in the bug-fix or feature addition lifecycle. Possible status entries include: Reported, Diagnosed, Fix Created, Fix Tested, Fix Released, Deferred To Next Version, Deferred Indefinitely, Scheduled for Version #x, Feature Request, and Not a Bug. It is important to agree upon which categories count as open so that lists can be made focusing on issues that need to be worked on, vs. closed issues that don't need further effort to resolve.

- **Description.** The description will be added to over time. It should include symptoms, information necessary to create or reproduce the reported problem, description of root cause, suggested requirement for a new feature idea, and so on. Often this can be a substantial text field.

- **How found.** Was it found in peer review? During integration testing? Via a customer complaint? It's useful to know how bugs are being found or feature ideas are being created. Keeping this data can help in assessing whether process improvements such as increasing peer reviews are in fact helping to find bugs earlier.

- **Root cause.** It is nice to have a separate field that specifies the cause of a defect independent of the description, to make sure that a concrete root cause is identified. In an ideal world, this is a category field that attributes the defect to one of: Requirements, Architecture, Design, Implementation, Documentation, and so on. But the real world is a messy place, so having a text field to explain messy situations is also a good idea.

- **Location.** Along with the root cause, it is very useful to record the location(s) of a defect. For implementation defects this would include the file name and procedure name. For requirements defects, this would include the particular requirement or section of requirements that was defective.

- **Corrective action.** This describes what was done to fix a defect or address other issues (this might be part of the description, but it is better to have a separate field). It might well include improvements to the development process in addition to more specific fixes to the particular bug in question.

- **Issue owner.** This is the name of the person who is in charge of resolving the issue.

Many embedded system development teams just use a spreadsheet with one column for each of the above data fields and one row for each issue, and find it adequate for their needs. However, once a project gets complex you may need to move to a real issue tracking tool.

24.3. What's a bug, really?

There are several tricky points that project teams run up against in bug tracking. They have to do with figuring out what is (and isn't) a bug, when to start tracking bugs, and how to assign priorities.

24.3.1. Is it a bug or an issue?

A classical software defect (or bug) occurs when the implemented code doesn't match the requirements. But a bug might be something else beyond that. It might be that the code perfectly implements a requirement, but the requirement is wrong (a requirements bug). It might be that the system works exactly as intended, but the customer hates it. It could just be that someone thought up a new feature idea and wants it put into the next release.

For these purposes a bug could be almost anything. That is why many software tools to help with bug tracking are called issue tracking rather than bug tracking tools. Beyond that, bugs and defects are clearly bad, while issues are … well … who knows what they really are? While it might seem like a minor thing, hearing there is an issue with software you wrote might not feel as threatening as being told your code has bugs.

So, for tracking purposes, a bug or defect or *issue* is any of the following:

- A report of a perceived mis-functioning of the system (which might or might not have been in accordance with the intended functionality)
- A desired change or modification to how the system works
- Any other information that the developers should know or take into account when fixing or modifying the system

---

Bugs are just the starting point.
Track all issues you find worth tracking.

24.3.2. When does an issue count for reporting?

Once an issue tracking system is created, some screening process has to be put in place to keep the list clean, accurate, and up to date. There should a single person who is in charge of the issue list. (Others might be able to update it, but one person should be responsible for keeping it in good shape.) That person has to take into account the following points.

- **At what point in development do bugs count?** In many organizations issue reports only count when they are found in products after shipment. Defects found and corrected before the product ships might not count. However, as product development processes mature and become more rigorous, it is common to start tracking issues earlier and earlier in the development cycle, all the way up to doing so during peer reviews. When you start tracking issues is up to you, but tracking them earlier will give you better insight into your development process.

- **What counts as a valid issue?** Whether it is called a bug list or an issue list, it's worth thinking about what should be in the list and what shouldn't. It is our view that things should be kept in the issue list if tracking them helps developers. Categories can be added such as feature request so that entries aren't deleted just because they aren't a classical bug or defect. It's a good idea to keep false alarms in the database, so repeated reporting of something that was judged not to be a bug will be noticed. (For example, if customers are complaining frequently about something that is an intended feature, having a false alarm entry in the issue database will help resolve repeated reports quickly, without going through an entire bug analysis effort each time.)

- **What should priority be based on?** Priority is sometimes called severity, which brings out questions such as: if an issue is just a minor nuisance for users but absolutely has to be resolved, is that a severe issue or not? In our opinion, the most useful information is how important it is to resolve the issue, independent of how dramatic the effects of a bug are or whether the issue is easy or difficult to resolve. This makes priority a combination of severity and urgency. But, other approaches are possible so long as they are useful in the developer team's particular situation.

Additionally, the issue list owner has to screen for duplicate entries, which may be difficult. A single bug might manifest as more than one symptom. And, a particular symptom might actually be caused by more than one bug. Merging and splitting entries requires some thought and expertise, but is important to keeping the list relevant and free of clutter.

For more sophisticated issue lists, the issue list owner should also review entries for conformance to style requirements and to ensure that all required entries have been made. If an issue list is full of low quality information, its usefulness is significantly reduced.

24.4. Defect and issue analysis

A major goal of having an issue list is to have a single repository of data for bugs and other issues that can be analyzed and used to manage the project. The approaches to analysis can range from very simple to extremely sophisticated. We'll discuss some high level uses here. Deciding exactly which types of analysis to do is highly project specific.

24.4.1. Issue reporting

The most basic use for an issue list is reporting which defects are still open, along with status. A report of open issues is often used at periodic project management meetings. Not all issues in the list are equal in priority or effort required. But, at a minimum, it is important to be able to produce a list of open issues sorted in priority order so that critical and high priority issues can be given management visibility.

Keep in mind that the accuracy of the reports hinges upon the accuracy of the data in the issue list. If the data isn't very clean, then the reports aren't likely to be very useful in practice.

It is helpful to look for patterns in the issues found. For example, if there are several issues caused by improper use of interrupt masking (disabling interrupts at the wrong time), then it is worth looking for other places where interrupt masking is used to see if there are latent bugs elsewhere.

24.4.2. Identification of bug farms

A classic pattern of defects is the *bug farm*, which is a piece of code that consistently has many more bugs than other parts of the system. In many software systems, there will be a small number of modules that have most of the defects. You should periodically examine your issue list data to see if there are particular modules that have an unusually high concentration of defects.

If you identify a module with a significantly higher defect rate than other modules, it's time to ask some hard questions about why this module is the one with all the defects. It might be because the module is significantly more complex than other modules. It might be because the design is too obscure and difficult to understand. It might just be that it was created by an inexperienced team member and wasn't reviewed sufficiently well. But regardless of the problem's root cause, identifying the bug farms is a key first step in understanding why you might have more bugs than you'd like, and where you might be able to find them. After the bug farms have been identified, it can be useful to take one of the following actions:

- Perform additional reviews of the design and implementation of a bug farm module to see whether it can and should be improved.
- Perform reviews of the test plan to see if the module wasn't sufficiently well tested.
- Look for patterns in the issues detected to see if restructuring the module will help eliminate future similar problems.

> ### Look for bug farms.
> ### When you find one, throw the code away and
> ### re-create that module from scratch.

Sometimes (arguably most of the time) the right thing to do with a bug farm is throw the design and implementation away, and start again. Fixing defects is much more expensive than writing code. If the reason for a piece of code being a bug farm is that it was poorly designed or poorly implemented, putting fix upon fix into that code isn't going to make it well designed or well implemented. At some point, it is cheaper and less expensive to simply start over on that module. The difficult part is making the decision to do this, because for each new bug the incremental cost of fixing just that problem is low. Taken on its own, just fixing one bug seems much cheaper than the much larger cost of redeveloping the entire module. But, the additional question to ask is, "how do we know this is really the last, or nearly the last, bug we'll find in this module?" If you're dealing with a bug farm, the answer is that you are pretty much guaranteed there will be more bugs after the next one, and each attempted bug fix has a significant chance of introducing even more bugs as an unanticipated side effect.

24.4.3. Identification of process problems

The Root Cause field in the issue list can be useful for identifying and correcting process problems. For example, if a large number of defects are caused by problems handling null pointers, then the software process should be updated to pay specific attention to null pointers in reviews and testing. In general, any pattern of problems can suggest a way to improve the development process to try to reduce a source of those problems.

It is important *not* to use defect information to blame people for making mistakes! Doing that will quickly lead to withholding of defect information, and a negative development culture. Nothing will kill the usefulness of an issue database faster than punishing people because something they worked on shows up in that database. It's also risky to reward people who have few defects found, because that will create incentives to hide defects.

Don't use defect data to punish (or reward) developers.

24.5. Pitfalls

The biggest pitfall in keeping defect logs and tracking down root causes is pinning blame on an individual developer for a bug. In particular, it is essential that developers not be punished or have their careers affected in any way based on the attribution of a defect to them. It is best if root cause doesn't record the name of the person who made a mistake. Making it personal will not only alienate the individual blamed, but also create tremendous incentive for developers to bypass the issue list process, and likely create a counter-productive rift between developers and testers.

24.6. For more information

24.6.1. General topic search keywords
- Bug tracking

- Defect tracking
- Issue tracking

24.6.2. Recommended reading

Ganssle, J., "Firmware basics for the boss," *Embedded Systems Design*, part 1: February 2004, pp. 37-40; part 2: March 2004, pp. 45-48.
A boss-oriented discussion of some basics of embedded software development.

Chapter 25
Run-Time Error Logs

- Detect errors at run time, feed that information back to developers, and deploy bug fixes to current and future systems.

Contents:

Keep error logs in non-volatile memory. Keep as much error log information as you can afford. Periodic entries that a system is working normally can help indirectly determine when problems have occurred.

User error logs to identify causes of observed failures. Just as importantly, use them to detect problems before users even notice them.

25.1. Overview

There are two reasons to keep run-time error logs. One reason is to detect bugs that escape into fielded products. The other reason is to defend software developers from being blamed for non-software defects, and as a result avoid wild goose chases for software bugs that aren't really there. Both reasons can be equally important in practice.

Because software isn't perfect, it is often blamed for problems that aren't reproducible. The desktop computing culture approach to bugs is, as a first step, have the user reboot the system and try again. Most of the time, desktop computer problems that are fixed via a reboot are caused by software defects (not always, but often enough that it's reasonable to assume that this is what is going on).

Bug hunting in embedded systems can be more complex than desktop systems. Dirt in a mechanical system, adverse environmental conditions, electromagnetic interference, and any number of external factors can cause an embedded system to fail even if the software is, for practical purposes, perfect. When a system experiences a problem, but that problem can't be reproduced or isolated later, it leads to unhappy customers and frustrated developers. Unhappy field service personnel often blame software, whether that blame is justified or not. A good mechanism to help improve this situation is to incorporate run-time error logging and performance instrumentation into the final product.

25.1.1. Importance of run-time error logs

Having a way to detect, report, and analyze run-time problems can help improve your system over the long term. Consider what happens if a customer returns or reports a product as being defective. If a software defect is in fact responsible for a problem, some record of its effects might be in the error logs, even if it is just the fact that a watchdog-induced system reset occurred. That way, software developers will know they have encountered a software defect, and have some idea of what happened to cause a customer to return a product as defective. On the other hand, if the error log shows normal system operation, then developers might be able to avoid presumptive blame and wasted time trying to deal with a problem that might not be theirs.

If error log data can be collected from apparently working units, that might reveal incipient problems (error log entries) that can be fixed before a customer actually has cause to complain.

There are certainly non-software causes for not being able to find problems in units returned as defective. For example, units might be returned from distributors as defective when the distributor's real business objective is simply to reduce inventory levels of slow-selling (but non-faulty) products. Intermittent field problems might be due to dirt or corrosion rather than software. Systems might be returned as defective because maintenance technicians mis-diagnosed problems. But, whatever the case, having error logs in a system gives you some guidance as to whether software is more or less likely to be the problem.

25.1.2. Possible symptoms

Your system can benefit from better run-time error logs if:

✘ Problems are found during system test that can't be diagnosed, especially intermittent problems.

✘ A high percentage of returned units don't have a reproducible problem.

✘ A high percentage of service calls result in a no trouble found report, meaning the equipment is working properly when the service technician arrives.

✘ There is no error logging capability in the system. For example, if a system fails, there is no indication stored in non-volatile memory that a failure has occurred, nor what type of failure took place.

25.1.3. Risks of not keeping error logs

➤ High warranty repair costs, high maintenance costs, and unhappy customers due to problems occurring in the field that can't be diagnosed and fixed.

➤ Excessive software developer time spent attempting to reproduce defects of unknown origin, especially if there is presumptive blame on software for any system fault of unknown origin

25.2. Error logging

It is common for desktop systems to have sophisticated error logging and remote failure reporting capability. But, what about embedded systems? It might be unrealistic to have an embedded system e-mail error information to developers, or even get the attention of a human unless something catastrophic has happened. On the other hand, when something serious enough to attract attention does happen, the problem needs to be fixed, and enough information needs to be available to have an idea what needs fixing.

For many embedded systems it can take days or even weeks of troubleshooting to figure out what (if anything) actually went wrong in the software for systems that have failed in the field. Even simple error logging can make a huge difference in diagnosis. It can also give clues to unexpected problems that are happening in the field in units that are maintained or returned even though a software defect hasn't (yet) caused a high profile failure in the field. But to do this, there need to be good logs kept in every deployed system.

25.2.1. How to log

Embedded system error logs can range from very simple to complex, depending on available system resources and the perceived value of collecting extensive error data. Starting simple is a good idea; complex logs can come after the developers have gained experience in knowing what information they need most.

The simplest approach is to have a single byte of non-volatile memory (often EEPROM) that contains the most recent error code generated by the program. This is a minimalist approach, but at least that byte will give a starting point as to where to look if there is a problem. A more robust, but still inexpensive, approach is to keep a queue of the most recent few error codes (for example, 8 or 16 most recent error codes or system events). This provides some context for analysis, and avoids situations where several errors occur almost at once, with a seemingly minor error over-writing a more important error message in a single-byte event log.

If you have a significant amount of run-time modifiable flash memory available, then you might have room for an extensive error log. How much data you record, and how many different events you write into the error log will depend on your situation and experience. But, having an error log of any kind is the most important first step to take. As non-volatile memory becomes less expensive and more readily available, it is likely you will increase the logging capabilities of your system over time and from one project to the next.

Keep error logs in non-volatile memory.
Keep as much error log information as you can afford.

Keep in mind that non-volatile memory has wearout effects. Make sure that your error log is designed so that it doesn't over-write the log memory so often that it wears out the memory cells. It is common to have wearout limits of 100,000 to 1,000,000 writes depending on the memory technology being used, so this is something to check for your system.

25.2.2. What to log

As with deciding how often to log, deciding what to log depends on your resources, situation, and system. Here are some ideas of things commonly logged.

- **System resets.** Every time a system reset occurs, it should be considered as a log entry, especially if your system has the capability to retain multiple log entries. The cause of the system reset is also important – was it the user pressing a hardware reset button? Was it a power off/on cycle? Was it a watchdog timer reset? Most system resets, and especially a series of closely spaced system resets, indicate something bad has happened.

- **Run-time errors.** Many run-time functions can return an error, and these errors should be checked for and recorded. Some examples of run-time errors include: failure to allocate memory from the heap, stack overflow, communication port data errors, memory parity errors, and data checksum errors.

- **Assertion violations.** Assertions are checks inside your code that everything is as you expect. In the most general sense, an assertion is a check for an impossible condition, such as a state machine entering an invalid state, or sensors delivering related values that can't possibly correspond to a real physical system. If the assertion is violated, then there is a problem somewhere in the system, and that should be recorded.

- **Hardware failures.** If possible, it is good to include some run-time checks of hardware, especially I/O ports, for correct operation and out-of-range sensor values. When those occur they should be logged.

- **Non-computer equipment failures.** In most cases there are ways to tell how well external equipment being controlled by the embedded system is operating. Logging problems with external equipment not only helps diagnose those problems, but also helps shield software developers from unfair blame when problems occur. One simple problem to log is loss of control loop closure, which happens when an actuator is commanded to a position, but related sensors show that the commanded position isn't reached within acceptable tolerance and acceptable delay.

- **Operating conditions.** If you have a large amount of error log memory available, you may wish to periodically snapshot the operating conditions of the system, then freeze that history when an error takes place to help with later diagnosis.

- **Time stamps.** It is helpful if each entry in the error log can be time stamped. Even if time of day isn't available, a simple timer value recording how long it has been since the system was last reset can give an idea as to how problems are spaced apart. An error log showing one month each between four system resets is a much different situation than a system which resets four times in an hour.

It is good to have a master list of all error codes available, and is best to coordinate use of the error log so that errors from different modules and different sources have a consistent, well thought out organization to them. It is also important to test the error logging mechanism as part of system test to make sure errors are actually being recorded properly. For example, be sure that if you keep a limited history you actually throw away the oldest error log entries and not the newest ones when the history buffer is full.

> Log everything that you think will help diagnose problems.

25.2.3. Recording system reset

The trickiest information to preserve is how long a system operates between resets, because a system reset tends to prevent effective writes to an error log. In some systems, a reset jumps to a particular high-priority interrupt service routine, and that routine can record the reset (assuming the system is still stable enough to do that). But, this capability isn't always present, and there may be situations such as loss of power in which it doesn't really work.

One way around the problem of recording resets is to maintain a non-volatile memory location that is written once in a while during normal operation with the current system up time. For example, you could update that location once per hour with how many hours the system has been running. A 16-bit unsigned integer can hold more than 7 years of hours counted this way. Then, when the system reboots, it can create an error log entry recording the reboot event, including the integer hour value at the time of reboot. (For completeness a 16-bit counter rollover should generate an error log entry as well, just in case your system manages to run for more than 7 years without an error log message.) That timer can be reset – or not – after every reboot depending on your preference, with the understanding that you might have up to a one-hour error on accumulated time after each reboot since the timer value after the last-written hour entry is lost when the system reboots.

Robust reboot logging schemes tend to be based on logging when the system is up, and inferring from that information when the system has crashed and recovered.

> **Record all system resets by inferring them from periodically updated "system is working" information.**

25.3. Error log analysis

Error log analysis can range from simple to sophisticated depending on the amount and detail of data you collect, how you get access to the data, and how many units send you data.

25.3.1. Identifying failure causes

The simplest use of error log analysis is to look at failed units and try to determine what has gone wrong. This involves looking at the captured error log information and using it to guide a search for the problem. This is the most important use of an error log, so thought should be given during design as to which error log messages would be most useful for this task. If you have the space, collecting a little more data than you think you need is better than collecting too little data.

Another use of error log analysis is proving that the software didn't fail, and that any problem was likely from another source. This can be done in part by noting that no error log entries are present. But, the argument can be strengthened by recording data indicating normal operation. Lack of an error log entry doesn't prove there is no software defect (it could be something that doesn't generate an error log entry). But, with an error log it is much easier to understand what has happened, and it is more difficult for anyone to simply accuse developers of being the source of a field problem because they (the software developers) don't have evidence to suggest otherwise.

> **Use error logs to identify causes of observed failures.**

25.3.2. Identifying latent defects

Error log analysis can look at units which seem to be working properly to determine if problems are taking place that the user hasn't noticed. A really robust system might suffer significant problems, but be so good at recovery that the user doesn't happen to notice.

For example, watchdog timer trips once or twice a day might go unnoticed if the system recovers quickly and the system being controlled doesn't exceed its normal operating parameters. This doesn't mean everything is OK. It means that the developers are living on borrowed time, and eventually this problem will escalate into a highly visible issue. Better to know about it and correct it before anyone complains!

> **Use error logs to detect problems before systems fail hard.**

It is a good idea to collect data from representative units in the field, even if no problems have been reported. For example, every time a system is maintained by a factory service representative, it could be standard procedure to download the error logs and send them back to developers for analysis. This should be a standard requirement for beta test sites, since they are expected to cooperate in observing and reporting system performance. At the very least, systems used for engineering development and test should have their error logs examined to see if unexpected events are taking place that weren't noticed by testers. In general, the more systems that can be examined for error log anomalies, the more likely you are to find a latent problem before it becomes a visible issue.

25.4. For more information

25.4.1. General topic search keywords
• Error logs
• Assertions

25.4.2. Recommended reading

Grundmann, B., "Using flash memory to diagnose system bugs," *Embedded Systems Programming,* July 1996, pp. 64-73.
    Discusses flash memory error logs and failure analysis.

CRITICAL SYSTEM
PROPERTIES

Chapter 26
Dependability

- Dependability is a measure of how likely it is that a system will fail.
- Determine the type and level of dependability required for your system (*never fails* is an unrealistic goal).
- Creating dependable software is an especially difficult challenge, but a combination of good development process, system state scrubbing, and carefully considered use of software diversity can help.

Contents:

Reliability measures a system's ability to operate defect-free for a given period of time. Availability is the probability the system will be operating at any given instant. Serial and parallel reliability equations can help predict reliability for hardware having random independent faults.

Software doesn't have random independent faults, so reliability modeling is difficult. Good process enables, but does not guarantee, high quality software. Software state scrubbing can keep systems running, including periodic reboots. Diverse software can help, but it isn't a silver bullet.

Include a clearly stated goal: what does it mean for your system to be dependable? Also include a fault model and strategies for fault mitigation.

26.1. Overview

Every embedded system has some requirement for dependability. (Many also need safety and security as well, but we cover those in subsequent chapters.) Dependability requirements might not be written down for your system, but they surely exist. For example, is it OK if the software in your system crashes every 30 seconds and requires a reboot? Probably not. How about every hour? Once per day? Once per month? Once per year? Once per 10 years? At some point there is a failure rate that is acceptable, and the purpose of doing dependability analysis is understanding what that point is, and how you plan to get there.

26.1.1. Importance of achieving dependability

It is common for embedded system developers to say they want their software to *never* fail. While that's a great desire, it is an unrealistic engineering goal. Every system will fail eventually. And, as your failure rate approaches *never* the cost to create such a system approaches infinity. So you need to pick an acceptable failure rate, and then figure out how you are going to achieve that realistic goal.

> **Every system can fail.**
> **So, you need to decide what your acceptable failure rate is.**

26.1.2. Possible symptoms

You need to create or improve a dependability plan if:

✖ There is no stated dependability goal.

✖ Failures caused by software defects are not included in the dependability goal.

✖ There is no definition for what dependable or reliable means for this product. (How reliable is enough? What failures are the biggest problem?)

26.1.3. Risks of dependability gaps

➤ The product might be too undependable, because there was no target set to encourage the development team (including testers) to put enough extra effort into dependability.

➤ The product will be too undependable because software failures aren't taken into account in dependability projections.

➤ It will be impossible to evaluate whether the product is dependable enough, because there is no measurable definition for dependability. Thus, dependability will just happen (or not) instead of being designed for.

26.2. Hardware dependability

Dependability is an umbrella term for the degree to which a system can be relied upon to function as desired. Dependability has many aspects, but the two most common issues for embedded systems are reliability and availability. Even though this book is mostly about embedded software, dependability is classically discussed in terms of hardware. So, first we'll discuss hardware dependability, and then explain how those ideas extend to software (or not, because software fails differently than hardware in some important ways).

26.2.1. Faults and failures

Just because some little thing goes wrong inside an embedded system doesn't mean that there is a catastrophe. Some faults are no big deal; others matter a lot. Pinning down the results of a particular fault takes a lot of analysis, but it is useful to have a way to speak about how small faults cascade into larger problems.

Faults are what happens when hardware gates mis-function, a bit is corrupted in memory, or a piece of software encounters a buggy line of code.

Failures are instances in which a fault is said to activate, meaning that it results in an incorrect computational result. For example, if a fault results in a bit being corrupted in memory, the failure doesn't happen until that bit is read and causes an incorrect computational result. If the corrupted bit is never read, the fault never activates to cause a failure. If the corrupted bit is used in a computation but by chance doesn't lead to an incorrect result, then a failure doesn't occur.

Errors occur when a failure activates into an observable deviation from how the system is supposed to work. Not all failures result in an error, because a failure might not disrupt operation enough to matter.

Thus, even a system with many faults can be dependable so long as techniques are in place to keep faults from activating into failures, and to keep failures from activating into errors.

26.2.2. Reliability

Reliability is the probability that a system will still be working some number of hours after it has been turned on. The longer a system has been turned on, the more likely that an error will have occurred at some point, and the lower the expected reliability. Rebooting a system starts a new period, with an assumption that a self test procedure ensures there are no residual faults in the system at the start of that new period.

> Reliability is a measure of a system's ability to work completely failure-free for a certain length of time, or mission.

Here is an example scenario for computing reliability. Consider a jet aircraft. A jet engine has a certain probability of failure for every hour of operation. The longer you fly, the more likely that a failure will just happen to occur. For a single-engine aircraft, you must have no engine failures between takeoff and landing, and that flight time is the *mission* time. So, to understand engine reliability in the context of an aircraft flight, you want to know the probability that the engine will operate failure-free for the entire length of that flight. For example, if reliability is 99.99% for that particular length flight, this means 9999 out of 10,000 flights of that length will successfully land without experiencing an engine failure (and, it also means that statistically speaking, one flight won't).

26.2.2.1. Computing reliability

Reliability can be computed for hardware using an assumption of random independent failures (in other words, any given component will fail at random with some probability of failure per hour). If components fail at a rate of lambda (λ) failures per hour, the reliability for t hours of continuous operation (called a mission time of t) is:

$$R(t) = e^{-\lambda t} \tag{26.1}$$

The exponential form of this equation makes it very difficult to have high reliability for long missions. Reliability goes down quickly as t gets large.

26.2.3. Reliability vs. MTBF

Mean Time Between Failures (*MTBF*) is the average length of error-free system operation. (Strictly speaking it should be called mean time between errors at the system level, but the term was coined before the formal distinctions among fault, error, and failure were made.) The longer MTBF is, the better.

The exponential form of the reliability equation also leads to a somewhat counter-intuitive result when comparing reliability to failure rates. Let's consider a λ of (1/1000)=.001, which is one failure per thousand operating hours. Because faults are random, this does not mean systems are guaranteed to fail by the end of a 1000-hour mission. Some will fail sooner, and some will fail later. How-

MTBF (hrs)	Mission time at 99% reliability	Mission time at 99.9% reliability	Mission time at 99.99% reliability
10	6 minutes	36 seconds	3.6 seconds
100	1 hour	6 minutes	36 seconds
1000	10 hours	1 hour	6 minutes
10,000	4.2 days	10 hours	1 hour
100,000	6 weeks	4.2 days	10 hours
1,000,000	60 weeks	6 weeks	4.2 days
10,000,000	11.5 years	60 weeks	6 weeks

Table 26.1. Example MTBFs for different reliability levels

ever, this does *not* mean that the probability of failure is one half for a 1000-hour mission. The reliability for 1000-hour mission is:

$$R(1000) = e^{-0.001*1000} = e^{-1} = 0.3679 \qquad (26.2)$$

After 1000 hours, only about 37% of systems will still be working. This means that if you put a hardware component in your embedded system with an MTBF of 1000 hours, you can expect 63% of systems to see that component fail *before* they have been used for 1000 hours.

Achieving high reliability can be very difficult. Table 26.1 gives the length of mission time to achieve 99%, 99.9%, and 99.99% reliability. Even at 99.99% reliability, 1 mission out of 10000 can be expected to fail. As you can see from the table, achieving high reliability for long missions takes very high MTBFs.

As an example of using this table, if you have a fielded system that is turned on continuously for a 10 year operating lifetime and you want fewer than 1 failure in 100 systems, you need to have an MTBF of 10 million hours ($\lambda = 10^{-7}$). Unfortunately, a reasonably reliable hardware component has $\lambda = 10^{-6}$ to 10^{-5}, which is much worse. For a reliability of 99.9%, the MTBF requirement is 10 times higher, and the required λ is even lower.

26.2.3.1. Serial component reliability

Most systems are made from multiple hardware components. Those components combine in a serial manner to give an aggregate system failure rate that is worse than the failure rate for any particular component. By *serial*, we mean that if any single component fails, the system fails. The formula for combining components is to multiply the reliabilities of each component $R(t)_i$ to get the overall system reliability $R(t)$. The basis of this formula is probability math – the system breaks if any one or more of the components breaks, so the system is working if you get lucky in that each and every component happens to be working at the same time.

$$R(t)_{serial} = R(t)_1 R(t)_2 R(t)_3 \ldots = \prod_i R(t)_i = \prod_i e^{-\lambda_i t} \qquad (26.3)$$

As you add components, the effect of even a small failure rate gets amplified because you are vulnerable to any failure within the system.

> Adding serial components reduces reliability dramatically.
> It only takes one component failure to cause system failure.

Reducing λ can be done to a degree by buying higher quality components. The US military tried this for many years and eventually gave up for most systems, because they just didn't buy enough components to drive the costs down through volume, and their components ended up being too expensive. If you need a lower λ for an electronic component, the best you can usually do is buy automotive-grade or industrial-grade components, which are rated for more extreme operating conditions than standard components, and therefore have a lower λ for any given operating environment. But, this will only improve λ a little bit.

All this means that as a practical matter you can't get highly reliable systems unless you can find a way to make the system keep working even when a component fails. That's why highly reliable systems incorporate redundant components.

26.2.3.2. Redundancy and parallel component reliability

The key to improving hardware reliability is adding redundancy. For example, install two components in *parallel* so that if one fails, the other redundant component can still keep the system running. This makes the system much more than twice as reliable. This is because hardware faults are, for the most part, random independent events. That means that if failures are unlikely (λ is small), the chance of all redundant components failing at the same time is very low.

$$R(t)_{redundant} = 1 - \left[\left(1 - R(t)_1\right)\left(1 - R(t)_2\right)\left(1 - R(t)_3\right)... \right]$$
$$= 1 - \prod_i \left(1 - R(t)_i\right)$$

(26.4)

This equation also comes from probability math. If you assume that only one out of all the redundant components needs to work for the system to operate, then the chance of a failure is the probability of all the components happening to fail before the mission is over, which is dramatically lower than for a single component.

> Adding parallel, redundant components results in
> dramatically improved system reliability.

Let's look at redundancy applied to jet engines as an example. Consider how many jet engines should be put on a jet aircraft to have a very high probability of making a flight across the Pacific Ocean without having all engines fail during

# Engines	R(11) at 50,000 hr MTBF	Mean Number of Missions Before Failure
1	0.999 78	4,546
2	0.999 999 952	20,665,853
3	0.999 999 999 999 999 998	$1.326 * 10^{17}$

Table 26.2. Multi-engine jet aircraft reliability example.

that same flight. (To be conservative, we assume that once an engine fails it can't be restarted in flight.) Assume an aircraft engine failure rate of $2*10^{-5}$ (50,000 hours between in-flight shutdowns), which is typical for a modern engine, and amazingly good for something so complex! The question is, how many engines are required for the plane to safely make an 11 hour flight across the Pacific Ocean? At λ of $2*10^{-5}$ for each engine, and using the single-component reliability we get:

$$R(11) = e^{-\lambda t} = e^{-\left(2*10^{-5}\right)*11} = 0.99978 \text{ for each engine} \qquad (26.5)$$

Table 26.2 shows the results of putting this engine reliability into the redundant reliability equation for 2 and 3 engines.

Aircraft require a mission failure probability of less than 10^{-9} per flight hour for catastrophic failures such as loss of all engines, which means a chance of less than $1.1 * 10^{-8}$ for an 11 hour flight. So by this math two engines aren't quite enough for a trans-Pacific flight ($4.84 * 10^{-8}$ chance of failure), and you need three engines or more to be safe. Two-engine aircraft have started making such flights in recent years, but are restricted to always stay relatively near a diversion airport (within 2 to 3 flight hours, depending on the type of aircraft) so that if one engine fails, the aircraft can land with very high probability before the other engine has a chance to also fail. This math doesn't take into account any possible common mode failures of engines at the same time. That is why an incredible amount of design and operational safety effort goes into eliminating such failures.

If you need to create a seriously dependable system, you will need additional expertise beyond this. This gives you an idea of how redundancy can be used to increase system reliability to very high levels.

26.2.4. Availability

Availability is a different way to view dependability. *Availability* is the probability that at any given instant the system will be operating properly, meaning it is error-free. Thus, if your system is up 95% of the time, it has an availability of 0.95.

Availability is primarily governed by the time between failures (MTBF, which includes repair time) and the time it takes to repair and recover the system from a failure. In most practical cases, availability can be expressed simply as:

$$Availability = \frac{\left(MTBF - RepairTime\right)}{MTBF} \qquad (26.6)$$

The big difference between reliability and availability is that availability is independent of mission time – it is the same regardless of how long the system runs. Thus, it is better suited to situations in which the emphasis is on making sure the system is almost always running (high availability) rather than making sure it runs for a certain amount of time entirely error free (high reliability). Any system with an availability of 99.999% or better (often called "five nines") is considered very good and can only achieve that goal via considerable effort in design and run-time system management.

Availability is the fraction of time the system is operational.

In some ways, high availability is easier than high reliability, because there is no exponential term making things difficult for long mission times. (That is not to say that very high availability isn't difficult to achieve in practice!) If possible, it is a good idea to find a way to make your system an availability-centric system rather than a reliability-centric system. One way to do this is to find a way for the system as a whole to keep operating even when the embedded computing system is momentarily inoperative. For example, use a watchdog timer and make sure a system reset happens fast enough that a computing system failure doesn't have time to progress to a user-visible product functionality error if the watchdog timer trips. This can be made to work in something like a water heater or thermostat where the time constants of the system being controlled are measured in minutes, but is not so easy in something like an engine control application where time constants might be measured in milliseconds.

Approaches to increasing availability typically use either redundancy or fast recovery. Some typical approaches include:

- **Standby computers,** ranging from hot standby with near-instantaneous switchover, to cold standby systems that must boot a spare computer before they can operate properly, to installed spares that must be manually reconfigured to take over system operation after a failure, but are already installed.

- **Fast system resets,** on the hope that resetting the system is likely to clear out any software problems and make the system run properly. This hope is often justified when a software crash is caused by memory leaks or corrupted data structures. But not all crashes can be cured with a reset.

- **Watchdog timers** to hasten recovery, assuming that a system reset will clear the problem. (See *Chapter 29. Watchdog Timers.*)

- **Periodic maintenance system resets** to clean out any accumulated software problems and restore the system to a freshly booted state. These maintenance resets can also be a good time to run diagnostics and self tests to look for latent faults. The trick to this approach is finding a good time to reset the system without disrupting system operation. In systems with a pattern of daily use, such resets are often scheduled late at night when the system is otherwise idle. For systems where continuous uptime is demanded, one can install two sets of embedded computers and ping-pong them so that one is always running and the other is running self tests. This approach also gives the advantage that if one computer dies, the other is still available for operation, increasing availability.

> Redundancy or fast recovery of non-redundant systems can
> increase availability.

26.2.5. Dispatchability

A close cousin to availability is dispatchability. *Dispatchability* is the probability that when the system needs to be turned on, it will work. Classically, dispatchability is used with reliability-intensive systems such as aircraft. For example, dispatchability is the probability that an aircraft will be fully working when it is time to take off, and reliability is the probability it will keep working once it is in the air. Most aircraft normally aren't allowed to take off with a major component failure, because the reliability math used to assess allowable flight mission time assumes that all redundant components are working at the start of the mission.

There is a natural antagonism between dispatchability and reliability. Reliability is enhanced by adding redundant components, so if one breaks there will be others likely to still be working. But, all those extra components means that, on average, *something* will be broken more often. Twice as much stuff to break means twice as many failures in a given time interval. Thus, systems designed for high reliability might have lower dispatchability (be at least partially broken more often) than ordinary systems.

Dispatchability can be increased by adding (surprise!) even more redundant components. The Boeing 777 aircraft, for example does this to reduce the chance the aircraft will be stranded at a remote location where spare parts aren't available. By adding additional installed spare components beyond those required for safety, the aircraft can switch to an installed spare and safely continue flying until there is a chance to replace that failed component, so long as no additional redundant components of that same type also fail. For example, if 3 redundant computers are required for safety, the 777 might have 4 computers. If one of the 4 fails, it can still fly safely on 3 while meeting the full measure of its reliability requirements. The 4th, broken, computer can be repaired at the next scheduled maintenance interval. If a second computer breaks before the next maintenance interval, then the plane might be grounded or restricted to short flights because it is left with only 2 working computers, and the reliability math assumes 3 working computers of that type to safely start a full length mission.

> High dispatchability means that a system will
> most likely be ready to start new missions.

The idea of extra redundancy for dispatchability can be used in any reliability-intensive system. Note that this approach actually increases component failures – because there are even more components to fail! But, dispatchability is improved, which is often the important thing. For example, a single cancelled overseas flight might cost an airline upwards of $1 million in direct and indirect expenses. With this high a penalty, spending considerable money on installed spares is still a financial win.

26.2.6. Support for computing hardware reliability

Hardware reliability calculations have been performed for many years in military, aerospace, and other similar domains. The usual approach is to employ a software tool which keeps track of various components as well as which components are redundant and which aren't. Standard failure rates are used for each component, and the tool calculates an overall system MTBF.

Failure rate data is readily available based on years of study of military systems. The most comprehensive source of data is the Reliability Information Analysis Center (RIAC), which makes component failure rate data available for various types of components, including electronics and mechanical components. Other, less comprehensive data may be available for other domains. For example, SAE has a few publications of reliability prediction models for automotive applications.

Calculations based on standard reliability data aren't precise predictors of failure rates for a particular design because of differing assumptions about usage, operating environments, sophistication of users, and so on. However, it is common for products in a particular application area to be a relatively constant factor different than these calculations. For example, in your application failure rates might be 30% as high as predicted by the calculations, and that percentage might well hold for all the products you make.

If you don't have a multiplier based on field experience for your domain, these calculations are still useful as relative measures. If you compare two different designs, the one with the higher calculated reliability number will have higher reliability. In other words, while the absolute reliability number might not be completely accurate without a calibration factor from field experience, a comparison will still tell which of two alternatives is more reliable.

26.3. Software dependability

From the preceding sections, it should be clear that analyzing and improving hardware reliability is a relatively mature and well understood discipline. It's natural to want to simply use these techniques to improve software reliability as well. Unfortunately, that doesn't work as well as you might hope.

Here's the problem. The hardware reliability math assumes random independent faults. If you put in two components and subject them to the same conditions, they are very unlikely to fail at the same time unless you grossly exceed their intended operating environment (for example, massive over-stressing of a structural component, or suffering a lightning strike if the system wasn't designed to withstand one). In general, you can count on independent failures for hardware.

In contrast, software components tend to have highly correlated failures for many problems. Given the same exact situation, two copies of software will often both fail the same way. So, if you put two copies of the same software in two redundant computers, you get a more reliable hardware system, but software reliability isn't improved – a situation that crashes software in one system is likely to crash the software in the other system.

There are three different relevant ideas that you can use to improve software reliability: improved software quality, software state scrubbing, and very carefully considered diverse software.

26.3.1. High quality software

The most effective way to improve software reliability is to get rid of bugs, to the extent that you can afford to do so. Bugs can occur in the code, in the design, in the requirements and even in the user manual. But, all of them count as bugs if they result in a system failure (*i.e.,* a system that doesn't do what the customer is depending upon it to do).

Hiring good developers is always a good starting point for improving software quality. So is providing them with good tools, a good working environment, realistic deadlines, a good set of requirements, testing support, and so on.

But, there is a limit. Providing a good environment isn't enough. To get really good software, you need a good software process. Can really great software be written without a process? Sometimes. But, there is high risk that software won't come out great all the time, and there is no way to know how good it is without a good process – you just have to ship the code and see what happens.

The problem is that we really don't know how to take a pile of source code and judge how reliable it is. Sure, if the software is a complete mess it's easy to offer an opinion that it isn't reliable. But that's just a good educated guess. The problem is that if the code looks pretty, that doesn't mean it is reliable. The only way we know how to assess reliability of code is to look at it in the context of the project design package and the process used to create that design package.

We'll discuss this more in the chapter on safety (*Chapter 28. Safety*), because the design techniques used to create safe code will also help create dependable code. But, even if you don't use heavy-duty techniques for creating critical code, a well defined, well executed process is very likely to result in more reliable software. How much? Beats us. But, typically, improved software process reduces the number of defects that make it to the field. And, it's the only way we really know to approach this problem.

> Good process enables, but does not guarantee,
> high quality software.

We really wish we could give you an easy recipe for putting a number on software reliability. But, unfortunately, the world just doesn't work that way.

26.3.2. Software state scrubbing

Some software bugs are activated randomly enough that it is reasonable to model them as random independent failures for dependability purposes. Classic random bugs come from sources such as:

- Memory leaks, where dynamically allocated memory is acquired but abandoned without being released (*e.g.,* a malloc or new without a corresponding free, or a data structure that fools a garbage collector into not reclaiming a piece of garbage). Memory leaks can cause random-seeming failures if they are invoked by time-varying event sequences.

- A corrupted pointer that causes the wrong memory location to be over-written.

- Failure to handle an error condition caused by a transient hardware failure which induces a corresponding software failure.

- Defects that occur with sensor values, when those sensor values have a lot of noise (so, whether software fails or not depends on the precise time of a sample).

- Non-robust responses to dropped network packets.

- Timing errors and race conditions that require a particular, relatively unlikely sequence of events to take place.

- Counter and timer rollovers.

Desktop software can often be restored to operation by simply rebooting the offending task or the entire machine. When that works, the problem was likely due to one of the above errors or something similar. One can argue that most software errors are of this type on desktop systems (or at least it certainly seems that way!). See *Chapter 30. System Reset* for more thoughts on this topic.

But, while some embedded systems do suffer these types of problems, it is not always safe to assume that system reboots will solve all, or even most of your problems. That's because these types of bugs are intentionally designed out of many embedded systems. For example, some embedded system design rules absolutely forbid the use of dynamically allocated memory, precisely to avoid crashes resulting from memory leaks.

At any rate, to the degree you expect your system to suffer random-seeming software failures, it makes sense to perform periodic maintenance reboots to clear those problems. If you have multiple redundant processors, it is sensible to space out the timing of those reboots to minimize the chance that all processors will, for example, just happen to run out of heap memory due to memory leaks at exactly the same time.

> Periodic system reboots can help avoid unscheduled downtime.

Beyond system reboots, there are more subtle scrubbing techniques that might be effective. These include:

- Monitor task status in your operating system, and restart any task that has crashed, thrown an unrecoverable exception, violated an assertion, or otherwise misbehaved.

- Re-initializing hardware components periodically (for example, the direction and speed settings of I/O ports) in case they have become corrupted.

- If you are using an operating system, shut down and restart tasks periodically, which (depending on the OS) frees any memory that has been leaked within that task's allocated memory.

The effectiveness of these measures will depend on your software and your situation. They are worth using, but they won't solve problems that crash multiple copies of a particular task or crash a task repeatedly. For example, if your aircraft autopilot crashes whenever you cross the International Date Line (which happened to a flight of US F-22 Raptor aircraft in February 2007), rebooting your computers during a mission might not be possible or might not help. Neither will having many redundant but identically buggy copies of that same defective software that all crash at the same time when they cross the Date Line.

26.3.3. Diverse software

It would be really great if you could figure out how to create two pieces of software that failed independently. If you could do this, you could use all the tried and true hardware dependability techniques which are based on an assumption of independent failures. In practice it is extremely difficult to get software modules that fail completely independently (so, that is bad news for ultra-critical applications). But, in practice it isn't too hard to get *some* level of independence, and that moderate level of independence helps if you can get it without spending too much money to get it.

BEWARE – this isn't a silver bullet! A little software diversity is easy to get. A lot of diversity is very difficult to get, and knowing how much diversity you actually obtain is even harder.

> Diverse software can help, but it isn't a silver bullet.

First, an important word of caution. Many people (including us), think that if you have limited time and resources, you're better off making one really good version of software than attempting to make two independent versions, which are each not nearly as good on their own. There will likely be too many bugs that are the same in both versions. (In other words, two buggy versions doesn't beat one good version.) But, if you can get a second somewhat different version almost for free, and doing so doesn't lead you to reduce the quality of your primary version, then maybe it is worth doing. Be careful, be thoughtful, and realize that truly free software is a rare thing indeed.

> **One good version is better than two poor quality versions.**

That having been said, here are some tricks that might be helpful. (These approaches are inspired by the research of Lui Sha at the University of Illinois, who has done research in this area for many years.)

26.3.3.1. Use different versions of third party software

If you are using third party software that has frequent updates, you can consider using multiple versions of that software (different updates) in different redundant processors. This way, a bug introduced by a new update is less likely to cause problems with both processors. Trying this approach with two redundant tasks on the same processor is likely to be trickier, because you have to make sure that different tasks link to different versions of software components such as libraries that might have changed, and that the OS doesn't mind this happening.

> **Multiple versions of third party software can provide some diversity, but can be difficult to manage.**

As an alternate approach, if you are releasing a new version of your own software, you could consider having a mechanism that falls back on the old version if the new version fails. This is a key idea in the dependable upgrade strategy (Sha, 1998).

26.3.3.2. Have a simple version as a fallback plan

In some situations, it is worthwhile to make two versions of a piece of software – a simple one and a complex one. The reasons why this might be effective are twofold: (1) simple software tends to be less buggy, and (2) simple algorithms often need fewer resources to execute. So you might, for instance, have an expensive, complex, fast CPU with a main control algorithm, and a slower, simpler, cheaper CPU with a backup simple algorithm to provide some level of redundancy. This approach is based on ideas in (Bodson, 1993).

The way this works is that a full-featured algorithm runs in normal operation. For example, a rather sophisticated control algorithm might read multiple sensors and try to optimize system behavior for performance, energy conservation, and so on. But, what happens when that control algorithm crashes? Or a required sensor fails, depriving that algorithm of data it needs to control the system? The system might first try a reset in case it is a transient software problem. But, if that fails, the system might then switch over to a simpler algorithm that is less optimized, less likely to be wrong, and that needs fewer sensors to compute a reasonable (but not as optimized) answer.

> A fallback simplified algorithm can provide resilience against both hardware and software faults.

How you apply this principle depends on the specifics of your system. But, to pick a simple example, let's say you're building a household hot water heater. Your normal operational software might try to do energy conservation by modeling how much hot water is currently in the system based on recent demand and time of day. But, that software might crash, or it might consistently run out of hot water. If that happens, you might switch to a very simple control algorithm (or even an electromechanical control system) that keeps the tank full of hot water all the time. It's not as efficient, but it is simple and less likely to run out of hot water. (You'd also want to annunciate an error of some sort indicating the energy optimization feature isn't working properly, or at least record it in the system's error log.)

26.3.3.3. Other approaches

There are heavier-weight approaches that are often proposed, and may be tempting. For example, you could use two different operating systems in the hopes that they won't fail the same way. You could use two different programming languages, two different libraries, two different design teams who went to universities in two different countries, with two different native spoken languages, and so on. The problem is that there is a good chance that by the time you have gotten this serious about highly dependable software, most of your bugs aren't in your implementation any more – they are more likely in your requirements. And things like different programming languages and operating systems won't fix requirements defects. This opinion is supported by the experience of the Boeing 777 design team, which attempted to create highly diverse implementations of software and decided it was unlikely to produce benefits worth the cost for just this reason (Yeh, 1998). Other teams still believe heavyweight software diversity is worthwhile. But, if you aren't a true expert in this area, probably it is best to build one good version instead of multiple redundant versions of software.

26.4. Dependability plan

Now that we've discussed the elements of dependability, let's talk about how to apply that information to an embedded system development project. Every embedded system should have a dependability plan, even if it is only a few items in the system requirements. To be effective, a dependability plan needs to cover at least the following elements: a dependability goal, anticipated faults, and planned dependability approaches.

26.4.1. Dependability goal

A dependability goal is more than just a number. The number has to mean something that is relevant to your system and your customers. To set a dependability goal, first ask: "What does it mean for our system to be dependable?"

Typical answers might include that a dependable system:

- Doesn't crash

- Doesn't give a wrong answer

- Doesn't have system state excursions too far beyond control loop set points (in other words, it maintains stable control)

- Doesn't miss a scheduled data sample

- Doesn't lose acquired data

- Responds to user inputs within a certain period of time

- Warns the user if something is about to go wrong (*e.g.,* low battery warning)

- Must keep working even if one component fails (*fail operational*)

- Must immediately shut down to a safe state if a component fails (*fail safe*)

- Must work even if transient failures occur

It is seldom the case that a system needs to be dependable in every single respect. Moreover, since building dependable systems can be expensive, it is important to think carefully about which dependability characteristics matter, and which don't. After giving this topic some thought, create a short list of the dependability attributes you really care about.

> **A dependability plan must have a clearly stated goal:**
> **what does it mean for your system to be dependable?**

The next part to setting a dependability goal is asking how close to perfection you really need to be. The system that *never* fails has yet to be built. Partly that is because designers miss some ways for a system to fail and therefore don't protect against them. And, partly that is because *never* is a really, really long time. "Never fails" is just unrealistic, even if that is what you and your customer would like to have. So, how long is long enough to be close enough to *never* for your purposes?

After you have an idea of a numeric target for your goal, you also need to find a way to measure whether the system meets that target. That measurement must be something useful, but also something you can readily measure. Here are some examples of dependability goals with varying degrees of specificity and different approaches to the problem.

Unrealistic goal: "System shall never crash" (never is a really long time!)

Poorly stated goal: "System shall be reliable" (how reliable is that?)

Unrealistic goal: "Software shall be defect-free" (that is almost impossible to achieve, and even if you could do that, how would you know you haven't missed a bug?)

Incomplete goal: "Hardware MTBF shall be at least 10,000 hours" (what about software?)

Better goal: "Mean time between system failures from all sources shall be at least 2000 operating hours"

Better goal: "System availability shall be at least 99.99%, including software outages and maintenance downtime."

Very difficult goal: "Mean time between unsafe system operations shall be at least 250,000 years." (If you are only relying upon testing, that is a very long test period! But, this is an actual safety specification for a rail system component. See *Chapter 28. Safety* for a discussion of this sort of requirement.)

26.4.2. Anticipated faults

Once you have a goal, you need to think about what sources of faults you want to protect against, and what sources of faults you aren't going to worry about (either because they are too unlikely, or because guarding against them is going to just be too expensive). In dependable system design, this is called selecting a *fault model.* Here are some examples of fault models that you might, or might not, decide to include in faults you guard against:

- Hardware component failure (out of specification; transient failure due to electromagnetic disturbance; background radiation induced soft errors; catastrophic failure)
- Software fault (incorrect answer; timing problem; run-time exception)
- Loss of power supply
- Corrupted network message
- Corruption of program image in non-volatile memory
- Sensor faults
- Actuator faults
- Faults in equipment being controlled
- Operating environment too hot or two cold
- Lightning strikes
- Liquid spill or immersion

There might be many others, depending on your system and application domain. Nonetheless, it is important to list all the faults you are trying to cover with your dependability approaches. (Note that you need not provide perfect operation when these faults occur – you just have to account for them somehow in achieving system dependability goals.) More dependable systems tend to include a wider variety of possible faults in their fault model.

> A dependability plan must include a fault model:
> what fault effects are you going to mitigate?

26.4.3. Planned dependability approaches

Once you know the types of faults you need to deal with, you need to create dependability approaches for each one. Each approach might be specific to a particular fault, but might also be a general technique that helps with many different faults. Making the argument that all the faults are adequately covered by your dependability approaches is a bit of an art, but it is important to at least think about what coverage you are getting. In other words, are your approaches leaving any big holes that will cause problems?

Some typical dependability approaches are discussed in the previous section. Some additional general techniques that are helpful include:

- Retry operations that fail. Often the failure will go away if it is due to a transient fault.
- Use sanity checks on sensor inputs to help detect failed sensors before they cause incorrect outputs.
- Run self tests on hardware components when possible.
- Use an integrity check of the program image (for example, a CRC of program memory) to ensure it is uncorrupted.
- Use a CRC or checksum integrity check on network messages.
- Check to see if actuators respond to commands accurately to detect actuator faults.

Achieving dependability requires significant attention to detail, and can take tremendous effort for extremely dependable systems (for example, aircraft flight control software). On the other hand, keeping in mind these steps can help you improve the dependability of even a relatively simple product by understanding what your dependability goals are and thinking about how to protect against the type of faults you expect to encounter.

> A dependability plan should include
> general strategies for fault mitigation.

26.5. Pitfalls

The two main pitfalls in dependability are not planning for dependability up front, and not taking into account that software dependability is different than hardware dependability.

Getting a system to be highly dependable requires a significant architectural commitment to dependability, as well as selection of high quality components. Once a system has been built, trying to make it significantly more dependable as an after-thought doesn't work very well.

It's vital to realize that software and hardware dependability are inherently different, because hardware mostly fails randomly, and software failures are often correlated. Thus, simply using multiple copies of the same buggy software isn't going to help that much with dependability in the general case.

26.6. For more information

26.6.1. General topic search keywords

• Dependability
• Reliability
• Availability

26.6.2. Recommended reading

Punches, K., "Design for Reliability: a checklist", *EDN*, November 21, 1996, pp. 149-156.
A good intro-level overview to electronic reliability calculations and methods.

Kalinksy, D., "Design patterns for high availability," *Embedded Systems Programming*, August 2002, pp. 24-33.
A high level survey of various software fault tolerance approaches.

Meyer, B., "Every little bit counts: toward more reliable software," *IEEE Computer*, November 1999, pp. 131-133.
A good synopsis of current techniques for reliable software.

26.6.3. Additional resources

http://www.theriac.org
The Reliability Information Analysis Center (RIAC), which has extensive reliability resources, although most data is for hardware.

http://www.dependability.org
Starting point for the dependability research community.

26.6.4. References

Sha, L., "Dependable system upgrade," *Real Time Systems Symposium*, 1998, pp. 440-448.
Suggests keeping old versions around to use as a diverse copy if the newest revision of software fails.

Bodson, M., J. Lehoczky, R. Rajkumar, L. Sha, D. Soh, M. Smith, & J. Stephan, "Control reconfiguration in the presence of software failures," *32nd Conference on Decision and Control,* December 1993, pp. 2284-2289.
Describes the simplex method, which involves using a simple but dependable software module as a diverse copy of a complex primary software module.

Yeh, Y.C., "Design considerations in Boeing 777 fly-by-wire computers," *High-Assurance Systems Engineering Symposium,* November 1998, pp. 64-72.
Gives an architectural description of and lessons learned from designing the B777 safety critical computing systems, including an observation that perfectly diverse software was too difficult to create.

Chapter 27
Security

- Embedded systems are increasingly subject to attack, and must address security.
- Your system must have the right amounts of secrecy, authentication, integrity, privacy, and availability.
- Secure systems combine different elements to mitigate the most important threats, and have the ability to improve security over time.

Contents:

27.1. Overview

Embedded system developers must address *security*, which can be thought of as the ability of a system to deliver expected services despite malicious attacks. Sometimes there really is no threat. But, much more often, the threat is real (or will soon be real). You have to assume that any embedded system will be attacked eventually. The question is not if you need security, but rather how much security you need.

There are many types of attacks, but we'll use the generic term *malware* to indicate software that is attempting to compromise the embedded system in some way. This lets us avoid hair-splitting among the sometimes subtle differences among viruses, worms, Trojan horses, spyware, and other forms of malicious software.

27.1.1. Importance of adequate security

Most embedded systems have some requirement for security, even if it is very simple. Any embedded system that is connected to a network (including embedded control networks and modems) must have a security plan. The threats to an embedded system might be less intense than those experienced by typical financial systems, but they need to be dealt with in an appropriate way nonetheless.

A security plan helps define what threats you are worried about (and which you aren't), as well as how much effort needs to be spent to make the system sufficiently secure. In some cases it might be very little effort indeed. But the important part is knowing that you did the right thing, instead of taking a chance because you haven't thought hard enough about security.

27.1.2. Possible symptoms

✖ There is no written security plan.

✖ Your system is connected directly *or indirectly* to the Internet (even if the network your system is directly connected to is not Ethernet).

✖ Your system can be connected to a laptop or other computer for maintenance.

✖ Your system has a telephone modem or is designed to be connected to one.

✖ Your software contains trade secrets or otherwise should be protected from examination and copying.

✖ There is incentive for users to modify or repurpose your product in a way you don't wish to have happen (for example, converting an inexpensive digital video recorder sold below manufacturing cost that runs on Linux into a general purpose Linux computer).

27.1.3. Risks of inadequate security

➤ Your system could be attacked, infected, or otherwise compromised remotely via a network connection, modem connection, or infection from a maintenance computer.

➤ Your system could be copied, or trade secrets revealed via access to the system software.

➤ Your system could be modified or corrupted in a way that makes it dangerous to operate, increasing your legal risk if there is an accident involving your system.

➤ Your system could be modified to be used for some other application, causing financial loss if your business model involves subsidizing hardware costs and profiting from service contracts.

27.2. Embedded security overview

There is no way to cover all of security in a single chapter. You need to read many books to learn about security – and then continually keep up to date because the field changes on a monthly or weekly basis. But, what we can do is outline the basics, define relevant terms, and discuss how security issues are likely to affect embedded systems in a general way.

27.2.1. Aspects of security

There are several different aspects to security. It is typical for embedded systems to have different emphasis on those aspects depending on the application domain. For example, a safety critical embedded system might worry the most about integrity and authentication, and even be willing to give up some secrecy or privacy to achieve higher integrity. In other systems, the tradeoffs will be different. Briefly, aspects of security you should worry about include:

- **Secrecy:** keeping others from having access to information. In network communications this is primarily done via encryption. In embedded systems there is also the issue of whether someone can recover secret information if they purchase or otherwise gain physical access to the device.

- **Authentication:** ensuring that only authorized entities can operate the system. For user interfaces, this is classically done using passwords as part of a log-in system. For networks this can be done either via encryption (which also provides secrecy), or secure message authentication codes.

- **Integrity:** ensuring that data or the system has not been tampered with. For network messages and the contents of memory, tampering can be discovered by checking data against a secure authentication code. Encryption can sometimes help, but it is important to have data integrity checks to ensure encrypted messages haven't been corrupted.

- **Privacy:** ensuring that data about a user is not revealed. This differs from secrecy because in many instances it is desirable to reveal data to a trusted party, but in a way that doesn't connect that data to a user. For example, an automobile manufacturer might want to collect data about typical speeds at which their cars operate, but not collect information about the driving habits of specific individuals. The notion of privacy varies significantly depending on culture and the history of the country in which the system is being used.

- **Availability:** ensuring that the service provided by the system remains available despite attacks. Internet-connected systems can suffer from denial-of-service attacks, where the goal of the attack is to make the system unavailable, even if it cannot be broken into. In embedded systems that provide safety services, such as providing safety warnings or controlling a dangerous process, a denial of service attack might lead to unsafe situations. A related attack is attempting to drain the power of battery-operated systems so that they are forced to shut down pending battery replacement.

> **Your system may require one or more of:**
> secrecy, authentication, integrity, privacy, and availability.

27.2.2. Embedded-specific attacks

There are many ways in which an embedded system can be attacked, including:

- **Break-ins,** where the attacker attempts to gain direct control of a system. For example, an attacker might attempt to log into a system remotely. A common way to do this is using a factory-programmed default account name and password, or using a password guessing program to try commonly used user id and password strings. (Hint: using a password consisting of the word "password" is not just trite; it is really bad security practice. Unfortunately, many people still do this. But we're sure you're not one of them.)

- **Intercepting communications,** possibly with attempts to breach any encryption to compromise secrecy or privacy. Wireless network messages are particularly susceptible to interception.

- **Spoofing communications,** or otherwise creating malicious message or message envelope information in an attempt to trick the embedded system into acting upon those messages. For example, telephone caller ID information is easily faked by someone who wants to invest a little time understanding how that system works.

- **Playing back communications** that were previously intercepted, in an attempt to get an embedded system to repeat actions at the time of the attacker's choosing. For example, a valid message to unlock doors in a car might be played back after the car owner has gone. (This is related to a *man in the middle* attack, where a malicious entity intercepts communications, potentially modifies them, then forwards them on to the intended destination.)

- **Physical analysis.** In this situation, the attacker has complete physical control of a system, and can disassemble it into components and perform whatever analysis is desired. For many desktop systems, it is assumed that only good guys have physical access to the system to be protected. But, in many embedded systems it is easy for an attacker to gain physical access to the system under attack.

- **Inserting malicious updates.** Many embedded systems have a mechanism to perform updates. It is possible to provide malicious updates, either directly in the case of a system owner who wishes to do so, or indirectly. For example, a web site might proclaim to have a software update for an embedded system, but might actually be distributing malware.

- **Coordinated multi-system attacks.** Embedded systems often control the consumption or release of energy. For example, an electric household hot water heater controls both consumption of electricity to heat the water, and the temperature of the water that is provided to hot water faucets within a house. While there might be little to be gained by attacking one system individually, attacking a large number of systems concurrently might produce dramatic results. For example, turning on all the electric hot water heaters in a city at once might conceivably lead to an electric utility overload and subsequent blackout.

> Think about all the ways your system can be attacked, including attacks that assume the system's user or owner is hostile.

27.2.3. Attack probability and motivation

There are as many variations on potential attacks as there are clever attackers. The real question about vulnerability is often: why would anyone bother to attack us? Typical motivations include:

- **Direct incentive.** Someone might be paid to attack a system directly to get it to change its function. For example, an attacker might make a system fail in a highly publicized way for the benefit of a competitor. Or, someone might benefit directly from a system malfunctioning. An attack might be something as comparatively minor as getting green lights at a traffic intersection by spoofing the emergency vehicle priority signals (yes, people build illegal devices to do this), or might be as serious as compromising alarm systems as a prelude to a burglary. Also, someone might be paid to find out secrets about your system to reveal them to a competitor.

- **Extortion.** Someone might threaten an attack in an attempt to be paid off for not attacking. A small demonstration attack to give credibility to the threat might be part of an extortion scheme.

- **Indirect incentive.** Someone might be paid or otherwise benefit indirectly from attacking an embedded system. For example, any computer with an Internet connection might be attacked so that it can be used as a source for sending spam e-mail. In that case the attacker is paid by how much e-mail is sent, and isn't actually interested in the primary function of the embedded system.

- **Revenge.** Someone might attack a system to exact revenge upon a former employer who either uses the system or manufactures the system. You must assume this type of attacker has access to special information, such as factory maintenance passwords and knowledge of potential system vulnerabilities.

- **Bragging rights.** Some people break into systems because they find it fun, or challenging, or desirable to further their professional career. For example, in January 2008 a 14-year-old boy modified a television remote control transmitter to control track switches in the light rail system of the city of Lodz, Poland, derailing four vehicles and injuring twelve people (Baker, 2008).

- **Cyber warfare.** It is clear that governments see embedded systems as attractive targets with a part to play in military strategies. For example, an adversary might attempt to turn off electricity to a large section of a country to cause distraction in concert with traditional military actions.

For any particular embedded system it might be difficult to say whether an attack is likely or not. But it is also difficult to look several years into the future and decide that none of the above motivations will become relevant at some point while the system is still in service. Therefore, it is wise to include basic countermeasures for the most disruptive threats, and have a plan for how to react to increased levels of threats after the system has been deployed.

Ask yourself "how could someone make money from attacking my system?" And, even if it is a very small amount of money per system, so long as in aggregate there is money to be made, it is likely someone will eventually attempt to compromise your security.

> If there is a way to make money from attacking your system,
> you can be sure it will eventually happen.

27.2.4. Elements of typical countermeasures

It's impossible to enumerate every security technique that might be used, but doing so is beside the point. In general, good security is attained using a mix of techniques appropriate to a particular application and anticipated set of threats. Below is a list of typical building blocks.

- **Encryption.** This involves scrambling data so that nobody can guess what the original data is unless they have a secret key value to decrypt the message. Good encryption is CPU intensive. Encryption schemes are often broken over time, so an encryption scheme that is great today might be obsolete tomorrow. Similarly, encryption keys tend to grow in size over time to counter increases in computing power available to attempt key guessing attacks.

- **Secure authentication codes.** These involve computing a secure hash, or secure digest, which is a pseudo-random bit pattern created from the data to be protected. For example, a 128-bit message might have a 16-bit authentication code that is created by mixing together the 128 bits of data in a cryptographically secure manner. In a good authentication code, it is very difficult to change the message in a way that just happens to have the same authentication value, and difficult to compute a new authentication value to match modified data, unless you have a secret key. Computing and verifying the authentication code requires a key, just as with encryption, although authentication codes don't provide any secrecy. Rather, authentication codes function in a way that is similar in some respects to checksums. It is very important to note that cyclic redundancy codes (CRCs) are not secure, even if a secret polynomial or starting value is used. A secret CRC polynomial is easy to reverse engineer, and should never be used as a secure authentication code method.

Encryption is expensive and slow.
User lighter weight mechanisms when secrecy isn't important.

- **Login procedure.** A traditional login procedure with user name and password can be used to restrict access to an embedded system, just as it is used in a desktop system.

- **Password management policies.** Password management policies set rules for password construction and changes. For example, a password management policy might forbid easy-to-guess passwords, require at least one numeric digit, require a minimum password length, and so on. A change policy might require that passwords be changed from factory-set default when the system is installed.

- **Data length checks.** A common software vulnerability is a buffer overflow attack. In this type of attack, a large block of data is sent as a program input or a network message. The program processing the data makes an assumption that the data is smaller than a certain size (either a pre-set size, or a size included as a field within the data message). The program then mistakenly over-writes its own program or data with the incoming data, spilling the excess past the reserved buffer area. This in turn might overwrite code or data that changes the behavior of the system, or sometimes even give the attacker complete ability to access anything in the system. Defending against this type of attack requires that all data be checked to ensure that it is no larger than the buffer allocated to hold it. Despite the apparent simplicity of this countermeasure (making sure input data fits into allocated buffers), buffer overflow vulnerabilities remain widespread.

- **Data validity checks.** Software often assumes that inputs it receives will be valid. Sometimes, invalid data can cause a software problem that crashes the system or even causes the system to perform undesired operations. If software assumes that only a certain range of values can come from an external source, it must reject any invalid values or take the risk of this type of attack.

- **Sequence numbers.** Desktop and enterprise systems are often based on transactions or events, in which each relevant piece of data is sent exactly one time. This means that networks must provide a way to detect missing or duplicated messages. However, embedded systems are often state-based, and send the same message repeatedly or without any particular sequence number or time stamp. This means that embedded systems are often vulnerable to playback attacks, in which a message is intercepted, stored, and played back later to cause the system to replay a previous behavior. This vulnerability exists even for encrypted messages – you don't need to know how to create a new packet if you can just play back a pre-encrypted packet you have saved from a previous valid transmission. This vulnerability can be reduced by having a tamper proof, changing sequence number or time stamp in each message.

- **Good software quality.** Many systems are compromised by attackers who exploit software bugs or lax coding practices (for example, software that is missing length checks on input strings). Good software quality helps make your system more secure, especially if you emphasize finding security-related software defects in testing and peer reviews.

There are many other security techniques, many of them quite sophisticated. But, the above list provides some basics that are useful in providing at least minimal security.

27.3. Attack vectors (network and otherwise)

A classical security horror scenario involves a computer connected to the Internet that is attacked by someone in a faraway country intent on destroying society. If you are working on systems that control significant infrastructure such as national electric power grids, then you are almost certainly at risk for this type of attack, and should be getting significant help from security experts. But, what about the rest of us? A single Internet-connected thermostat isn't exactly a lynchpin of national security.

Unfortunately, we all have to worry about potential attacks. While high profile attacks on less obvious embedded system targets aren't splashed across the newspapers, they are quietly happening. More importantly, there is no way to know if a year or two from now your system will suddenly be an attack target of choice – which is a problem if you are designing systems that will operate for tens of years. Therefore, what you need to do is make a reasonable effort to plug huge holes in security, and make an informed, well-reasoned engineering trade-off as to how much security will be enough.

For our purposes, let's assume that an attacker's goal is to break into a system and cause it to take an unsafe or undesired action, or compromise privacy by in-tercepting messages. (There are many security threats that aren't quite like these, but these are the basics that will get you thinking.) Let's talk about the different ways someone might get into your embedded system.

In each case we discuss somewhat minimal security precautions. It may be that these precautions are enough, but often they are not. However, if you are not even taking these basic steps or considering these points, then you need to improve your security approach.

27.3.1. Internet connection

This is the obvious path for infection. If your embedded system is connected to the Internet, you can expect it to be the target of an attack, as all Internet-con-nected computers are.

Additionally, you are vulnerable to messages being intercepted, manipulated, or otherwise exposed to the Bad Guys. So, even if your embedded system isn't broken into by malware, it might be the target of spoofed messages. For exam-ple, if household hot water heaters or thermostats are on the Internet, a simplis-tic attack might just be to send them all "turn yourself on" messages. More subtle attacks are possible (for example, as discussed in Koopman, 2004).

If you have an internet connection, you should treat security as seriously as you would for a PC or other general-purpose computer. You should expect se-curity to be a significant and ongoing effort.

> **If you have a direct or indirect connection to the Internet, you can count on being attacked.**

27.3.2. Factory-installed malware

In 2008, there was a rash of factory-installed viruses that came with new con-sumer electronics, including music players, digital picture frames, and GPS navigation devices (Robertson, 2008). One suggested source for the infections was desktop computers used for testing, with a theory that viruses could have propagated from those desktop machines to the embedded systems. But, it is not too difficult to envision future situations in which workers at overseas factories are paid by outsiders to install viruses on purpose (for example, viruses that steal passwords or credit card numbers and report them over available Internet links to criminals).

The tricky part about this threat is that it can affect systems which might not have any source of infection after shipment. Moreover, this sort of problem can be bad publicity for the producer of the component. Inspection of units before they are sold could help. But, you can simply consider this a special case of off-line contamination (discussed next).

> People who manufacture or maintain your system can be attackers.

27.3.3. Off-line spreading of malware

A generalization of the factory installed attack is any off-line attack. The scenario is that someone manages to load malware into a handheld service tool, toy, digital camera, or other electronic device. That device later connects to an embedded or desktop system. The malware then spreads. While this might seem like a lot of trouble to go through, it has already happened. In 2008 there were reports of digital picture frames being used to spread malware to computers, bypassing the need for network access (Gage, 2008). It seemed that this attack was a purposeful one against digital picture frames, with the aim of infecting PCs connected to the picture frames for the purpose of collecting passwords. It is unclear whether infection of the frames was done intentionally by factory staff or by external attackers. There's no reason someone couldn't attempt to infect other systems this way as well.

You should consider any method of attaching to an embedded system a potential source of threats. This includes embedded networks, serial ports, USB ports, Bluetooth connectivity, flash memory slots and any other way in which the external world can connect to your device. If data can be exchanged with the outside world, there might be a way for malware to attack your system. This includes both intrusion into the system and skimming (or copying) data from the connection.

> Computers that connect to your system can attack it, even if you aren't Internet-connected at the time of the attack.

Some minimal countermeasures for off-line contamination include:
- Encrypting or securely authenticating data transferred to or from other systems.

- Using a secure authentication code on software updates to prevent sneaking malware into updates.

- Ensuring that data transferred into a system cannot easily corrupt memory with buffer overflow attacks. (For example, ensure that the maximum length of a data packet is enforced, and that the length of a packet received matches the packet's length field.)

27.3.4. Indirectly Internet connected

Many embedded systems are indirectly connected to the Internet. If your system has an Ethernet or wireless connection that relies upon a firewall or other device to protect it from the Internet, then it likely has most of the same problems as other Internet-connected systems. You have to make sure the firewall really will provide the protection you are relying upon. It is common for there to be back-door paths into a supposedly protected network that bypass firewalls. And, firewalls aren't perfect. While using firewalls is a good idea, putting all your eggs into one security basket and leaving your embedded system with no security features at all isn't the best plan. For example, (Geer, 2006) describes an infection of the Davis-Besse nuclear power plant by the Slammer worm, which bypassed the normal firewall by coming in through a contractor's telephone modem connection into the plant's internal network.

Many embedded systems are indirectly connected to the Internet or other computers by non-Ethernet embedded networks, such as CAN or a network running a proprietary protocol. It is frequently argued that this makes them safe from attack. Unfortunately, this argument is just wishful thinking. If it is easy for malware to install itself on an Internet-connected computer, it's not that hard for it to know how to talk to some other network protocol. Whether someone would go to that trouble or not is another matter – but assuming it can't happen is a bad idea. This is simply a form of the fallacy of security through obscurity (see the pitfall section at the end of this chapter).

Using a non-Ethernet network doesn't keep out attackers.

A recommended approach for embedded networks is to assume that attacks can occur over them originating at any node. Unfortunately, typical embedded networks provide little in the way of support for security. That makes this an extremely challenging problem for which there aren't any easy solutions.

In practice, this means you should be very cautious any time you hook up Internet-connected systems to an embedded system. You have to assume in any security analysis if an intruder can get in to the gateway node that interfaces to you embedded system, they will be able to do whatever they want from that gateway node. To the maximum degree possible, don't connect critical systems to the Internet directly or indirectly. If they must be connected indirectly, don't count on the interface from Ethernet to non-Ethernet protocols to provide much additional security.

27.3.5. Modem connected

Any embedded system with a modem is subject to attack. Programs known as war dialers have been used for decades to systematically find modems, even those with unlisted numbers, to break into computers. (The name war dialing is said to date back to the 1983 movie War Games, which featured that technology in its plot.) Embedded systems with modems that have little or no security are common, and fairly easy to break into. For example, Shipley & Garfinkel (2001) report the results of a war dialing experiment. If you use a system with a modem, it is imperative that you assume you will be attacked just as if you were on an Internet-connected system.

Modems will be attacked. Unlisted phone numbers don't help.

Some minimal security practices for modem systems include:
- Change user names and passwords from the factory defaults.
- Require strong user names and passwords.
- Use a dial-back scheme, in which calling the modem causes it to dial back to a predetermined authorized connection number. Beware of using caller ID for authentication – it is easily faked.

27.3.6. Unauthorized users

Sometimes an attack comes not from a network, but rather from a user who has physical access to the system. If physical attackers have some constraints, such as not causing obvious physical damage to the computing enclosure for fear of being noticed, you can use standard techniques such as password protection for user interfaces. This is particularly applicable if you have multiple classes of users (users, system administrators, and factory maintenance personnel for example).

It's important to be realistic about passwords. They will get written on scraps of paper and taped to equipment. They will be set to something easy to remember. They will be given to people who probably shouldn't have them so as to save a drive in to work in the middle of the night or a walk across a large industrial complex. Especially problematic are factory maintenance passwords, which are often the same for all machines in a class, and which are impractical to change across all those systems if they are revealed to the public. Count on them being revealed one way or another.

People will use weak passwords if you let them.
If you insist upon strong passwords, they'll write them down and
tape them to the system console.

Minimum password security recommendations:

- Consider building in the ability to support password policies (*e.g.,* using strong passwords).

- If you wish to use factory technician passwords or other passwords that are the same on every system, you have to assume that eventually clients or competitors will figure them out. Plan accordingly.

- Consider using a unique per-system factory password instead of the same one for all systems (but, there needs to be an easy way for technicians to determine that password on a service call).

- Consider using a physical key instead of a password, as is done on cash registers to authorize overrides. While keys can be duplicated, doing so involves more effort than simply giving someone a few characters or numbers over a telephone or on a web site posting, reducing the likelihood of broad dissemination.

- Assume that any "secret" master passwords, product-wide access codes, or other back door mechanisms will be written down and posted on the web.

27.4. Intellectual property protection

Sometimes your security concerns include a need to protect proprietary software or data in your system. Patents help protect an idea, and are useful for both hardware designs and algorithms. Copyrights protect the expression of an idea, and are useful for protecting software implementations. Patent and copyright protection can help to an extent, but often aren't a complete solution. In particular, those sorts of legal protections aren't going to help you if you are trying to protect trade secrets, trying to deter reverse engineering of your system, or trying to deter manufacturers of clones that will be sold in markets in which your patents and copyrights aren't enforceable.

> **Patents and copyrights help prosecute intellectual property thieves.**
> **But they don't stop anything from being stolen.**

Unfortunately, protecting software inside an embedded system is difficult to do well. Once you sell a system and let a user have ownership of it, they can do anything they want to it. They might leave visible tamper marks that void a warranty, but that only helps if the system costs so much they are unwilling to absorb the loss of warranty protection (or the entire cost the system) to find out what is inside.

It is relatively easy to hire companies that will reverse engineer systems to find out what is inside a system, right down to the transistors inside custom integrated circuits and memory contents. Tamper-resistant technologies exist, but they provide only some help. As a practical matter, anything tamper-resistant now won't stay that way for very long. All tamper resistance does is make someone spend a few thousand dollars more to find out what is in your system. In some cases that might be enough deterrent, but in others it won't be.

Despite the fact that it's essentially impossible to prevent a determined adversary from discovering what's inside your product, there are practical and legal reasons to take some steps to protect your intellectual property. You might as well make it hard for them to steal from you if you can do so in an affordable way.

> Take steps to make it difficult
> to read out your software from deployed units.

Here are some minimal steps to increase protection of your intellectual property:

- Build the software without debugging information included in the compiled image, to make it slightly harder to reverse engineer. In particular, strip out symbol tables if your compiler supports that for production builds. In small systems the symbol tables aren't kept with the program so as to save memory space, so this might already be done for you.

- Use the security fuse, if present, to disable easy read-out of flash memory in your microcontroller after it has been programmed and verified in the factory.

- If it makes sense in your situation, use standardized (and therefore inexpensive) tamper-resistant modules such as smart cards in key parts of your system.

- Embed copyright notices and other unique markers in your code to make it easier to prove that code was copied from you, if copiers aren't sophisticated enough to detect and change those markers.

- Intentionally include some bugs, Easter eggs, dead code segments, weird inefficient ways of performing a computation, or other apparent design errors. This makes it easier to prove in a legal setting that someone whose code has those same strange elements must have copied from you. As a simple example, somewhere in your code if you want to decrement a counter, do so by adding 597 and then subtracting 598. It's still a decrement operation, but then you get to ask a jury "why would someone who wasn't copying the code do it that way instead of just subtracting 1?"

27.5. Security plan

Now that we've discussed the elements of security, let's talk about what should be in a basic security plan. Every embedded system should have a security plan, even it if is a very simple one that says "we've thought about this hard, and we don't think there are any security threats we need to worry about in this particular system."

27.5.1. Security plan elements

A basic security plan should address at least the following elements:

- **Security goals.** What does being secure mean to your system? Are you worried about privacy, secrecy, authentication, theft of trade secrets, *etc.*? Are you worried that an attacker can cause unsafe operations? Start with a solid definition of what secure means in the context of your system, and use this definition to evaluate which things matter (and which don't) in your particular situation. Include, to the degree possible, a cost/benefit goal so you know how much security is enough.

- **Plausible attacks.** What attacks are likely to be encountered given its intended usage? This is often in the form of representative attack scenarios. But you could also start with a list of system features that are likely to present a vulnerability (for example, an Internet connection to the device is always worth considering as a security vulnerability).

- **Failure criticality.** What attacks are likely to cause critical security failures, and which ones will just be a nuisance? Prioritizing the importance of attacks will help in deciding which ones are worthy of countermeasures. One way to do this is using a table with one row per threat, and annotate that row with criticality and countermeasures.

- **Countermeasures.** What countermeasures do you have (or should you have) to mitigate the high criticality threats?

> A basic security plan should include:
> security goals,
> plausible attacks,
> critical failures, and
> countermeasures.

Those elements will help you organize attacks you are concerned with and your countermeasures. However, there is an additional crucial dimension to the plan. How do you plan to evolve the system as threats change over time? To address this, you need to include in the plan some other elements, including:

- **Update strategy.** If new threats emerge (or old threats increase in criticality), how will you deploy improved security countermeasures to your product? This should include not only dealing with fixes for your own software, but dealing with fixes of third party software that may be running on your system. If you are planning on using the Internet to distribute security updates, keep in mind that this opens you to attacks on the update mechanism.

Even if your system doesn't have an Internet connection and relies upon users to perform updates, how do you know that an attacker won't set up a web site with malicious updates and trick users into installing them?

- **Monitoring strategy.** How will you know what threats are actually resulting in attacks on your systems? You will have to monitor what the Bad Guys are trying to do to your systems over time to be able to respond to the ever-changing threat environment. This also includes a way to keep track of whether any third party software you use has had security fix releases.

> Include an update strategy and a monitoring strategy to improve your security plan.

27.5.2. The *no security* plan

Sometimes it is appropriate to have no real security features in an embedded system. For example, you might be willing to trust that a user has no incentive to break into or modify your system. Or, you might be forced to assume that your customer will provide an isolated embedded control network or a corporate firewall that ensures attackers from outside the corporation won't be able to attack your system.

In the case that you don't design in security features but instead depend upon the user to provide a secure environment, you should still have a security plan that includes the following elements:

- A statement to be provided to the user saying, more or less, that you don't provide security features and it is the user's responsibility to ensure the system is not attacked.

- A list of assumptions or requirements for the system to still be reasonably secure in operational use. For example: "CAUTION: This product must be connected to an Ethernet network that is entirely isolated from the Internet and is accessible only to trusted parties. An attacker with network access can mount a successful attack on this device if connected even indirectly to the Internet." You should talk to your lawyers about the exact wording you wish to use.

The *no security* plan is quite common in embedded systems, but often not stated in clear terms to the user.

> If you aren't providing security assurances, tell the user.

27.6. Pitfalls

There are many common security blunders and misconceptions. We address only some of the more common ones found in embedded systems here.

- **Security through obscurity.** Hiding design information or relying upon an attacker to not know how something works does not provide effective security. This has been proven time and again. Someone with enough motivation or patience to attack you will be able to figure out how you did anything. This especially includes home brewed encryption algorithms. Use a standard algorithm, not one you made up yourself. Your home-made cipher almost certainly will be easy to crack by someone who wants to do that.

- **Non-Ethernet protocol / proprietary protocol.** Keeping your protocol secret is a variant on attempting obscurity. Someone will figure it out if they want to. (Or, a disgruntled former employee will reveal it!)

- **Unlisted modem number.** Keeping a phone number unlisted doesn't help against war dialing attacks, which try every possible phone number in sequence under automatic software control. Again, this is an attempt at obscurity that doesn't work.

- **Secret design information.** You have to assume that any secret you have will be revealed one way or another, with the exception of a unique random cryptographic key assigned on a per-unit basis (so long as you keep no record of what key was assigned). In other words, the *only* thing that should need to be a secret is the secret key itself.

- **Standard password or identical crypto key on all units.** It's really convenient to have a magic password (a type of *back door*) that will let you tell someone over the phone how to log into their system when they've forgotten their own password. It's also incredibly insecure. Someone will figure it out, trick it out of an employee, beat it out of an employee (informally known as rubber hose cryptography), find it via reverse engineering, or bribe an employee to obtain it.

- **Putting default or back door passwords in manuals.** Manuals for almost every system can be found on the Internet. If you insist on creating a factory default or master password, don't put it on the Internet in your on-line manual.

- **Master or manufacturer keys.** A great many cryptographic applications are simplified if you assume that each manufactured device has the same master key or manufacturer key inside it. The problem is that it doesn't take much effort to recover such a key from a purchased unit, and once the key is out, every system in the field has been compromised at once. If you use a manufacturer key, someone *will* figure it out. Instead, use a different key for each system in the field. Key distribution without a manufacturer key is more difficult and expensive, but is required if you're really serious about security. As a case in point, consider that the automotive security Keeloq system was cracked by recovering the manufacturer key from a single unit (Indesteege, 2008), while the competing Lear automotive security system was never cracked during its 10 year designed production lifetime. Keeloq relies upon secret designs and a secret manufacturer key. The Lear system design was published in a US patent (Koopman, 1994) but uses completely different keys for every single transmitter, so cracking one transmitter provides no help in cracking other transmitters.

27.7. For more information

27.7.1. General topic search keywords
- Computer security
- Critical infrastructure
- Threat analysis
- SCADA security

27.7.2. Recommended reading

Anderson, R., *Security Engineering: A Guide to Building Dependable Distributed Systems,* 2nd ed., Wiley, 2008.
A thick but readable book on security, with considerable discussion of high-end embedded system applications such as automated tellers and transportation ticketing systems. The author has a few chapters available as a free preview on his web site.

Geer, D., "Security of critical control systems sparks concern," *IEEE Computer,* January 2006, pp. 20-23.
Describes security issues with Supervisory Control and Data Acquisition (SCADA) and Process Control Systems (PCS) applications.

Koopman, P., "Embedded System Security," *IEEE Computer,* July 2004, pp. 95-97.
Explains some of the direct and indirect ways embedded systems might be attacked.

27.7.3. References

Baker, G., "Schoolboy hacks into city's tram system," *Telegraph Media Group* (telegraph.co.uk), January 11, 2008
News story about a 14-year-old boy who modified a television remote control to change track configurations on a city tram system, injuring passengers and derailing four trams.

Gage, D., "Virus from China the gift that keeps on giving," *San Francisco Chronicle,* February 15, 2008.
Malware installed in the factory is spread by digital picture frames to PCs.

Indesteege, S.; Keller, N.; Dunkelman, O.; Biham, E. & Preneel, B., "A practical attack on KeeLoq," *Advances in Cryptology – Eurocrypt 2008*, LNCS Vol. 4965/2008, Springer, 2008.
Describes an attack on Keeloq that exploits the presence of a secret master key. Spending a bit of effort on one device reveals the shared password of all devices. Keeping the algorithm and master key secret bought Keeloq some time, but ultimately did not prevent someone from breaking the device's security.

Koopman, P. & Finn, A. US #5,377,270; *Patent Cryptographic Authentication of Transmitted Messages Using Pseudorandom Numbers*; Koopman & Finn, Dec. 27, 1994.
Describes a lightweight cryptographic protocol used in millions of vehicles (the main competitor to Keeloq). It was designed for a 10 year production lifecycle, and wasn't broken during its designed lifetime despite publication of the algorithm in this patent. (As far as we know it still hasn't been broken, although no doubt the NSA could make short work of it if they really wanted to break into people's cars.)

Robertson, J., "Your next gadget may come with a pre-installed virus," *USA Today*, March 14, 2008.
Reports of iPods being infected with malware by a PC used for testing, then being shipped to customers.

Shipley, P. & Garfinkel, S., *An analysis of dial-up modems and vulnerabilities*, 2001.
Describes a large-scale war dialing experiment that found 46,192 modems in the San Francisco Bay area. One of these modems gave unprotected access to a system that controlled a high-voltage power transmission line. Other systems should have been more secure as well.

Chapter 28
Safety

- Any system that controls the release of energy via an actuator has the potential to cause safety problems.
- Safety Integrity Levels (SILs) help categorize how stringent safety techniques need to be.
- Using hardware safety mechanisms is often a good way to reduce the required integrity level of the software portion of a system.
- Every system should have a safety plan including a list of safety functions and a safety design strategy.

Contents:

28.1. Overview

A surprising number of embedded systems have some aspect of safety critical operation. Medical, aviation, nuclear power, and other such devices have obvious safety issues.

But, often the safety aspect is somewhat indirect or is only a small part of the functionality. For example, is a household hot water heater that contains software safety critical? (What if it overheats water, leading to a risk of scalding?) Is a cell phone safety critical? (What if it doesn't work when you need to call for an ambulance?) Is an electronic door lock safety critical? (What if it lets an intruder into your hotel room when it is supposed to be locked or won't let you out if there is a fire?)

28.1.1. Importance of ensuring an appropriate level of safety

Building a safe system requires understanding what aspects of your system can produce unsafe situations, how critical those potentially unsafe situations are, and what you should do to avoid those situations. There is essentially no product that is perfectly safe in every conceivable way. But, there are general practices and standards that can be applied in many cases to tell you how much effort on safety is appropriate. Few embedded system are as safety critical as an aircraft autopilot. But, most embedded systems have some safety concerns, even if minor.

28.1.2. Possible symptoms

Because embedded systems commonly have some aspects of safety in their design, you need to look more closely at safety if:

✘ There is no written safety plan.

Beyond that, the specifics all depend upon the situation. However, there is a general-purpose high-level question that will often tell you whether you need to worry about safety. It is:

✘ If you, the system designer, set out to try your hardest to write software that would make the system do something that was dangerous, could you cause an unsafe system behavior?

This may seem quite aggressive. After all, you'd hope that the system designer wouldn't want to design an unsafe system! But still, this question is very relevant for testing to see if you have safety concerns.

The point is this: if you have a system that could conceivably be made to behave in an unsafe way, then safety is a relevant concern. While you might not intentionally produce an unsafe behavior, how do you know unsafe behaviors can't happen unintentionally, for example as the result of a software bug? They might seem unlikely to happen, but that isn't the same as being sure they can't possibly happen.

Therefore, we argue that if an unsafe behavior is conceivable, you must not only avoid that unsafe behavior, but also make sure you know that you have avoided it via positive steps in the design process. While it might seem unlikely for a problem to happen by chance, you can't say you are safe until you have ensured that it really won't happen. In practice, this means you should have a safety plan. We'll explain how to create one in this chapter.

28.1.3. Risks of insufficient attention to safety

➤ Your system might injure or kill people.

➤ Your system might damage property.

➤ Your system might exhibit other unsafe behaviors, including injuring animals or damaging the environment.

➤ You and/or your company might be held accountable via the legal system for losses caused by your system.

Safety is a particularly risky area to get wrong in the United States because of the popularity of lawsuits for defective products that cause injuries, and the astonishingly large monetary awards that can result.

28.2. Embedded safety

Achieving a high level of safety for systems that contain software is difficult, and requires some significant specialized expertise. Therefore, what we will do is discuss how to tell how much of a problem safety is for your situation, and survey the general approaches that can be used for different levels of safety.

28.2.1. Terminology

A *mishap* is a generic term for an event in system operation that is somehow unsafe or potentially unsafe. (Mishaps can also be called *loss events*.) It is helpful to define more precise terms for how a mishap might manifest:

- **Hazard:** a situation in which software displays unsafe behaviors, but a mitigation technique works successfully. The fact that a hazard happened exposes the system to a potential for a safety problem, but no unsafe outcome occurred.

  Hazard example: automatic doors are commanded open when a bus is moving, but an automatic lock stays in place, keeping the doors closed.

- **Incident:** a situation in which software displays unsafe behaviors and mitigation techniques don't work. An injury or death might have taken place, but circumstances were fortunate and it didn't happen.

  Incident example: automatic doors on a bus unlock and open, but nobody is leaning against the door at the time so there is no injury.

- **Accident:** the same as an incident, except circumstances are unfortunate and someone is injured or killed.

Accident example: automatic doors on a bus unlock and open while someone is leaning against the door, and they fall out.

Note that the difference between an incident and an accident is usually beyond the system's control. Either one can be caused by the same system embedded system misbehavior, and whether someone gets hurt depends on external circumstances.

28.2.2. What, exactly, is safe software?

Strictly speaking, a piece of software taken in isolation is neither safe nor unsafe. The same identical software can be safe in one system and unsafe in another. It all depends on the system context and how the software is used.

Taken as a whole, any embedded system will directly or indirectly contribute to mishaps with some probability – hopefully a very low probability. Thus, safe software is software which has a sufficiently low probability of contributing to an accident when it is incorporated in a particular embedded system design.

It is a common misconception to think that if you make bug-free software, it will be safe software. While buggy software is undesirable in a safety critical system, bug-free and safe aren't the same thing. Bugs occur when software fails to do something it is supposed to do. To the degree that safety requires correct functionality, bugs in safety-related functions certainly matter. (For example, when you press the brake pedal in a car, the brakes are supposed to activate.) But, unsafe situations can occur from many other sources, including:

- Software that exhibits an extraneous function (for example, car brakes that activate when they aren't supposed to).
- Software based on unsafe requirements (for example, car brake lights that have a long delay in turning on after the brake pedal is depressed, where the long delay is specified in the requirements and exactly met by the software implementation).
- Software and requirements that are safe for expected situations, but cause an accident under unanticipated operating conditions (for example, car brakes that stop a car so quickly in a non-emergency situation that it is hit from behind by a following car with less capable brakes, which can't stop as quickly).

This means that merely getting software to be bug free (as difficult as that is!) only goes part way to ensuring a system is safe. Safe software should have the following properties:

- Correctly provides safety-relevant functionality when required
- Does not provide unintended, unsafe functionality
- Is not built upon requirements that omit safety-relevant functionality or include unsafe functionality

- Handles unforeseeable operating conditions without contributing to an accident

> **Safe software does all the safe things it is supposed to do and avoids unsafe actions.**

Getting all these aspects to software safety right is difficult to pull off – especially when it includes situations nobody could be expected to foresee. Thus, in the Real World, systems are as safe as we can reasonably make them given constraints on time, budget, and the limited scope of human ability to understand our systems and their operating environment.

28.2.3. How big an issue is safety in your system?

Getting something to be *perfectly* safe is, in general, impossible. But, the good news is that in many cases it's not too hard to get things to be safe enough for everyday use. After all, life is not perfectly safe. Even if you never drive, never fly, and never leave your back yard, there is still a non-zero probability you'll be struck and killed by lightning. Or a much lower probability you'll be injured by a meteor falling out of the sky (one person has been hit that we know of, but it was non-fatal). Or develop cancer from radon gas seeping into your basement. Thus, the relevant question isn't "is it safe," but rather "is it safe enough?"

> **No system is *perfectly* safe in all possible situations. The question is, "is it safe enough?"**

The usual way to approach this problem is to rank potential accidents by their probability and their consequence. High probability events with high consequences tend to make a system unsafe. Low probability events with low consequences tend to have no negative effect on system safety. But, how often is often enough? As it turns out, an analogy to death by lightning isn't a bad starting point. You can argue that so long as the consequences of using your system don't make life in general noticeably less safe than it already is, there is no point in trying to do better than that. As a real life example, approximately 50 people per year are killed in the US by lightning vs. approximately 140 people per year in airline crashes (these numbers are generally representative; the exact numbers depend on data source and years covered). That's not much of a difference, so most people consider planes safe enough to be worth the risk, especially since the alternate of driving is riskier per mile than flying by most accounts.

There are many ways to look at this topic and many ways to argue about relative safety. But the point is that at some level people are willing to accept risks to gain benefits from using a system. The art is in getting risks low enough, and benefits high enough, that the small risks involved in using a system are well worth taking.

28.2.4. Safety Integrity Levels

The most commonly prescribed way for embedded software designers to handle safety is to use the notion of a Safety Integrity Level (*SIL*). There are variations on this idea, but a common approach is to assign five SIL numbers, from 0 through 4, to different levels of safety and assign targets for how often a mishap at that level can occur. Below is a composite sketch of how SILs typically are assigned (but realize in your particular situation they might be a bit different):

- **SIL 4 – Catastrophic.** Unsafe software behavior would be very likely to kill one or more people.

- **SIL 3 – Critical.** Unsafe software behavior would be likely to cause injury, or possibly death depending on the circumstances.

- **SIL 2 – Significant.** Unsafe software behavior could possibly cause injuries, but ordinarily would not, depending on the circumstances.

- **SIL 1 – Minor.** Unsafe software behavior would be unlikely to cause injuries, but would cause operational limitations that could in turn contribute to an injury in adverse circumstances.

- **SIL 0 – Nuisance.** Safety is unaffected for practical purposes.

The higher the SIL, the more important it is to avoid unsafe software behaviors.

As you can see, the circumstances in which an unsafe software behavior takes place have a lot to do with whether an accident actually occurs, or can reasonably be expected to occur. The SIL level is applied based on the severity of a potential accident if mitigation techniques are unsuccessful. The idea is to use mitigation techniques to reduce the probability of a particular accident severity to an acceptable level. Typical target levels per system during operation are:

SIL 4: one mishap per 1,000,000,000 hours
SIL 3: one mishap per 10,000,000 hours
SIL 2: one mishap per 100,000 hours
SIL 1: one mishap per 1,000 hours
SIL 0: one mishap per 100 hours

In other words, mishap rates should be reduced to these levels or lower for systems to be acceptably save.

Safety Integrity Levels (SILs) assess how critical software safety is for a particular system. SIL 4 is the highest, most critical level.

As a practical matter, SIL 0 and SIL 1 issues can be dealt with more or less normal development practices. SIL 0 failures are, by definition, not safety problems. SIL 1 problems can happen often enough that they are likely to be encountered and corrected during normal system testing or early deployment, and are at low risk of actually causing an injury.

Handling problems at SIL 2 and above is more difficult. The target rate of occurrence is far longer than typical test cycles. If you test for only 2000 hours and don't see a safety problem, that doesn't really tell you if you've met a 100,000 hour goal! Determining whether adverse events occur infrequently enough to meet SIL 2 criteria via testing is difficult and expensive.

SIL 3 and SIL 4 are considered *safety critical* integrity levels. The software has to be safe, or unacceptably severe mishaps are likely to happen. Worse, it's hopeless to ensure SIL 3 and 4 criteria are met via testing alone, because the required target intervals for mishaps are too long to measure that way. So, you need other methods, which we will discuss.

28.3. Safety analysis techniques

We'll discuss three basic safety analysis techniques that work well in combination. There are many, many other possible techniques that can and should be used in combination with a high-SIL system.

A good place to see the range of techniques available is the safety standard IEC 61508-7, Annex A, which contains a 90-page list of hundreds of techniques with summary descriptions. If you want to develop safety critical software, you need to follow that standard or a similar one applicable to your application domain.

28.3.1. HAZOP (HAzard and OPerability)

The *HAZOP* technique is a methodical way of coming up with potential safety problems in your system. It involves applying guide words to your system requirements and asking "if that happens, is it unsafe?" The guide words are chosen to negate or modify the requirement under consideration to do a what-if analysis of what might happen if the requirement were violated. For example, the guideword *late* applied to a requirement of "system shall respond to input X within 100 msec" asks the question: "what happens if the system responds *later* than 100 msec?" Guidewords vary by domain, but a starting point for embedded system guidewords is:

- no – the required action is not taken
- reverse – the opposite of the required action is taken (*e.g.,* turning something off when it is supposed to be turned on)
- more – increase in value
- less – decrease in value

- early – happens earlier than specified
- late – happens later than specified
- wrong order – sequence of events happens in the wrong order

The result of a HAZOP analysis is a list of hazards for the system that describes both what the hazard is and how the system is likely to react to that hazard (e.g., what the unsafe behavior is). For example, "If the *valve* is *opened late* the pressure vessel might explode."

> HAZOP uses guide words in a structured approach to looking for unsafe situations.

For hardware, a HAZOP can take into account likely hardware failure modes. But for software, failure behaviors can be quite arbitrary. If there is a software bug, it is very difficult to make accurate predictions about what the software will or won't do. Thus, as a practical matter, the result of the HAZOP will be an identification of safety-relevant software requirements. In other words, if any requirement is violated or omitted and that results in a non-trivial hazard, then you have to consider the requirement safety critical, and the software implementation must get that requirement right if you want your system to be safe.

28.3.2. PHA (Preliminary Hazard Analysis)

A *PHA* ranks the various hazards in a system so that attention is focused on the most important ones. The list of hazards can come from anywhere, but a HAZOP is a good way to start generating this list.

The usual process for a PHA is to assess the probability of each hazard and its consequence, then rank them according to *risk* (which is a combination of both factors). High probability + high consequence is the most dangerous type of

RISK	CONSEQUENCE			
	CATASTROPHIC	CRITICAL	MARGINAL	NEGLIGIBLE
FREQUENT	*Unacceptable*	*Unacceptable*	*Unacceptable*	*Undesirable*
PROBABLE	*Unacceptable*	*Unacceptable*	*Undesirable*	*Tolerable*
OCCASIONAL	*Unacceptable*	*Undesirable*	*Tolerable*	*Tolerable*
REMOTE	*Undesirable*	*Tolerable*	*Tolerable*	*Negligible*
IMPROBABLE	*Tolerable*	*Tolerable*	*Negligible*	*Negligible*
INCREDIBLE	*Negligible*	*Negligible*	*Negligible*	*Negligible*

(Left axis label: PROBABILITY)

Figure 28.1. Example risk table, based on IEC 61508 (Redmill,1998). Actual risk entries in table may vary depending on application.

hazard and is the most important to mitigate. One way to do this is via a risk table, which shows both probabilities and consequences, then ranks each combination as to severity of risk. Figure 28.1 shows a risk table of the type used by the IEC 61508 standard. There is no single optimum way to assign table entries to risk levels. For example, an occasional critical risk might be unacceptable or undesirable depending on the particular system. Nonetheless, Fig. 28.1 is a good starting point for many embedded applications.

To use a risk table, first the consequence of a fault is determined by analyzing the response of the system to that fault. For hardware, the probability is determined by using a classical reliability prediction equation (see *Chapter 26. Dependability*). The risk is then determined by looking at the intersection of the consequence column and probability row. For example, in Fig. 28.1, a critical consequence and occasional probability would give a risk level of undesirable. If that risk is too high, we change the design to reduce probability, or the way the system is used to reduce consequence, and then re-evaluate risk for the new system.

A risk table uses consequence and probability to assign a level of risk to a particular safety concern.

If you try to use this table in the context of a safety evaluation, you'll notice that the various names for rows and columns don't quite align with the SIL levels. The assignment of SILs is based on the amount of *reduction* in risk that is deemed appropriate for a system (Redmill, 1998). This can be based on a risk table result, or just on the consequence if the probability is unknown. So, while high risks tend to get high SIL levels, there is some room for expert judgment in how SILs are mapped to risks.

For software, PHAs are more difficult, because it's difficult to know how often software will fail in the abstract. Reliability equations don't apply very well to software, because failures don't follow the random independent assumption required by hardware reliability equations. So, using a risk table for software is fraught with peril.

Instead, software failure consequence is used to determine a SIL, and that SIL mandates how rigorous a software process is required to ensure the level of software risk is appropriate.

This might all sound a bit fuzzy and, well, it *is* fuzzy. Ultimately, good embedded system safety approaches require someone experienced to guide them. If this is your first safety critical project, get some help. Unfortunately, there are no easy answers.

28.3.3. FTA (Fault Tree Analysis)

Fault Tree Analysis is an alternate way to look at system safety. The idea is to start with a set of undesirable outcomes (mishaps) and work backward to see

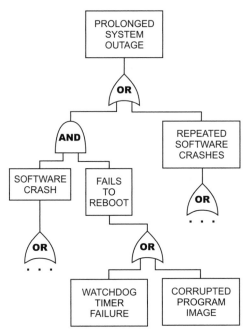

Figure 28.2. Example portion of a Fault Tree. In this example, it is assumed that a prolonged system outage is unsafe.

what might cause those outcomes. You then look for (or design in) redundancy within the system to eliminate single points of failure that can lead to an accident. In the context of a PHA, adding redundancy to avoid accidents is a way of lowering the probability of a particular accident occurring.

FTA involves a graph with nodes that represent undesirable system behaviors, AND gates, and OR gates (Figure 28.2). The notation puts the mishap at the top of a tree. Factors that can cause the mishap are put in nodes below the mishap itself. If a factor on its own can cause the mishap, it is put through an OR gate. If a factor must combine with another factor to cause the mishap, those combined factors are put through an AND gate. Each factor is then decomposed further until the graph is sufficiently detailed (how detailed that needs to be is a matter of judgment). In an ideal case, every item at the bottom of the FTA tree goes through at least one AND gate on its way to the top, meaning that there is no single point of failure that can lead to the mishap.

The root items (mishaps) for the FTA come from three sources. The first is a critical system failure discovered using a Failure Mode and Effects Analysis (*FMEA*), which is a hardware analysis technique that hypothesizes hardware component failures and determines the result of each such failure on the system. The second source is system failures identified by using a HAZOP process. The third source is brainstorming by design engineers of possible unsafe situations that might have been missed by the other two techniques, often based on mishaps that have occurred with previous or similar systems. It is always possible to fail to foresee a mishap, but by using methodical techniques such as these you are much less likely to miss something compared to just only spending a few minutes brainstorming potential problems.

> Fault Tree Analysis (FTA) uses a mishap as the root of a tree, then identifies contributing causes through AND and OR gates.

The tricky part of FTA is including software. If a software component is involved in a behavior that can conceivably produce a mishap, you need to assume that behavior can take place unless something is done to mitigate it. This means either you need to prove it just can't happen (by using a very rigorous development and validation process), or there needs to be some alternate safety mechanism *and*ed with it in the fault tree to mitigate the risk. Both strategies are possible.

28.4. Avoiding safety critical software

The previous section probably seemed unsatisfying. There was no formula or recipe that is guaranteed to create a safe system. Unfortunately, that's the way things are, at least today.

There are two general approaches to improving software safety. The first, and the best way if you can manage it, is to add a non-software safety mechanism so that if the software fails, the system remains safe. The second, more arduous, approach is to use a software design methodology designed for safety critical systems.

If you can, include a simple, dependable hardware component that on its own ensures the system is safe. In this case, the software is no longer safety critical, because there is a hardware safety net in place. There are at least three high-level approaches to doing this:

28.4.1. Hardware implementation of critical functions

The simplest, and least flexible, approach is to relegate all critical functions to hardware, and leave non-critical functions in software. The assumption is that hardware doesn't have design defects, but software does. This assumption only holds for relatively simple hardware. Programmable logic and complex chips are quite likely to have design errors, so using those doesn't count as using a simple hardware safety device! An example of the type of hardware we are thinking of is something like a fuse that burns out when too much current goes through a system, or a mechanical bi-metallic disc thermostat device to control temperature.

> Simple non-digital hardware implementations are easier to get right than software implementations for safety critical functions.

In pursuing this approach, it is essential that safety be *completely* ensured by hardware. It should be impossible for software to compromise safety, even if the programmer (hypothetically) tried as hard as possible to do so. If software can bypass the hardware implementation in any manner, then this approach isn't going to ensure system safety, because the software must still avoid unsafe behaviors.

As a practical matter, systems that use hardware for critical functions tend to use software for monitoring and human interface, and use hardware for actual control functions.

28.4.2. Hardware gating of critical functions

Performing critical control entirely in hardware can sacrifice a lot of system efficiency or performance. Often, the point of software is to optimize system performance in some way (better control, less energy usage, longer equipment life, and so on), beyond what is practical with mechanical controls. So we'd like to use software, but we want to avoid the cost and hassles involved in creating high-SIL software. What we'd like is to get the benefits of software functionality combined with the benefits of a hardware safety net.

A hardware gating approach can give the benefits of software functionality with hardware safety. It only works if there is a property that can be checked by hardware to ensure system safety. Additionally, the system has to immediately return to a safe state if the software is shut down by the hardware detecting a safety violation. The hardware mechanism takes the form of a gate or switch that the software must pass through to apply energy to an actuator.

As an example, consider a water heater controlled by software. The software might do a good job of ensuring just the right amount of hot water is available at just the right time for minimum energy cost. But, if the software over-heats the water, someone could get scalded. A hardware gating architecture could use a mechanical temperature sensor connected to a switch. The switch would be closed under normal circumstances, and the software could energize the heating elements at will. But, if the tank water got to the point that it was scalding hot, the mechanical switch would open, making it impossible for the software to further heat the water. Heat will dissipate from the tank over time, so the system naturally reverts to and stays in a safe state if the software is prevented from commanding more heat. In this situation it is impossible for the software to exhibit unsafe behavior, assuming that the mechanical switch doesn't fail. And, even if the switch does fail, the software also has to fail to result in a scalding water mishap. From a FTA point of view, the switch adds an AND path to the software's ability to overheat the water, removing software as a single point of failure.

Hardware safety gates disable software outputs when the system enters an unsafe state.

It is possible to simply use a mechanical thermostat to heat the water. But, the software approach gives much more flexibility in managing thermal energy. For example, software might let water in a storage tank cool down at night when nobody tends to use hot water, saving energy. The software might then warm up water temperature just before family members typically take showers each day. The hardware safety net prevents the software from causing injuries due to overly hot water, without getting in the way of implementing energy saving strategies.

In general, this approach tends to be possible when the following criteria are met:

- There is a property that is easy to measure without software, and that can be used to control a gate.
- The gate can be used to disable actuators.
- The system will remain safe or quickly return to a safe state when the gate disables actuators. Ideally, the system becomes increasingly safe with time as energy dissipates from the system.
- It is possible to detect when the system is just about to become unsafe so as to trigger the gate,

  OR

  It is acceptable for the system to be slightly unsafe for the brief period of time it takes for the gate to open and the system to revert to a safe state.

Depending on the situation, the gate may close and permit the software to resume control of the actuator as soon as the unsafe situation has been resolved. Or, a software defect may be deemed so critical that manual intervention is required to reset the gate to permit further operation. Even if resetting the gate requires manual intervention, other functions of the software can continue to operate.

Clearly this approach has limits, but it is nonetheless a very powerful architectural pattern for creating safe systems.

28.4.3. Hardware safety shutdown

A more draconian approach to ensuring system safety is to completely shut down the software any time it attempts to do something unsafe. This is the basis for fail-safe behavior. It is essentially the same as the gate approach with the exception that the gate is applied to the power input to the microcontroller itself. This means that the microcontroller shuts down whenever it does something unsafe (think of it as a circuit breaker, except with a trip condition that has to do with some unsafe situation in your system). In most cases the processor stays shut down until a human operator resets the system, so as to avoid software repeatedly trying to cause an unsafe situation, being reset, and then rebooting only to try something unsafe again.

> Hardware can perform a safety shutdown of the entire system
> when software attempts to put the system in an unsafe state.

The simplest shutdown system is a panic button that can be activated by a human operator. (Often these are large red switches – you've seen them on escalators and perhaps gasoline pumps.) When creating a panic button of this type, it is important to ensure that the button effects cannot be masked by software. For example, a panic button should interrupt a microcontroller's power supply, or at the very least be connected to a non-maskable interrupt. Having software read the panic button and then shut itself down (under software control) is seldom a safe approach all on its own, because it trusts malfunctioning software to turn itself off. Thought should also be given to what happens when the panic button is released or reset – does the system start back up automatically, potentially recreating its unsafe behavior?

A related technique is a hardware safety mechanism that engages when the computer shuts down. An example is a mechanically triggered emergency brake that is activated whenever the control computer shuts down, whether that shut down is caused by a software crash or the triggering of a safety shutdown system. This approach helps dissipate any kinetic energy in the system that becomes uncontrolled when the computer crashes.

28.4.4. Human oversight

When it is impractical to create a hardware shutdown mechanism, the next best thing is often to use a hardware detector to activate an alarm, and then make dealing with the situation a human's job. This is sometimes the only choice when recovering from a potentially unsafe situation requires positive and thoughtful action rather than an automatable emergency shutdown. There are numerous human interface issues involving whether the alarm is going to be noticed and whether a human operator can realistically handle the situation. Additionally, it is important that the human be able to control the system well enough to recover to a safe situation even if the software is malfunctioning (typically this is done via use of emergency mechanical controls).

> If hardware safety nets become too complex, consider using
> hardware to activate an alarm, and let a human deal with things.

28.5. Creating safety critical software

If there is no feasible way to use a hardware safety mechanism, then you need to use a well thought out, high quality software engineering process to create your software. Moreover, you need to follow good recommended practices for analyzing and recording your software design package to help ensure safety. The specifics of best practices vary from industry to industry, but they follow the same general approach:

- Determine the SIL of your software.
- Use a list of recommended techniques to develop and analyze the software, with more techniques required at higher SILs.
- For higher SILs, use redundant hardware (multiple embedded controllers) to minimize the chance of a run-time hardware error causing a mishap.

Many industries have their own safety standard, but an up-to-date one in widespread use is IEC 61508. If your industry doesn't have a standard for safe software development, this is the best place to start doing your homework.

28.5.1. Safety plan

A safety plan documents the process used to analyze system safety and enumerates the mitigation techniques being used to ensure safe system operation.

In general, your safety plan should have, as a minimum, the following:

- A statement of potentially unsafe system behaviors (potential mishaps).
- A mitigation strategy for each potential unsafe behavior.

This can be done, for example, with a set of fault trees, with each diagram in the FTA having a potential unsafe behavior as its root. Additional information to back up this plan is helpful. A more rigorous approach is using the Goal Structuring Notation, which annotates a fault tree-like structure with more information (Kelly, 1998).

It should be noted that not all mitigation strategies are technical in nature. In some cases, it is justifiable to use a mitigation strategy in the form of a warning label (*e.g.,* "WARNING – don't put your necktie into the paper shredder intake!"). In low risk situations of minor injuries, and if ethical considerations permit, it might suffice to just put a warning in the user manual or take out an insurance policy to cover the cost of settling claims.

> **Every embedded system should have a safety plan.**

28.6. Pitfalls

This chapter doesn't teach you enough to design safety critical systems.
We hope that it shows you the types of things you need to learn in more detail to get started in the area of safety. Consider it a first step in safety critical system literacy.

The most important thing to avoid is the ostrich technique – sticking your head in the sand and not even knowing what risks you are taking. A well considered examination of safety issues and risks is essential for every embedded system project. Beyond that, here is some general guidance to avoid the most common pitfalls.

- **Attempting SIL 3 software on your own.** Creating software that satisfies SIL 3 requirements is difficult, and shouldn't be attempted on your own if you have no experience with safety critical software. There are a lot of things to know, and it is unreasonable to expect any one developer to be really good at all of them. If you are trying to do SIL 3 for the first time, get some help from folks who have done it before.

- **Attempting SIL 4 software in general.** SIL 4 is the highest level of criticality. If you have any choice at all, avoid SIL 4 software and use hardware safety techniques instead. For recent standards, the difficulty of executing the techniques required to create SIL 4 software is truly staggering. Unless you work in an industry that has very significant experience in creating safety critical systems, don't even try SIL 4 software.

- **Attempting to test in or add on safety.** If your software was not designed to a particular SIL level, and you discover it has safety critical functions, your best bet is to toss out the parts of the software that are safety critical and start them over. Making good safety critical software is all about following a rigorous and documented process. If you didn't do that, you can't expect to go back and backfill things. Inevitably, you will find that you need to do something differently. Just start from scratch on the critical software pieces using a good process appropriate for your SIL level. It is certain to be cheaper and quicker than attempting to salvage existing code.

28.7. For more information

28.7.1. General topic search keywords
- Software safety
- Safety integrity level

28.7.2. Suggested reading

Redmill, F., "IEC 61508: principles and use in the management of safety," *Computing & Control Engineering Journal*, October 1998, pp. 205-213.
A tour of IEC 61508, one of the newest and most comprehensive software and hardware safety standards.

Kelly, T., "A systematic approach to safety case management," *SAE 04AE-149*, Society of Automotive Engineers, 2003.
Describes the GSN method for annotating fault trees to create a safety case.

28.7.3. References

International Electrotechnical Commission, *IEC 61508, Functional safety of electrical/electronic/programmable electronic safety-related systems*, Geneva, 1998.
This standard is primarily concerned with industrial process control, but is also intended to serve as a foundation for other safety standards in the future. The

most useful sections are probably: section 2 (hardware), section 3 (software), and section 7 (list of techniques).

Motor Industry Software Reliability Association (MISRA),
http://www.misra.org.uk
Publishes guidelines for dependable automotive systems, including a somewhat older SIL-based approach that can be thought of as a predecessor to IEC 61508. (MISRA Report 2, "Integrity", February 1995.) The main difference is that MISRA guidelines include human operators, and IEC 61508 does not. A newer set of automotive guidelines is being developed as ISO 26262, which is an adaptation of IEC 61508 to automobiles.

Kelly, T., *Arguing Safety – a systematic approach to safety case management,* DPhil Thesis, YCST-99-05, Department of Computer Science, University of York, UK (1999).
This thesis explains the GSN method for creating pictorial safety cases that are, essentially, fault trees annotated with additional information. The 2003 Kelly paper listed in the suggested reading section is a more accessible description of GSN.

Chapter 29
Watchdog Timers

- A watchdog timer resets the system automatically if there is a system crash or task hang.
- Every task within the system should contribute to watchdog timer kicks.
- Every embedded system should use a watchdog timer.

Contents:

29.1. Overview

In its simplest form, a *watchdog timer* is a hardware counter that starts at some initial value and counts down toward zero. When the watchdog count reaches zero, it resets the entire processor. Avoiding resets of the processor is desirable, so the application software is designed to *kick* (some people say *pet*) the watchdog once in a while to cause the watchdog to re-initialize its counter, avoiding a processor reset. If the software takes much longer than expected to complete its tasks, the idea is that the watchdog won't be kicked in time, and the processor will be reset. There are variations on this idea, but the general concept is to use a hardware timer (the watchdog) to detect when the processor has hung and initiate a system reset to un-hang the system. We'll call the time it takes for the watchdog to count to zero after it has been kicked its *timeout interval.*

29.1.1. Importance of using a watchdog

Using a watchdog timer is a common practice in embedded systems. If used properly, it can allow a system to automatically recover from a hang or crash without operator intervention. If a watchdog timer isn't used (or is used improperly), embedded systems may have a much more difficult time recovering from intermittently encountered software or hardware defects. Many embedded microcontrollers have built-in watchdog timers; it's a shame not to use one if it is already there.

A watchdog timer doesn't actually prevent the system from experiencing a momentary hang or slowdown. What it does do is provide a quick way to recover from such a situation without requiring external intervention to reset the system.

29.1.2. Possible symptoms

If your system is behaving in the following ways, you can benefit from using (or improving your use of) a watchdog timer:

✘ System crashes or hangs (fails to respond to inputs) and must be reset manually to recover.

✘ Some tasks hang or die without being noticed in a multi-tasking system, but other tasks keep running.

✘ System becomes extremely slow in some situations, requiring manual intervention such as a system reset.

✘ Design reviews reveal the watchdog timer isn't activated, or isn't set to a good timeout value.

✘ A timer interrupt service routine is used to kick the watchdog to avoid a watchdog timer trip (this is a bad practice).

29.1.3. Risks of not using a watchdog

➤ System failures due to temporary operating conditions that cause system hangs and crashes.

➤ Service calls and equipment returns due to crashes or bogged down system response, when very small transient problems could have been made invisible to the customer with a quick automatic watchdog reset.

29.2. Watchdog timer overview

Most embedded systems perform some sort of real time interaction with the outside world. Because of this, they have deadlines or expected response times. If the system takes significantly longer than expected to respond to an input, or misses its deadline, it can be considered broken in that it failed to perform as expected. In many cases, especially in embedded applications, resetting the system can clear whatever problems took place and restore normal system operation, or at least force a safety shutdown. Therefore, in practice, it is always appropriate to use a watchdog timer in embedded systems.

Every embedded system should use a watchdog timer.

29.2.1. Watchdog timer operation

Figure 29.1 shows a typical, if simplified, *watchdog timer* arrangement. The microcontroller is driven by a clock, and spends its time running application programs for an embedded system. The watchdog is a separate hardware circuit, which uses a clock to count down toward zero. Using two independent clocks can help detect a fault in the microcontroller's clock. But most non-critical systems use the same clock for both the microcontroller and the watchdog to reduce costs.

The RESET line is a signal that performs a hardware reset on the microcontroller if the watchdog timer counts down to zero without being kicked. The KICK line is a signal the microcontroller uses to kick the watchdog,

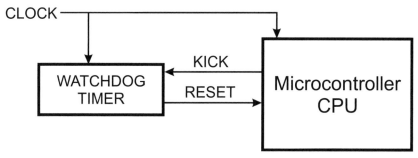

Figure 29.1. Watchdog timer hardware approach.

returning the watchdog's counter to its initial value and restarting the watchdog timeout interval.

> **If the watchdog timer reaches zero without being kicked by the application software, it resets the system.**

A typical system might work in the following way. When the system is reset, the watchdog timer is turned off. The microcontroller then performs whatever startup functions are needed, and kicks the watchdog the first time. This first kick starts the watchdog, and it must be kicked again before it counts down to zero to avoid a reset. Once started, there is no way to turn off the watchdog except as part of an overall system reset. It's important to ensure that software can't turn off or alter the operation of the watchdog once it is started, or else the system would be vulnerable to a software defect that accidentally turned off the watchdog timer and then crashed.

29.2.2. Watchdog effectiveness

You should use a watchdog timer. But they aren't magic. You must understand what they protect against and what they don't. Consider the fault model (the nature and types of faults) that a watchdog protects against. Watchdog timers perform a system reset if the program takes an unexpectedly long time to execute. This encompasses both faults that cause the system to become very slow and faults that cause a complete stop or hang. The specific fault sources encompassed by this fault model are many, including:

- Interrupt service routines or high priority tasks that retrigger too frequently, starving the main loop or lower priority tasks for processing cycles.
- Software that enters an unintended infinite loop (for example, a while statement with an exit condition that is always true, but was eventually supposed to turn false to terminate the loop).
- Corrupted data structures that cause software to enter an infinite loop (for example, a circular chain of pointers that is followed without end).
- Loops that run longer than intended (for example, a memory copy operation that copies far more memory than intended, perhaps due to a corrupted pointer or count value).
- Hardware faults that cause the system to hang.

There are however, some faults that watchdog timers provide no protection against, including errors in arithmetic calculations, many errors in conditional logic, incorrect requirements, and so on. And, it is entirely possible that corrupted instruction memory will produce a program that doesn't crash. Nonetheless, watchdog timers are readily available, and work well for enough system faults that they are worth using. The point here is simply that they don't provide bulletproof protection against all possible faults.

> Watchdog timers provide great value, but they aren't magic.
> It takes more than a watchdog to make a system safe and robust.

29.2.3. Variations on watchdog timers

There are many variations on watchdog timers, and we'll list some common ones here.

29.2.3.1. Software-settable watchdog parameters

It is common for the microcontroller to be able to set up the watchdog timer as part of its reset sequence. Usually the timeout interval can be set. Sometimes the watchdog can be turned on and off, although we think it's better to make it impossible to turn one off once it has turned on.

29.2.3.2. Unlock sequence

In a simple watchdog, reading a single I/O address or memory address might suffice to kick the watchdog. But, a program might accidentally access that address (for example, due to a corrupted pointer or loop that scans through memory). So, some watchdog timers require writing a sequence of specific values to a particular address to reduce the chance a kick can happen by accident.

29.2.3.3. Watchdog activated during startup

In some systems, particularly safety critical systems, the watchdog has a pre-loaded timeout value and is activated via hardware as soon as the system resets. This helps guard against system hangs during initialization and software defects in the watchdog setup software. But, it also means programmers have to put kicks in the right place during initialization to keep the system from being reset even before normal operation starts.

29.2.3.4. Windowed watchdog

A windowed watchdog timer has both a minimum and maximum delay before a kick will be effective. Kicking a windowed watchdog timer too soon results in a system reset, just as happens if a kick comes too late. This approach helps guard against a situation in which a software defect happens to call the watchdog kick routine repeatedly while doing nothing else.

29.2.4. Software watchdog

If you don't have special-purpose watchdog timer hardware, a software watchdog can be used in a pinch. So long as some hardware timer is available (perhaps a general-purpose counter/timer used for timing tasks or even providing time of day), a software watchdog timer can be implemented by decrementing a variable on every hardware timer tick or rollover. That same variable can be re-initialized via a kick subroutine call. A hardware watchdog timer is preferable because buggy software can accidentally re-initialize the software watchdog timer's counter value (for example, via a wild pointer store), and hardware isolation prevents that. But, a software watchdog timer is better than not having any watchdog.

29.3. Good watchdog practices

Good practices for watchdog timers revolve around reducing loopholes that prevent the watchdog from detecting some types of problems.

> Make sure there is no way for your system to
> kick the watchdog if it has partially crashed.

Typical good practices are:

- **Make sure all tasks are executed between kicks** . Every periodic thread or task in the system has to be executed before the watchdog can be kicked. It's important that it be difficult for a program to be partially hung, but still be able to kick the watchdog timer. For example, putting a watchdog kick inside a loop within a single task is a bad idea because the program might be stuck inside that task forever, yet still kick the watchdog on schedule.

- **If practical, kick the watchdog timer in only one place.** In a main loop-style system, the watchdog should only be kicked at the end of the main loop, or possibly between calls to various task routines within the single main loop. In an RTOS-style system, things are more complicated, but the watchdog might, for example, be kicked within the lowest priority periodic task in the system. (Assuming that all other tasks are run, if the lowest priority task meets its deadline then everything else probably did too – but this takes some thought and care to get right.)

- **Make sure it is impossible for any task in your system to crash without tripping the watchdog timer.** For every task in your system, ask whether that task hanging or crashing will be detectable via a watchdog timer reset. In the example of a low priority task kicking the watchdog, this means the low priority task must make sure all higher priority tasks are still executing properly before the watchdog is kicked.

- **Use the right size timeout interval.** A timeout interval that is too big leaves too much room for a system to slow down without triggering a watchdog reset. But, a timeout interval that is too close to the running time of a correctly operating program risks occasional watchdog resets for no good reason. Recall that watchdog timers work by resetting when a program takes an unexpectedly long time to execute. If you don't have a really good idea how long your program should take, you don't have a good idea of what *unexpectedly* means (and neither does your watchdog timer!). Make sure you aren't on the verge of tripping the watchdog in normal operation. A simple way to do this is to increase and decrease the timeout interval to see what triggers a watchdog reset in normal operation, and make sure you have some safety margin in the setting you use based on that.

- **Keep track of watchdog resets.** Watchdog resets can take a system that is mostly working and make it appear to be working perfectly to a customer (so long as resets are fast and infrequent enough, nobody will notice them). But, if a system resets, something has gone wrong. It is good to have a way to tell if a system is resetting so frequently that something needs to be fixed. How frequently that might be depends on the application. But, for example, if watchdog resets are happening during system test, it's important to know so the source of the problem can be tracked down and fixed before the final system is shipped. Something as simple as a red LED that stays on for a few minutes after a system reset might suffice, although an error log stored in non-volatile memory is nice if you can implement one (see *Chapter 25. Run-Time Error Logs*).

29.4. Pitfalls

While there is no one single right way to use a watchdog timer, there are definitely some wrong ways to use them.

- **Don't kick the watchdog with a timer interrupt service routine.** In some systems, a special timer ISR is just used to kick the watchdog. That ISR is driven by a hardware timer, and all it does is kick the watchdog and terminate. In this arrangement everything except the timer ISR can be dead, and the watchdog will still be happy. While this might technically meet a requirement to use a watchdog timer, it would be more honest to simply turn off the watchdog and be done with it.

> **Don't kick the watchdog timer from within a timer ISR.**

- **Don't turn the watchdog off after it has been turned on.** Some systems have hardware that permits the watchdog timer to be turned on and off at will. Avoid doing this. Every time you turn the watchdog timer off, you're operating without a safety net. Leave the watchdog on. If you have an operation that takes too long, either set the watchdog timer to a larger value, or, even better, break the long operation down into smaller pieces.

29.5. For more information

29.5.1. General topic search keywords
- Watchdog timer

- Heartbeat timer

While not a watchdog timer, a related concept is called a heartbeat in networked systems. The idea is that a task runs once in a while to tell other tasks or computers it is still alive. This approach is vulnerable to the problem of kicking an ISR with a timer interrupt service routine (sometimes the heartbeat task is all that is left running after a partial system crash), but it is nonetheless effective for speeding up detection of a system that has suffered catastrophic failure.

29.5.2. Recommended reading

Murphy, N., "Watchdog Timers," *Embedded Systems Programming*, November 2000, pp. 112-124.

A discussion of watchdog timers and implementation approaches.

Chapter 30
System Reset

- A system reset can be an effective way to recover from a system fault and re-store operation.
- Controlled systems must not be left in an unsafe or undesired state during the reset process.
- Software must carefully determine system state after a reset to achieve continuity of control.

Contents:

External resets can involve a hardware reset button, soft resets, and power cycling. Internal system resets can be caused by resource exhaustion, a watchdog timer, or intentional maintenance reboots.

Well behaved resets leave the system in a safe state during the reset, including situations in which the system never reboots. Rapidly repeated resets in which the system never regains stable operation require special handling.

30.1. Overview

All systems have to be reset for various reasons. There are two challenges in doing this: actually performing the reset when it needs to be done, and ensuring the system provides safe and stable behavior after the reset.

Performing the reset can be done by a person or automatically. For a person, you need to decide what the reset procedure is (perhaps it is a hardware reset button, or perhaps it is something more complicated). Automatic resets are most often performed by a watchdog timer.

30.1.1. Importance of a good system reset strategy

Ensuring the system behaves well after a reset can be tricky. It is important to realize that any equipment being controlled by the embedded system might still be operating when the microcontroller is reset. Therefore, something needs to be done to keep the system stable and safe during the reset.

Once the controller has completed its reset, it has no notion of what state the rest of the system is in. The controller must gather information about system state before it attempts to assert control. Additionally, the controller must avoid repeated resets that result in an *undead* system – one that is really dead, but tries to act as if it is still alive and asserting effective control.

30.1.2. Possible symptoms

You need to pay additional attention to system reset behavior if any of the following is true:

✘ There is no practical way for a person to reset your system.

✘ Resetting your system during operation could cause problems with equipment it is controlling. For example, equipment could become unsafe during a reset or if the controller never restarts.

✘ Repeated resets of your system could cause controlled equipment to become unsafe.

30.1.3. Risks of poor reset behavior

➤ Unnecessary service calls or equipment returns when a system reset could have solved the problem but didn't work properly.

➤ Equipment damage or customer loss because a reset system introduces control system perturbations.

➤ An unsafe situation caused by continual system resets not clearing a problem in operating equipment.

30.2. Ways to reset a system

There are two ways to reset a system: externally and internally.

30.2.1. External system resets

External system resets can be invoked by a user when the system doesn't seem to be performing properly. Typical reset methods include:

- **A hardware reset button,** put someplace accessible but not too noticeable. The advantage of this technique is, assuming it is attached to a non-maskable interrupt pin, no software defect can prevent the reset.

- **A soft reset feature,** such as holding down two particular buttons for a count of ten. This approach does not require an additional button for reset, but might not work if software has crashed.

- **Power cycling,** including removing and replacing batteries. This approach is inconvenient for users, but it can be effective as a reset technique of last resort. If you have a carry-through capacitor so that the system doesn't lose memory during a battery change, then consider whether you need a hardware reset switch. At the very least, tell people in the instructions how long they need to leave the batteries out of the unit to be sure a reset will take place.

> **Provide a way to externally reset your system, even if it is just removing and replacing the batteries.**

For better or worse, people have been conditioned to accept the occasional need to reboot a desktop computer as an ordinary and necessary operation. (We find this a deplorable situation, but that is the way the world is.) So they might not feel too timid about resetting your embedded system if they realize there is a reset button available to them. Make sure that repeated external resets won't damage your system, or put in limits if that is an issue. For example, if you have a compressor that will be damaged if it is power cycled too quickly, put in a time-out that prevents a compressor startup for a period of time after a system reset.

30.2.2. Internal system resets

Systems can reset themselves internally as well. This is especially useful for unattended system operation. Internal reset types include:

- **Watchdog timer resets.** The most commonly used internal system reset is a watchdog timer (see *Chapter 29. Watchdog Timers*), which performs a reset when software is hung or takes too long to perform a computation.

- **Resetting when resources are exhausted.** For example, resetting when malloc, new, or other dynamic memory allocation returns an error because memory has run out.

- **Resetting periodically as a maintenance technique** to clear accumulated software data structure errors, or to perform self test.

It is desirable for internally generated system resets to be as invisible to users and controlled equipment as possible. This is often done via a combination of performing resets when the system is idle and restarting the computer system very quickly to achieve normal operation before the overall product suffers noticeable effects.

30.3. Well behaved resets

Once you've gotten the system to reset, you must ensure that things are well behaved from that point on. In particular, you might have a piece of equipment or process you are controlling. But, resetting the microcontroller doesn't suspend (or reset) the laws of motion and thermodynamics! So, it is important to think through what will happen while your system is resetting and how it will gain control of the system when it comes back into operation.

30.3.1. Behavior during the reset

Once a system reset is initiated, it's important to ensure that the system as a whole remains well behaved from that point on. Ideally, you should use hardware techniques to ensure that actuators don't perform unsafe operations when the system is reset. Depending on your system this might involve commanding actuators to a known safe value (such as off), or making sure actuators stay where they are during a reset on the assumption that the system won't change its behavior much during the time it takes to perform a reset.

> **Ensure that the system will be well behaved**
> **if the microcontroller suddenly crashes.**

When considering behavior during the reset, ask yourself what happens if the system fails to restart after it is reset. One cause of a reset might be a hardware problem that leads to a software crash, and the microcontroller might not be able to recover and restart normal operation. Or, a reset might be caused by loss of power, which could take a while to resolve. It's important if the system resets and doesn't restart successfully that everything be left in a relatively stable and safe state, and that there be some way for people to know intervention is required.

30.3.2. Behavior after the reset

Once the system starts re-initializing itself, make sure that the initialization process doesn't send spurious actuator values as part of the reset process. For example, make sure that output values are set to something benign, or at least safe, before powering up output pins. It is worth observing the behavior of a system during reset in a test lab to look for glitches or other spurious values on output pins with an oscilloscope or other diagnostic tool.

Once the system has been reset and starts running its application software, it must collect information about the outside world before attempting to send actuator values. Many control approaches require the software to keep track of the state of the system (for example, as a value kept in the integrator of a control law). That state information has to be set to track the real world before control loops can be trusted to operate properly.

Ensure that the microcontroller doesn't do anything during system startup to destabilize the system being controlled.

As a minimum, you should sample all inputs before asserting any output value. But, if you keep a history of inputs for filtering or control operations, you need to initialize histories to values that won't cause bumps in system control outputs.

As a simple example, consider a thermostat that uses a moving average of the last 5 temperature readings to turn a heater on or off. If the moving average data points are initialized to zero on system reset, then the heater will very likely turn on when the system is reset even if the system is already hotter than it is supposed to be. This will happen even if temperature has been read once, because the four zero data points in the history buffer will outweigh the one actual temperature value. Solving this problem either requires pre-loading history buffers with a newly sampled temperature value or waiting a while (at least 5 temperature samples in this case) before enabling actuators.

Similar problems can be expected in any system that filters data or uses an integrator in a control system.

30.3.3. Repeated resets

There are advantages to designing a system that rides through a controller reset so as not to disrupt things with an emergency shutdown. For example, you might have a purely electromechanical safety timer (*in addition to* a watchdog timer) connected to an emergency shutdown system. That safety mechanism would have a timeout value much longer than the time it takes to reset the microcontroller, but fast enough to prevent the system from becoming unsafe if control ability is permanently lost. If the processor crashes and doesn't come back on line quickly enough, the safety timer would shut down the entire process. But, if the processor resets quickly enough to restore operation and kick that safety timer, the system will continue operation and ride through the processor reboot event.

One scenario to worry about is repeated resets. If the system repeatedly resets itself and reboots, it could seem to the safety timer that the microcontroller is operating when really it is suffering repeated faults. There are two strategies that can help with this situation.

(1) Ensure that system operation control is restored before the system can issue an "I'm OK" output or kick an external safety timer. This means, for exam-

ple, kicking the safety timer after all sensors have been read and actuators set to updated values, not simply when the microcontroller starts running the application software.

(2) Keep a count of system resets (for example, in on-chip EEPROM), and turn the system off or refuse to attempt a reboot if too many resets have happened in without a suitable interval of reset-free operation. For example, each time the system boots you could increment the value in a counter, and for each hour of error-free operation you could decrement that value. If that value is greater than some threshold (say, 3, meaning that the system has rebooted 3 times without a full hour of failure-free operation), the system could refuse to resume operation without human intervention.

> Make sure that repeated resets won't cause your system to become unsafe.

30.4. For more information

30.4.1. Recommended reading

Murphy, N., "Forget me not," *Embedded Systems Programming*, June 2001, pp. 39-44.
    Discusses data integrity during system resets.

Chapter 31
Conclusion

The chapters in this book have taken us through the development cycle: selecting a development process, requirements, architecture, design, implementation, V&V, and critical property evaluation. We hope that you've found some useful techniques, and that they make your process more effective, your products better, and your professional life more satisfying. (And, just maybe, give you a little more time and energy for evenings and weekends!)

> All of us can strive to do better.

There are certainly other important aspects of embedded system development beyond the ones we cover here. Three key areas are process improvement (ways to improve the quality of your process), project management (how you manage the process), and people (how you make your developers happier and more productive). And there are many other technical areas to know about in embedded systems.

> The ideas in this book aren't the final word;
> learning never ends.

One of the rewarding things about working with embedded systems is that there is always something more to learn and something new to do. We hope this book has given you some useful ideas, and wish you the best on your continuing journey.

Index

D

E

J

K

L

M

P

Q

S

U

V

About The Author

Philip Koopman is an Associate Professor at the Carnegie Mellon University Electrical and Computer Engineering Department. Additionally, he is a faculty member of the Institute for Software Research (ISR). After his undergraduate education at Rensselaer Polytechnic Institute, he served as a US Navy submarine officer in the Cold War. After receiving his PhD from Carnegie Mellon, he architected embedded control CPUs for Harris Semiconductor and then created embedded system architectures for a variety of United Technologies Corp. applications such as elevators and automobiles. He returned to Carnegie Mellon and has worked on wearable computers, software robustness testing, graceful degradation, cyclic redundancy codes, embedded networks, safety, and embedded security. He has written an assortment of books and academic papers, and holds 25 U.S. patents in areas such as embedded CPU design, embedded communications, geographic location-aware services, and vehicle security. His current research interests include lightweight software processes for embedded systems, embedded system security, and architectural support for dependability and safety in distributed embedded systems.

Web link: **http://www.ece.cmu.edu/~koopman**

E-mail: **BetterSoftware@koopman.us**
(Unfortunately due to high e-mail volume not every query can be answered.)